triumphlearning™
Common Core Coach
Coordinate Algebra
GEORGIA

Georgia Common Core Coach, Coordinate Algebra   T124GA   ISBN-13: 978-1-61997-971-0
Contributing Writers: Leslie Aiuvalasit, Colleen O'Donnell Oppenzato   **Cover Design:** Q2A/Bill Smith   **Cover Illustration:** James Matthew Crosley

Triumph Learning® 136 Madison Avenue, 7th Floor, New York, NY 10016

Contents

Problem Solving   Performance Task

* Transition Standard

3

Grade 8

Coordinate Algebra

Analytic Geometry

The Number System

Know that there are numbers that are not rational, and approximate them by rational numbers.

Number and Quantity

Quantities

Reason quantitatively and use units to solve problems.

Geometry

Similarity, Right Triangles, and Trigonometry

Prove theorems involving similiarity.

Define trigonometric ratios and solve problems involving right triangles.

Congruence

Make geometric constructions.

Geometric Measurement and Dimension

Explain volume formulas and use them to solve problems.

Expressions & Equations

Analyze and solve linear equations and pairs of simultaneous linear equations.

Work with radicals and integer exponents.

Algebra

Seeing Structure in Expressions

Interpret the structure of expressions.

Creating Equations

Create equations that describe numbers or relationships.

Algebra

Arithmetic with Polynomials and Rational Expressions

Perform arithmetic operations on polynomials.

Seeing Structure in Expressions

Interpret the structure of expressions.

Write expressions in equivalent forms to solve problems.

Creating Equations

Create equations that describe numbers or relationships.

Functions

Use functions to model relationships between quantities.

Functions

Interpreting Functions

Interpret functions that arise in applications in terms of the context.

Analyze functions using different representations.

Building Functions

Build a function that models a relationship between two quantities.

Unit 1
Relationships between Quantities

Units and Dimensional Analysis

UNDERSTAND When solving a problem, it is important to correctly identify the units being considered or measured. This may require converting a quantity given in one unit to a different unit. To do so, use **conversion factors**, such as 12 inches per ft or 0.001 meter per millimeter, to write a multiplication expression. Be sure to set up the conversion factors correctly so the result is stated in the appropriate units.

Paying attention to the units can help ensure that you perform the conversion correctly. Remember that 1,000 meters = 1 kilometer. Convert 8 meters to kilometers.

Try $\frac{1,000 \text{ m}}{1 \text{ km}}$: $\frac{8 \text{ m}}{1} \times \frac{1,000 \text{ m}}{1 \text{ km}} = 8,000 \frac{\text{m}^2}{\text{km}}$

The units in the result, $\frac{\text{m}^2}{\text{km}}$, are not the appropriate units.

Try $\frac{1 \text{ km}}{1,000 \text{ m}}$: $\frac{8 \text{ m}}{1} \times \frac{1 \text{ km}}{1,000 \text{ m}} = 0.008 \text{ km}$

The meter units cancel. The result is in kilometers, the correct unit.

You can convert units within a system of measurement or between different systems of measurement. Though it may require several steps, any unit of measure can be converted to another unit that measures the same property (length, volume, speed, and so on).

UNDERSTAND Examining the units as you perform calculations is a form of **dimensional analysis**. Dimensional analysis can aid in writing equations by determining how certain quantities can be combined. For example, to add or subtract two quantities, they must be expressed in the same units.

   7 cm + 1 in. ≠ 8 cm or 8 in.   7 cm + 2.54 cm = 9.54 cm

When multiplying or dividing quantities, units can combine or cancel out. Using dimensional analysis will ensure that you combine quantities by using operations that result in an answer that makes sense. This is especially helpful with rates of change.

Suppose you eat 3 apples per week. How long will it take you to eat a bag of 12 apples? The answer will be in some unit of time. Can you solve by multiplying the quantities?

$\frac{3 \text{ apples}}{1 \text{ week}} \times 12 \text{ apples} = \frac{36 \text{ apples}^2}{\text{week}}$

This answer above is not given in a unit of time, so try dividing the quantities.

$\frac{3 \text{ apples}}{1 \text{ week}} \div 12 \text{ apples} = \frac{3 \text{ apples}}{1 \text{ week}} \times \frac{1}{12 \text{ apples}} = \frac{0.25}{\text{week}}$

This is not a unit of time either. Try swapping the terms.

$12 \text{ apples} \div \frac{3 \text{ apples}}{1 \text{ week}} = 12 \text{ apples} \times \frac{1 \text{ week}}{3 \text{ apples}} = 4 \text{ weeks}$

A week is a unit of time, so this calculation makes sense.

⊷ Connect

A police officer saw a car travel 1,800 feet in 30 seconds. The speed limit on that road is 55 miles per hour (mph). Was the car speeding?

1 Determine the units given and the units desired.

The car traveled 1,800 feet in 30 seconds, so the speed can be found in feet per second. To compare this rate to the speed limit, we need to convert it to miles per hour.

2 Find the necessary conversion factors.

The distance conversion is from feet to miles. There are 5,280 feet in a mile.

The time conversion is from seconds to hours. There are 60 seconds in a minute and 60 minutes in an hour.

3 Write a dimensional analysis expression.

Remember that the result should be in miles per hour. It may help you to first set up an expression using only the units, so you can see how the units will cancel.

$$\frac{\cancel{ft}}{\cancel{s}} \times \frac{\cancel{s}}{\cancel{min}} \times \frac{\cancel{min}}{h} \times \frac{mi}{\cancel{ft}} = \frac{mi}{h}$$

Now write the expression with numbers.

$$\frac{1,800\ ft}{30\ s} \times \frac{60\ s}{1\ min} \times \frac{60\ min}{1\ h} \times \frac{1\ mi}{5,280\ ft}$$

4 Evaluate the expression. Determine whether the car was driving faster than the speed limit.

$$\frac{1,800\ \cancel{ft}}{30\ \cancel{s}} \times \frac{60\ \cancel{s}}{1\ \cancel{min}} \times \frac{60\ \cancel{min}}{1\ h} \times \frac{1\ mi}{5,280\ \cancel{ft}} \approx 41\frac{mi}{h}$$

▶ The car was traveling at about 41 mph, which is slower than the speed limit of 55 mph.

TRY

A car burns 0.85 gallon of gas per hour when idling. Express this rate in quarts per minute. Round your answer to three decimal places.

EXAMPLE A Dina took part in a diving competition. She dove 5 times, and her scores were 8.8 points, 9.0 points, 8.6 points, 9.5 points, and 9.2 points. If she calculates her score on an average dive, in what units should the answer be given?

1

Plan the calculation.

To find the average score, add up the individual scores. Then divide by the total number of dives.

2

Analyze the units.

All five scores have the same units: points. Adding them together produces a sum with the same units: points. Dividing that quantity by 5 dives will produce a quantity in points per dive.

▸ The average score should be given in points per dive.

EXAMPLE B A hospital's records indicate that, on average, 23% of babies born there are delivered by cesarean section. A total of 217 babies were born at the hospital last year, and a total of 220 were born this year.

What should be the expected number of babies born by cesarean section over both years?

1

Identify the quantities in the problem.

The numbers 217 and 220 stand for the numbers of babies born in given years, so they can be written as 217 babies and 220 babies.

The number 23% expresses the number of babies born by cesarean section out of all of the babies born. Remember that % stands for $\frac{1}{100}$. This quantity can be written as $\frac{23 \text{ cesarean births}}{100 \text{ babies}}$.

The question asks for a number of cesarean births.

2

Write expressions that give the answer in the desired units.

The quantities 217 babies and 220 babies have the same units, so they can be added together to find the number of babies born over both years.

217 babies + 220 babies = 437 babies

Now set up a multiplication expression to find the number of cesarean births.

437 babies $\times \frac{23 \text{ cesarean births}}{100 \text{ babies}} \approx$

101 cesarean births

▸ About 101 babies were expected to be born by cesarean section over that time.

Can you think of a situation in which a quantity could be given in pounds of vegetables per day?

Choosing the correct units is important for displaying data in charts and graphs.

EXAMPLE C The table on the right shows the quarterly profits for a company over a 1-year period.

Make a bar graph to display the data in the table.

Quarter	Profit
1	$167,581
2	$232,191
3	$97,502
4	$124,441

1

Choose a scale for the horizontal axis.

When time is a variable in a given data set, it is generally best to put the data for time on the horizontal axis. In this case, time is given in quarters, labeled 1 through 4. It makes sense to use a scale of 1 quarter.

2

Choose a scale for the vertical axis.

The other variable is profit, which is given in dollars. You could make a scale of $1, but that would result in a very tall bar graph.

The least amount is $97,502 and the greatest is $232,191. Given those numbers, it makes sense to use a scale in thousands of dollars and to begin the graph at $90,000. This means that you will be graphing numbers such as 168, 232, 98, and 124.

3

Construct the graph.

Remember to label the axes.

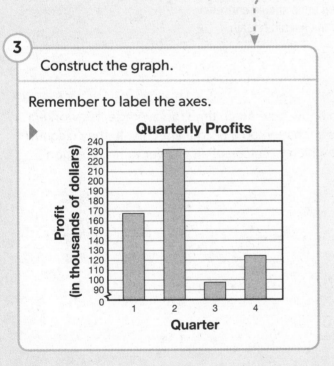

DISCUSS

Why might using a scale of hundreds of thousands of dollars make the graph misleading?

Practice

Write an expression for each conversion.

1. There are 1,000 grams in a kilogram. How would you convert 600 kilograms into grams?

   _____

2. There are 8 pints in a gallon. How would you convert 13 pints into gallons?

   _____

3. A cupcake shop sells an average of 14 dozen cupcakes a day to about 50 customers. What is their average sales rate, in cupcakes per customer?

   _____

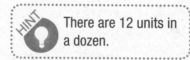 HINT There are 12 units in a dozen.

4. Write an expression that converts 50 liters per minute into milliliters per second.

   _____

REMEMBER The unwanted units should cancel out and only the desired units should remain.

Choose the best answer.

5. The owner of a pool cleaning business wants to know how much time, on average, his workers spend cleaning a pool. Last week, 7 employees each worked a 6-hour shift. In all, they cleaned 42 pools. Which is the most appropriate unit in which to calculate an answer to his question?

   A. pools per employee

   B. pools per day

   C. employees per pool

   D. hours per pool

6. Which is equivalent to 21.76 grams per minute?

   A.   1.306 kg/h

   B.   13.06 kg/h

   C.   36.267 kg/h

   D.   362.67 kg/h

Solve.

7. While traveling in England, Sonia noticed that the price of gas was 1.4 pounds (£) per liter. She wondered how that compares to the price of gas in Atlanta, where she lives. On that day, the exchange rate was £1 = $1.56. Set up and evaluate a conversion expression to find the equivalent price in dollars per gallon. Use the conversion factor 1 L = 0.26 gal.

8. Ravi has started a business importing handwoven and embroidered linen from India. His Indian supplier charges him 460 rupees per meter for the fabric. He wants to make a profit of $4 per yard. How much must Ravi charge per yard for the imported fabric? Use the following information:
    1 dollar = 57.3 rupees
    1 meter = 1.09 yards.

Use the table shown below for questions 9 and 10.

The following data show the population in a small town starting with the year 1980.

Year	1980	1985	1990	1995	2000	2005	2010
Population	2,782	3,219	3,788	4,490	5,176	6,490	6,151

9. To graph the data in a line graph, what units would you use for the horizontal axis? How would you label the axis? What scale would you use? _____

10. To graph the data in a line graph, what units and scale would you use for the vertical axis?

_____

11. **EXPLAIN** The graph on the right shows the recorded heights of tomato plants grown in a laboratory.

    How can you interpret the origin of the graph?

_____

_____

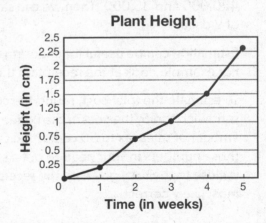

Plant Height

UNDERSTAND In arithmetic, the solution to an equation or the value of an expression is exact. The value of $1 + 1$ is exactly 2. However, in the real world, answers to problems are rarely exact. Measurements are often inexact because it is not possible to take an exact measurement. Sometimes human error causes inaccuracy. Other times, a value must be rounded.

For example, you may have used 3.14 in place of π. 3.14 is not the exact value of π, but the exact value of π cannot be written out and used to calculate because its decimal never ends.

The **accuracy** of an **approximation** or **estimation** is how close it is to the actual value. An approximation or estimation is always less accurate than an exact answer.

UNDERSTAND An approximation is a quantity used to represent a true measurement when the exact value cannot be determined or used.

Suppose you wanted to measure the length of your notebook. Using your ruler, you would likely find that it is about 21.5 centimeters wide. But is it exactly 21.5? Is it closer to 21.4? Might it be 21.400001 centimeters? If your ruler only has markings for millimeters, you could not use it to determine the width of your notebook to the nearest thousandth of a centimeter. So, instead, you use the approximation 21.5 centimeters to represent the true width, whatever it may be.

UNDERSTAND Estimation is different from approximation, because an estimate is made inexact on purpose in order to make calculations easier or to generalize about a population.

The population of a large city is generally given as an estimation in thousands of people, because it is a large number that changes continuously. It is extremely difficult to know the exact population of a city at any given moment. For example, if a census shows that Atlanta's population is 419,978 people and Vidalia's is 34,837, we can choose to round these to 420,000 and 35,000. Then we can say that Atlanta has about 12 times the population of Vidalia.

Estimation can be useful for checking a result. For example, look at the receipt on the right.

To estimate the total cost, round the cost of the sandwich to $5, the cost of the coffee to $1, and the amount of sales tax to 50 cents. You can easily add those numbers in your head to get a sum of $6.50. This is close to the total given on the receipt, so that total is most likely correct.

Dan's Diner	
sandwich.....................	$4.95
coffee..........................	$0.88
sales tax......................	$0.48
	$6.31

⟵ Connect

For each scenario given below, determine if the answer is exact, approximated, or estimated.

A. Cheryl has confirmed 143 guests for her party. She thinks that each guest will eat about half a pound of brisket, so she decides to order 0.5 lb × 150 = 75 lbs.

B. John received 4 identical boxes of a bestselling book at his bookstore. The first box contained 12 copies of the book, so he figured that the shipment included a total of 48 books.

C. Imani made a flag in the shape of an isosceles right triangle. She wants to put trim along the edges of the flag, so she measures each side with a ruler. She finds that each leg measures 10 inches and the hypotenuse measures 14.1 inches.

1 Examine scenario A.

In order to decide how much brisket to order, Cheryl has rounded the number of guests up to 150 to make it a more round number. Also, her determination that each guest will eat 0.5 pound of brisket is an estimate, since different people will eat different amounts. This is an example of estimation.

2 Examine scenario B.

The number of books in the box, 12, is an exact number. John will not find a fraction of a book in one of the boxes. The number of identical boxes, 4, is also exact. Therefore, their product is an exact answer.

3 Examine scenario C.

Even if the legs were exactly 10 inches in length, by using the Pythagorean theorem, you can see that the hypotenuse would be $\sqrt{200}$, or $10\sqrt{2}$ inches. Because 2 is not a perfect square, the number $10\sqrt{2}$ is irrational. Imani's ruler cannot possibly measure this exact value. Therefore, 14.1 inches is an approximation.

DISCUSS

In what other situations would the answer be in the form of an estimation? an approximation? an exact answer?

EXAMPLE A The diagram shows a cell phone with rulers set along its base and height.

Determine the area of the phone's screen. Discuss the accuracy of your answer.

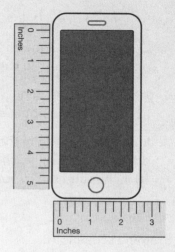

1

Determine the length and width of the screen.

The length of the screen falls between the $4\frac{1}{2}$-inch mark and the $4\frac{3}{4}$-inch mark on the ruler. Use $4\frac{3}{4}$ inches for the length.

The width of the screen falls between the $2\frac{1}{4}$-inch mark and the $2\frac{1}{2}$-inch mark on the ruler. Use $2\frac{1}{2}$ inches for the length.

2

Find the area.

To find the area, multiply the length and width.

$$4\frac{3}{4} \text{ in.} \times 2\frac{1}{2} \text{ in.} = 11\frac{7}{8} \text{ in.}^2$$

▶ The area of the screen is about $11\frac{7}{8}$ square inches.

3

Discuss the accuracy of your answer.

Both of the measurements taken with the ruler are approximations, because it was not possible to take exact measurements. Each measurement is approximated to the nearest quarter inch. The area that was calculated cannot be exact, because the measurements were not exact. Thus, the area calculated is also an approximation.

TRY

In the example above, both the length and width were rounded up to the nearest quarter inch. Try rounding each measurement down to the nearest quarter inch, and then calculate the area using those numbers. What is the difference between the calculated areas?

EXAMPLE B The table below gives the population from the latest census for three nearby counties.

County	Population
Jackson	324,109
Juniper	129,297
Pinewood	502,864

Find both an exact answer and an estimation for the total population of the region that consists of all three counties, and compare the results.

1 Find an exact answer.

Add the exact numbers to find an exact answer.

$$
\begin{array}{r}
324{,}109 \\
129{,}297 \\
+\ 502{,}864 \\
\hline
956{,}270
\end{array}
$$

2 Estimate the answer.

Round each number to the nearest thousand, and then add the rounded numbers to find an estimate.

$$
\begin{array}{rcl}
324{,}109 & \rightarrow & 324{,}000 \\
129{,}297 & \rightarrow & 129{,}000 \\
+\ 502{,}864 & \rightarrow & +\ 503{,}000 \\
\hline
 & & 956{,}000
\end{array}
$$

3 Compare the results.

The difference between the exact answer and the estimate is 270. Since the original numbers are in hundreds of thousands, a difference of several hundred is relatively small. In fact, if the exact answer were rounded to the nearest thousand, the result would be the same as the estimated answer.

DISCUSS

When would the exact answer above be more useful? When would the estimate be more useful?

Practice

For each situation, determine whether the situation involves an exact answer, an approximation, or an estimate.

1. A wedding planner needs to determine how many appetizers to order for between 200 and 220 guests.

   _____

2. A recipe that calls for 2 eggs is being doubled.

   _____

3. A square with a side 12 feet long has a diagonal of 16.97 feet.

   _____

4. An elevator has a capacity of 1,500 pounds. When 7 adults stepped onto the elevator, one of the passengers figured that the average weight of each adult is 150 pounds, for a total of 1,050 pounds.

   _____

5. Alicia looked at the thermometer and determined that the temperature is 14°C.

   _____

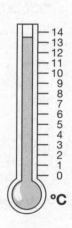

Choose the best answer.

6. Which of the following represents an exact quantity?

   A. The weather forecast for today calls for a high temperature of 81°.

   B. The rise of a hill is about 15°.

   C. A cat had a litter of 6 kittens.

   D. The maximum capacity of a bridge is 20,000 pounds.

7. For which of the following situations is an exact answer most needed?

   A. the maximum number of passengers on an airplane

   B. the number of spectators at a baseball game

   C. the number of blueberries in a batch of blueberry pancakes

   D. the number of people in a town

Solve each problem.

8. The picture on the right shows a bag of apples on a scale.

   If the apples cost $1.79 per pound, what will the cost be for the full bag? Discuss the accuracy of your answer.

   _____

   _____

9. A doctor has prescribed a medicine to be given in a dosage of 0.01 mL per pound of weight of the patient. What is the dosage for a 124-pound patient? Discuss the accuracy of your answer.

   _____

   _____

10. Estimate a 15% tip on a dinner bill of $39.51.

    _____

11. **COMPARE** The table below shows the monthly rainfall, in inches, in Macon over a period of 6 months.

Jan.	Feb.	March	Apr.	May	June
3.20	2.52	1.84	1.03	2.11	3.04

    Find the average monthly rainfall. _____

    Round each number to the nearest tenth of an inch, and find the average. _____

    Round each number to the nearest inch and find the average. _____

    How do the three different averages compare? What can you conclude about rounding, place value, and accuracy?

    _____

    _____

    _____

12. **CREATE** Think of a situation in which an estimate is more useful than an exact answer.

    _____

    _____

Interpreting Expressions

UNDERSTAND Mathematical expressions and equations can be used to model relationships and situations in the real world. Those models can be used to understand relationships between quantities and even to make predictions about them.

Expressions are made up of **terms**, which are composed of **constants** and/or **variables** joined together by mathematical operations such as multiplication and division. A constant that is multiplied by a variable is the **coefficient** of that variable. An expression may contain a single term or may be a string of terms joined together by addition and/or subtraction. Each part of a mathematical expression represents a different quantity or aspect of the real-world situation.

Constants are numbers that do not change. For example, in the expression $x - 1998$, the constant 1998 is always subtracted from the variable, x. If Ian was born on January 1, 1998, his age can be given by the expression $x - 1998$, where x is the current year. The year in which Ian was born, 1998, never changes; it is a constant.

A variable is a letter or symbol that stands for a number and can take on different values. In an equation with two variables, there is often a **dependent variable** (or output value) and an **independent variable** (or input value). Ian's age, y, can be found by using the equation $y = x - 1998$. Ian's age and the current year change periodically, so they are represented by variables. Ian's age, y, depends on the current year, x, so y is the dependent variable and x is the independent variable.

UNDERSTAND The coefficient of a variable often represents a rate. A rate tells how one quantity changes in relation to another quantity.

Suppose that a babysitter charges a $10 fee for each job plus $8.50 per hour of babysitting. The expression $8.50h + 10$ gives the total charge for a job that lasts h hours. The variable, h hours, can take on different values according to how many hours the job lasts. The coefficient, 8.50 dollars/hour, represents the rate, or the amount billed for each hour. The constant, 10 dollars, is the flat fee that is charged for every job, regardless of how many hours it lasts.

The rate 8.50 dollars/hour relates how the charge in dollars changes as the number of hours increases. Notice that when the rate is multiplied by the variable, the units *hour* and *hours* cancel, giving a quantity in dollars.

$$\frac{8.50 \text{ dollars}}{\text{hour}} \times h \text{ hours} = 8.50h \text{ dollars}$$

The constant 8.50 is the babysitter's rate, the variable h is the number of hours, and the term $8.50h$ is the cost, in dollars, for a given length of babysitting time.

←← Connect

Jorge has five male turtles and two breeding pairs of rabbits. The total number of animals that Jorge has m months after purchasing the rabbits can be approximated by using the expression $4 \cdot 2^m + 5$. What does each part of the expression mean in the situation?

1 Identify and examine the variable.

The variable in the expression is m, which represents the time, in months, since Jorge bought his rabbits. In this expression, the variable is an exponent. It means that for every month that passes, the term 2^m has another factor of 2; in other words, it doubles.

2 Examine the constant 2.

In the expression 2^m, the number 2 represents the repeated factor in the related multiplication (the number that is multiplied by itself m times). For every increase in m, the term is multiplied by 2. You can think of 2 as the rate of change in this situation.

3 Examine the constant 4.

A constant multiplied by an exponential expression represents an initial population. In this situation, 4 represents the number of rabbits Jorge started with.

4 Interpret the expression $4 \cdot 2^m$ in real terms.

We have found that, for every increase of 1 in the variable m, the term $4 \cdot 2^m$ is doubled. In the given situation, this means that the number of rabbits doubles each month.

5 Identify and examine the constant term.

The constant term in the expression is 5. It is added to the exponential term, and it is not affected by the value of the variable m. In the given situation, it represents Jorge's 5 turtles. Because all of the turtles are male, they will not reproduce, so their number will not increase from month to month.

TRY

A botanist places a single plant cell into a petri dish. The number of cells in the petri dish after h hours can be modeled by the expression 5^h. What does the number 5 in the expression mean in this situation?

EXAMPLE A Takashi is driving to his grandmother's house. He is driving at a constant speed and will not make any stops along the way. Takashi's distance in miles from his grandmother's house h hours after leaving can be described by the equation $d = 125 - 55h$. What does each part of the equation mean in the situation?

1

Identify and interpret the variables.

This equation contains two variables, d and h. The independent variable is h, and the dependent variable is d.

The problem statement identifies h as the number of hours Takashi has been driving.

The overall equation describes his distance, in miles, from his grandmother's house, so both sides of the equation must represent this quantity. So, both the variable d and the expression $125 - 55h$ must represent Takashi's distance from his grandmother's house.

2

Identify and interpret the coefficient.

The coefficient of h is 55. In a linear equation, a coefficient often represents a rate of change. In this case, 55 represents Takashi's constant speed. Since the distance d is given in miles and the time h is given in hours, the unit for the speed will be in miles per hour. The coefficient indicates that Takashi is driving 55 miles per hour.

3

Identify and interpret the constant term.

The constant term in the equation is 125. When $h = 0$, $d = 125$, so 125 must be Takashi's initial distance, in miles, from his grandmother's house when he begins driving.

TRY

Emmett and his friends played a game that they invented. In the game, a team is awarded a certain number of points for each goal scored. A team loses points any time a team member commits a foul. The equation $p = 3g - 5f$ describes a team's score. What does each part of the equation represent?

EXAMPLE B Jenny pulled the stopper out of a full sink. The amount of water, in gallons, remaining in the sink for each minute that followed can be modeled by the expression $17 - 5m$. Interpret the parts of this expression.

1

Interpret the parts of the second term in the expression.

The second term consists of a variable, m, and a coefficient, -5. The variable m represents the number of minutes since the stopper was pulled.

The amount of water in the sink is changing. The variable m represents the amount of time passed, so the coefficient of m is the rate at which the water is changing. The coefficient -5 tells you that the amount of water is decreasing (because the rate is negative) at a rate of 5 gallons per minute.

2

Examine the effect of combining the two parts of the second term.

The term $-5m$ consists of a rate, $-5\frac{\text{gal}}{\text{min}}$, and an unknown amount of time, in minutes. Dimensional analysis helps you see how multiplying the coefficient and variable creates a value with different units.

$$\frac{\text{gal}}{\text{min}} \cdot \text{min} = \text{gal}$$

So, the product of a rate, $-5\frac{\text{gal}}{\text{min}}$, and a number of minutes, m, yields a new quantity, an amount of water in gallons. This is the amount of water that has drained from the sink.

3

Interpret the first term in the expression.

Before the stopper is pulled, $m = 0$ and the value of the expression is 17. So, the constant 17 represents how much water was in the sink before the stopper was pulled.

4

Determine whether the first and second terms are dependent on each other.

The original amount of water in the sink is not dependent on how much water drains from the sink per minute, nor on how much time has passed. The rate at which the water drains from the sink is not dependent on how much water is in the sink to begin with. So, the first and second terms are not dependent on each other.

DISCUSS

How much water will be in the sink after 4 minutes? Does this equation apply to that time?

Practice

Complete each sentence.

1. In the expression $7x - 9$, the variable is _____.

> HINT
> A variable is represented by a letter or symbol.

2. In the expression $3^y + 12$, the constant term is _____.

3. In the expression $90 + 5z$, the coefficient is _____.

4. In the equation $t = 0.7n - 1.3$, the dependent variable is _____.

Use the information below for questions 5–8. Choose the best answer.

A plumber charges a flat fee for each job, plus an hourly rate for the number of hours the job takes to complete. The total cost of the job, in dollars, can be modeled by the equation $y = 50 + 65x$.

5. What does the independent variable in the expression represent in this situation?
   A. the number of jobs, y
   B. the number of hours to complete the job, x
   C. the cost per hour, $65
   D. the total cost for the job, y

6. What does the coefficient in the expression represent in this situation?
   A. the number of hours to complete the job, x
   B. the cost per hour, $65
   C. the flat fee, $65
   D. the flat fee, $50

7. What does the constant term in the expression represent in this situation?
   A. the number of jobs, x
   B. the cost per hour, $65
   C. the cost per hour, $50
   D. the flat fee, $50

8. What does the dependent variable in the expression represent in this situation?
   A. the number of jobs, y
   B. the number of hours to complete the job, x
   C. the total cost for the job, y
   D. the flat fee, $65

Give an explanation for each question.

9. A colony of bacteria doubles in number every hour. The expression $250 \cdot (2)^h$ gives the number of bacteria after h hours. What does the constant 250 in the expression represent?

_____

10. Bryn is riding his bicycle at a constant speed from school to the library. His distance from the library in kilometers x hours after leaving school can be modeled by the equation $y = 20 - 12x$. What do x, y, 20, and 12 each represent in the equation? Be sure to specify units.

_____

_____

_____

11. INTERPRET The formula for the volume of a rectangular prism is $V = lwh$, where l is the length, w is the width, and h is the height of the prism.

    If you write the formula as $V = (lw)h$, what new entity does the product lw in the first term represent?

    _____

    In $V = (lw)h$, are the first term, lw, and the second term, h, dependent on each other?

    _____

12. EXPLAIN Ginny has 2 quarters. For every week that Ginny does all of her chores, her mother will increase the amount of money Ginny has exponentially. The equation $y = 0.5 \cdot 3^w$ describes the amount of money that Ginny has after w weeks of doing all of her chores. What does the term 3^w tell you about the situation?

    _____

Writing Equations in One Variable

Writing Linear Equations

UNDERSTAND In a **linear equation**, every variable is raised to the first power.

The equation $12x - 7 = -5$ is linear because the variable, x, is raised to the first power.

The equation $x^2 + 5 = 32$ is not linear because the variable, x, is raised to the second power.

The equation $r = \frac{2}{x}$ is also not linear. Remember that $\frac{2}{x}$ can be rewritten as $2(x^{-1})$.

Since x is raised to a power other than 1, the equation is not linear.

UNDERSTAND The solution to a linear equation in one variable is the value that, when substituted into the equation for the variable, results in a true number statement, such as $1 = 1$. Linear equations in one variable usually have one solution, but some have no solution and others have an infinite number of solutions.

To solve a linear equation in one variable, isolate the variable. You can manipulate the equation and get the variable by itself on one side. Some general steps for solving a linear equation in one variable are listed below.

- Add or subtract to get all variable terms on one side of the equation and all constant terms on the other side.

- If possible, simplify each side by combining like terms.

- Multiply or divide to remove the coefficient from the variable term.

To check the solution, substitute its value for x into the original equation and evaluate. If the result is a true number statement—if the numbers on both sides of the equal sign match—then your solution is correct.

UNDERSTAND Many real-world situations can be modeled by using linear equations. For example, linear equations can often be used to model situations that involve a constant rate. A plane flying at a constant speed of 600 mph covers a distance of $600x$ miles in x hours. The time it takes to fly 2,000 miles can be found by solving the linear equation $600x = 2,000$.

In a real-world situation, the possible values of a variable can sometimes be limited. In some cases—such as measurements of time or length—a variable can only take on positive values. Similarly, when finding the maximum number of people that can ride an elevator, for example, the solution must be a whole number, since you cannot have a fraction of a person.

⊣ε Connect

The sum of two consecutive even numbers is 110. What are the two numbers?

1 Examine the information given in the problem.

There are two unknown numbers in the problem, and their sum is 110.

The two numbers are described as consecutive even numbers. This means that the greater number is 2 more than the lesser number.

The numbers must be integers because only integers can be even or odd.

2 Define a variable and write an expression for each number. Then write an equation to describe the situation.

Let n be the lesser of the two numbers.

The greater number would then have the value of the expression $n + 2$.

The sum of the numbers is 110.

Write an equation.

$$n + (n + 2) = 110$$

3 Solve the equation for the variable.

$n + (n + 2) = 110$	Remove the parentheses.
$n + n + 2 = 110$	Combine like terms.
$2n + 2 = 110$	Subtract 2 from both sides of the equation.
$2n + 2 - 2 = 110 - 2$	Simplify.
$2n = 108$	Divide both sides of the equation by 2.
$\dfrac{2n}{2} = \dfrac{108}{2}$	Simplify.
$n = 54$	

4 Find the value of each number.

The value of n is 54, and n represents the lesser number.

The greater number is represented by $n + 2$. $54 + 2 = 56$.

▶ The two numbers are 54 and 56.

 DISCUSS

Interpret the solution for the problem shown above. Is the solution reasonable?

Writing Exponential Equations

UNDERSTAND In an **exponential equation**, the variable is the exponent of a constant, which is called the **base**.

The equation $6^s = 216$ is an exponential equation because the variable, s, is the exponent of a constant base, 6.

The equation $212 = t^4$ is not an exponential equation because the variable, t, is the base of the expression and the exponent, 4, is a constant.

UNDERSTAND The solution to an exponential equation in one variable is the value that, when substituted into the equation for the variable, results in a true statement.

For simple exponential equations, you can sometimes find the solution by using mental math and your knowledge of the powers of the base. For example, in the equation $2^{2x} = 64$, the base is 2. Thinking through the powers of 2, we know that $2^6 = 64$. So, the base, 2, must be raised to sixth power.

$$2^{2x} = 64$$
$$2^{2x} = 2^6$$

Now, you can set the exponents equal to each other and solve the resulting linear equation.

$$2x = 6$$
$$x = 3$$

UNDERSTAND Exponential equations can be used to model situations in which a rate changes in a uniform way. Suppose that a business currently has 5 employees and the number of employees at the business doubles every year. The number of years it will take before the company has 80 employees can be found by solving the equation $5 \cdot 2^x = 80$.

Just as in a linear equation, the values of a variable in an exponential equation can sometimes be limited. For real-world situations, it is always important to remember what a variable stands for and to set appropriate limits. When counting objects, you cannot have a negative number of objects. Sometimes, fractional values are appropriate—such as measurements of length or weight—and sometimes only whole number values will work—such as numbers of cats or dogs.

⌐ Connect

Tina raised the number 3 to a power and then added 19 to the result. She obtained the sum 100. To what power did she raise 3?

1

Examine the information given.

A number is raised to an unknown power. This means that the exponent will be represented by a variable. An equation with a variable for an exponent is an exponential equation.

2

Define a variable and write an expression for the exponential term.

The number 3 is raised to an unknown power. If x represents that unknown power, the exponential expression is 3^x.

3

Write an exponential equation for the situation.

After raising 3 to the unknown power, 19 is added the result. This addition sums to 100.

$$3^x + 19 = 100$$

4

Solve the equation.

$$3^x + 19 = 100$$ Subtract 19 from both sides of the equation.
$$3^x + 19 - 19 = 100 - 19$$ Simplify.
$$3^x = 81$$

Think through the powers of 3:

$3^1 = 3, 3^2 = 9, 3^3 = 27, 3^4 = 81$

Since $3^4 = 81$ and $3^x = 81$, $x = 4$.

▶ The unknown number is 4.

CHECK

Substitute $x = 4$ into the equation you wrote and verify the solution.

EXAMPLE A A parking garage charges a $2.50 base fee plus an hourly rate for each hour or portion of an hour. The sign on the right gives the prices for up to 3 hours of parking.

Write and solve a linear equation to find the hourly parking rate.

Parking Rates	
Up to 1 hour	$ 8.00
Up to 2 hours	$13.50
Up to 3 hours	$19.00

1

Examine the given information.

There is a base fee, which is a constant. The garage also charges an unknown hourly fee, which is multiplied by the number of hours spent in the garage. The number of hours is the coefficient of the unknown fee.

2

Define a variable and write a linear equation to describe the situation.

Let r be the hourly parking rate.

If a customer parks for up to 3 hours, the base fee is $2.50 and the total charge is $19.00.

$$3r + 2.5 = 19$$

3

Solve the equation for r.

$3r + 2.5 = 19$	Subtract 2.5 from both sides of the equation.
$3r + 2.5 - 2.5 = 19 - 2.5$	Simplify.
$3r = 16.5$	Divide both sides of the equation by 3.
$\frac{3r}{3} = \frac{16.5}{3}$	Simplify.
$r = 5.5$	

4

Interpret the solution.

The variable r represents the hourly parking rate. The solution is $r = 5.5$.

▶ The hourly parking rate at the garage is $5.50.

 DISCUSS

The cost to park in this garage can be represented by the expression $5.5h + 2.5$, where h = number of hours. What restrictions are placed on the variable h?

EXAMPLE B The number of bacteria in a petri dish doubles each hour. At the start of an experiment, there were 300 bacteria in the dish. When the scientist checked again, there were 4,800 bacteria. How much time had passed?

1

Examine the given information.

The number of bacteria doubles each hour, so the number is multiplied by 2 each hour. This situation can be modeled by an exponential equation with a base of 2. The original number of bacteria, 300, is multiplied by a power of 2. That product, after an unknown number of hours, equals 4,800.

2

Define a variable and write an exponential equation to model the situation.

Let h be the number of hours that have passed since the experiment began.

The experiment begins with 300 bacteria. The number of bacteria doubles each hour. After an unknown number of hours, h, there are 4,800 bacteria.

$$300 \cdot 2^h = 4,800$$

3

Solve the equation for h.

$300 \cdot 2^h = 4,800$	Divide both sides of the equation by 300.
$\dfrac{300 \cdot 2^h}{300} = \dfrac{4,800}{300}$	Simplify.
$2^h = 16$	

Think through the powers of 2:

$2^1 = 2, 2^2 = 4, 2^3 = 8, 2^4 = 16$

Since $2^h = 16$ and $2^4 = 16$, $h = 4$.

4

Interpret the solution.

The variable h represents the number of hours. The solution is $h = 4$.

▶ Four hours had passed since the experiment began.

CHECK

Substitute $h = 4$ into the equation you wrote and verify the solution. Then, reread the problem and make sure that the answer makes sense in the problem.

Practice

Write a linear equation for each situation. Use _x_ as the variable.

1. The sum of 12 and three times a number is 60. _____

2. The sum of 3 consecutive integers is 72. _____

3. A rectangle's length is 3 feet longer than its width. Its perimeter is 62 feet.

   _____

4. A washing machine repairman charges a flat fee of $50 per job and a fixed hourly rate. A job that takes 5 hours to complete has a total charge of $225. _____

Write an exponential equation for each situation. Use _n_ as the variable.

5. The product of 10 and a power of 4 is 2,560. _____

6. The sum of 13 and a power of 5 is 138. _____

7. The number of fruit flies in a population doubles every day. Everett caught 6 fruit flies. The next time he counted, there were 48 fruit flies. _____

Choose the best answer.

8. A rectangle's length is twice its width. Its perimeter is 156 meters. What is the rectangle's length?

   A. 13 m

   B. 26 m

   C. 52 m

   D. 54 m

9. A seamstress is making dresses to sell at a local craft fair. She charges $35 for each dress and pays a $75 fee to rent her booth at the fair. The expression $35d - 75$ gives the amount she earns at the fair, where d is the number of dresses sold. Which of the following is **not** true?

   A. The value of d can be any whole number.

   B. The value of d can be any integer.

   C. The value of d cannot be irrational.

   D. The value of d can be 0.

Solve.

10. The sum of 22 and five times a number is 57. What is the number? _____

11. What 3 consecutive integers sum to 96? _____

12. Maria has $12 more than Chris. Together, they have $72. How much money does each have?

   _____

13. The drama club ran a lemonade stand to raise money for its new production. The club made a profit of $2 on each glass of lemonade sold and also collected $67 in donations. At the end of the day, the club had raised a total of $171. The club president calculated that 18.5 glasses of lemonade were sold. Is this reasonable? Explain why.

_____

14. A triangle has sides with lengths that are consecutive odd integers. The perimeter of the triangle is 141 centimeters. Sketch the triangle and label the lengths of the sides, using the variable a. Then find the lengths of the sides.

The lengths of the sides are _____ cm, _____ cm, and _____ cm.

15. Genevieve's grade for her history class is the average of her midterm exam, final exam, and final paper. She received a 91 on her midterm and an 86 on her paper. What grade must she get on her final exam to receive a grade of 90 for the class? _____

16. Raul raised 4 to a power, then multiplied by 5 and added 1. The result was 321. To what power did Raul raise 4? _____

17. WRITE MATH   Eisa raised the number 2 to the power of twice a number n. She then added 9. The result was 13. Explain how you can find the value of n.

_____

_____

_____

18. EXPLAIN   The number of cells in a sample doubles every minute. A doctor started with a sample of 25 cells and predicted that, after 5 minutes, he would have 32 cells. Is his prediction accurate? Explain.

_____

_____

Writing Inequalities in One Variable

UNDERSTAND Both linear and exponential inequalities can be solved with the same steps you would use to solve equations. But when solving an inequality, you must remember this rule: if you multiply or divide both sides of the inequality by a negative number, you need to reverse the inequality sign.

$-4x \leq 16$ Divide both sides by -4. Reverse the inequality sign.

$x \geq -4$ This is the solution to the inequality.

UNDERSTAND The solution to an inequality is not a single number but a range of numbers. In the example above, any real number greater than or equal to -4 is a solution. In other words, the solution set includes -4, -3.5, 0, 2.125, and countless other numbers. One way to represent the entire solution is on a number line. The solution set $x \geq -4$ is graphed below.

When graphing a solution set on a number line, write the inequality so that the variable is on the left side and then follow these rules:

- When the inequality symbol is $<$ or $>$, place an open (empty) dot on the endpoint to show that it is not part of the solution.

- When the symbol is $\leq$ or $\geq$, place a closed (filled-in) dot on the endpoint to show that the number is part of the solution.

- When the symbol is $<$ or $\leq$, shade to the left of the dot.

- When the symbol is $>$ or $\geq$, shade to the right of the dot.

UNDERSTAND In some cases, you will need more than one inequality, or a **compound inequality**, to describe a situation. For example, a solution set may be represented by $x \geq -3$ and $x < 2$. The compound inequality described can also be written in the form $-3 \leq x < 2$.

If you graph both parts of a compound inequality on the same number line, the solution is the portion of the graphs that overlap.

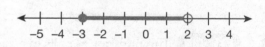

The solution sets for two inequalities sometimes do not overlap at all. The solutions for $x \leq 0$ and for $x \geq 5$ are graphed on the same number line on the right. There is no overlap because no value of x makes both inequalities true. The situation has no solution.

⬅ Connect

Ecologists studying a colony of rabbits in the wild found that the colony doubles in population every quarter of a year. At first count, the ecologists found 5 rabbits. After how many quarters will there be more than 40 rabbits? How long is this in years?

1

Examine the given information.

The rabbit population is multiplied by 2 from one quarter to the next, so the situation is modeled by using an exponential expression with a base of 2. The problem asks when the population will be more than 80 rabbits. The situation is modeled by an inequality with the greater than symbol, $>$.

2

Define the variable and write an exponential inequality.

Let q be the number of quarters since the ecologists first counted the rabbits.

At first count, the colony had 5 rabbits. The number of rabbits doubles, or increases by a factor of 2, each quarter. The number of quarters, q, determines how many times to multiply by the factor. We want to know when the number of rabbits will be greater than 40.

$$5 \cdot 2^q > 40$$

3

Solve the inequality for q.

Change the inequality symbol to an equal sign and solve.

$5 \cdot 2^q = 40$ Divide both sides by 5.

$2^q = 8$

Since $2^3 = 8$, $q = 3$.

The solution to the inequality is either $q > 3$ or $q < 3$.

4

Determine the solution.

Choose two numbers, one less than 3 and one greater than 3. Substitute each into the inequality and see which one results in a true statement.

Try $q = 0$.	Try $q = 5$.
$5 \cdot 2^q \overset{?}{>} 40$	$5 \cdot 2^q \overset{?}{>} 40$
$5 \cdot 2^0 \overset{?}{>} 40$	$5 \cdot 2^5 \overset{?}{>} 40$
$5 \cdot 1 \overset{?}{>} 40$	$5 \cdot 32 \overset{?}{>} 40$
$5 \not> 40$	$160 > 40$ ✓

5

Interpret the result.

Substituting a number greater than 3 in the inequality resulted in a true statement. The solution is $q > 3$.

▶ The population of rabbits will be greater than 80 after more than 3 quarters, which is $\frac{3}{4}$ of a year.

TRY

Graph the solution $q > 3$ on a number line.

EXAMPLE A Jonah subscribed to a new service that streams music over the Internet. The service costs $2.95 per month, but Jonah's rate is reduced by 15 cents for each new subscriber that he signs up. If there is no limit to the discount, how many users must Jonah recruit in order for him to listen for free?

1

Examine the given information.

Jonah's monthly payment, if he recruits no subscribers, is $2.95. His goal is to listen for free, or to reduce that payment to $0. For each new subscriber that he signs up, his monthly payment is reduced by 15 cents, so the rate of change is -0.15 dollars per person.

2

Define the variable and write a linear inequality.

Let x be the number of people that Jonah recruits.

The rate of the discount, -0.15 dollars per person, must be multiplied by the number of people, x, to find the dollar amount of the discount. This amount is subtracted from the base cost, $2.95. This discounted cost must be less than or equal to $0.

$$2.95 - 0.15x \leq 0$$

3

Solve the inequality for x. Interpret the solution.

$2.95 - 0.15x \leq 0$ Subtract 2.95 from each side.

$-0.15x \leq -2.95$ Divide both sides by -0.15. Reverse the inequality symbol.

$x \geq 19.\overline{6}$

▶ Jonah would need to recruit at least 20 people for the service to be free.

Since the calculations yielded $x \geq 19.\overline{6}$, why was the answer at least 20? What are the possible values of x in this situation? What are the possible amounts that Jonah might pay in a given month?

EXAMPLE B Olivia is going to the mall, where she plans to buy a coffee for $3 and some scented soaps for $4 each. She has a gift certificate for $11 that she wants to use, but she can spend no more than $35 in total, including the gift certificate. Write and solve a pair of inequalities to find the number of soaps that Olivia can buy. Then graph the solution on a number line.

1

Write two inequalities to model the problem.

Let s be the number of soaps that Olivia buys.

Since soap costs $4 per bar, the total cost of the soaps is $4s$. She will also buy a coffee for $3. The total amount that Olivia will spend is $4s + 3$.

She will spend at least $11: $4s + 3 \geq 11$

She will spend no more than $35: $4s + 3 \leq 35$

2

Solve the inequalities.

$$4s + 3 \geq 11 \qquad 4s + 3 \leq 35$$
$$4s \geq 8 \qquad\qquad 4s \leq 32$$
$$s \geq 2 \qquad\qquad s \leq 8$$

▶ $2 \leq s \leq 8$

3

Graph the solution set.

First, graph each inequality on its own number line.

$s \geq 2$

$s \leq 8$

Find the part of the number line where the graphs overlap. Consider the context of the problem. Olivia cannot buy a partial bar of soap, so only integer solutions make sense. Graph the integers in the region of overlap to show the solution set.

DISCUSS

Can Olivia buy only 1 soap? Can she buy 10 soaps?

Practice

Solve each inequality.

1. $9x - 7 < 65$

_____

2. $-2a + 13 \leq 23$

_____

3. $2 \cdot 3^n > 54$

_____

4. $7b - 19 \geq 2b + 1$

_____

5. $1 - 5y > y - 3$

_____

6. $\frac{1}{2}(4^d) + 2 \leq 130$

_____

Graph the solution to each inequality.

7. $12c + 7 > 10c + 1$

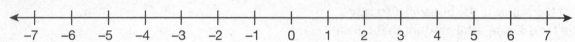

8. $19 - 3t \geq 34$

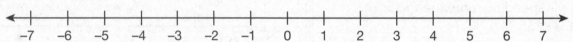

9. $3 \cdot 2^n + 1 < 25$

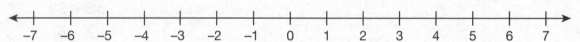

For each situation, write and solve an inequality.

10. The sum of 2 consecutive integers is greater than 73.

Write an inequality to describe the situation. _____

Solve the inequality. _____

Find the pair of integers with the least sum. _____

11. The length of a rectangle is 2 inches more than its width, and its perimeter is no more than 68 inches.

Write an inequality to describe the situation. _____

Solve the inequality. _____

What are the greatest possible dimensions of the rectangle? _____

Find the solutions that solve both inequalities.

12. $4x < 15 - x$

$x + 17 > 2x + 14$

_____

13. $6y - 9 > 2y + 19$

$10 - y > 7$

_____

14. $s + 1 \geq -19 - s$

$4s - 7 \geq 6s + 1$

_____

Find and graph the solutions that solve both inequalities.

15. $2x - 1 > -5 - 2x$

$3x + 5 < 13 - x$

_____

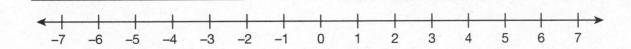

16. $12 - y \leq 15$

$6y - 13 \geq y + 7$

_____

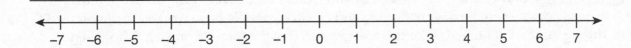

17. $-3 > 4n + 5$

$11n + 10 \geq 10n + 10$

_____

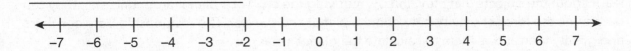

Solve.

18. **APPLY** A petri dish contained 50 bacteria at 8:00 A.M. The number of bacteria triples each hour. After what time will there be at least 1,350 bacteria in the petri dish? _____

19. **IDENTIFY** Jose's math grade is the mean of his three exams. His grades for the first two exams were 82 and 93. What grade must he earn on his third exam to have an average greater than 90 for the class? Express your answer as a compound inequality. Keep in mind any constraints on the variable.

_____

LESSON 6

Writing Equivalent Equations

UNDERSTAND An equation describes the relationship between different quantities. Those quantities may be represented by constants or by variables. You can rewrite an equation in order to see that relationship from a different perspective.

To determine how many inches are in 12 feet, you can use the equation $i = 12f$. This equation gives the number of inches, i, in terms of f, a given number of feet. But suppose that you wanted to know the number of feet in 156 inches. In that case, you are interested in the quantity represented by f.

$i = 12f$ Divide both sides of the equation by 12.

$f = \dfrac{i}{12}$

This equation is equivalent to $i = 12f$, but it highlights the quantity of feet. Plugging in a number of inches for i immediately yields a value in feet. This example involved rearranging a relatively simple equation. However, you can use the same concept to highlight quantities in more complicated equations.

UNDERSTAND Gravity is one of the fundamental forces that govern how objects interact with each other. Since the days of Galileo and Newton, people have worked to understand it. Through experimentation, scientists determined that the force of gravity, F, between two objects depends on their masses, m_1 and m_2, and r, the distance between them. The formula to calculate the force of gravity is:

$$F = \dfrac{(6.67 \times 10^{-11})m_1m_2}{r^2}$$

Astronomers searching the universe to discover new planets have used this relationship to learn about the objects that they find. By studying the orbit of a planet around its star, they can determine the force of gravity between the planet and the star. The relationship between mass and gravity then allows them to calculate the planet's mass.

You can rearrange the formula for the force of gravity to be a formula for the mass of one of the objects.

$F = \dfrac{(6.67 \times 10^{-11})m_1m_2}{r^2}$ Multiply both sides by r^2.

$Fr^2 = (6.67 \times 10^{-11})m_1m_2$ Divide both sides by $(6.67 \times 10^{-11})m_2$.

$\dfrac{Fr^2}{(6.67 \times 10^{-11})m_2} = m_1$ Swap the sides of the equation.

$m_1 = \dfrac{Fr^2}{(6.67 \times 10^{-11})m_2}$

This equation is equivalent to the force equation, but it highlights the mass m_1. If you know the mass of the star, m_2; the distance between the planet and the star, r; and the force of gravity between them, F, this equation yields the mass of the newly discovered planet.

⊕ Connect

The formula below converts a temperature from degrees Celsius, C, to degrees Fahrenheit, F.

$$F = \frac{9}{5}C + 32$$

Write an equivalent formula to convert a temperature from degrees Fahrenheit to degrees Celsius.

1

Examine the problem.

The given formula represents degrees Fahrenheit, F, in terms of degrees Celsius, C. The problem asks you to find the reverse relationship: degrees Celsius, C, in terms of degrees Fahrenheit, F. To find this formula, you need to isolate the variable C on one side of the equation.

2

Write an equivalent formula.

When rewriting equations or formulas, it is often easiest to apply the order of operations in reverse. For example, the right side of the given formula involves both multiplication and addition. If you were evaluating the expression on the right side of the formula, you would multiply first and then add. But to undo these operations and isolate the variable C, start by undoing the addition (through subtraction) and then move on to undo the multiplication (by dividing).

$F = \frac{9}{5}C + 32$	Subtract 32 from each side.
$F - 32 = \frac{9}{5}C$	Divide both sides by $\frac{9}{5}$.
$\frac{5}{9}(F - 32) = C$	Reverse the equation.
$C = \frac{5}{9}(F - 32)$	

▶ To convert degrees Fahrenheit to degrees Celsius, use the formula $C = \frac{5}{9}(F - 32)$.

3

Check your answer.

Use the given formula to convert 35°C to degrees Fahrenheit.

$$F = \frac{9}{5}C + 32$$

$$F = \frac{9}{5}(35) + 32$$

$$F = 95$$

Now, use the formula you wrote to convert 95°F to Celsius.

$$C = \frac{5}{9}(F - 32)$$

$$C = \frac{5}{9}(95 - 32)$$

$$C = 35$$

Since the result is the same temperature we started with, 35°C, the formula appears correct.

 TRY

The ideal gas law states that $PV = 8.31nT$, where P = pressure, V = volume, T = temperature, and n = the amount of gas. Rewrite the equation to determine a formula for n.

EXAMPLE Juanita works as a salesperson at an electronics store. She earns a base salary of $400 each week plus a 10% commission on her total sales. Her weekly pay is described by the equation $p = 400 + 0.1s$, where p is her total weekly pay and s is her total weekly sales. Juanita did not keep track of her sales last week, but her pay was $1,380. Rewrite the given equation to isolate s. Then find her total sales.

1

Rewrite the equation to isolate s.

To begin, subtract 400 from both sides.
$$p = 400 + 0.1s$$
$$p - 400 = 0.1s$$

Now, divide both sides by the coefficient of s, 0.1. Since $0.1 = \frac{1}{10}$, you can multiply both sides by the reciprocal of $\frac{1}{10}$, which is 10. Be sure to put the expression on the left side of the equation in parentheses, so that the multiplication is distributed to both terms.
$$p - 400 = 0.1s$$
$$10(p - 400) = s$$
$$s = 10(p - 400)$$

▶ Juanita's sales in terms of her pay is expressed by $s = 10(p - 400)$.

2

Find Juanita's sales for the week.

Substitute 1,380 for p into your equation. Solve the equation.
$$s = 10(p - 400)$$
$$s = 10(1,380 - 400)$$
$$s = 10(980)$$
$$s = 9,800$$

▶ Juanita's total sales last week were $9,800.

CHECK

One week, Juanita's sales were $6,500 and her pay was $1,050. Substitute these numbers into both equations and confirm that true statements result.

Problem Solving

In the distance formula $d = rt$, d is distance traveled, r is rate of speed, and t is time. How could you find t if you knew d and r?

James will travel 250 miles from Savannah to Atlanta. If he drives at an average speed of 50 miles per hour (mph), how much time will he spend driving?

PLAN

We are given a distance, d, and a rate of speed, r. The unknown quantity is _____, t.

Rewrite the given formula to isolate t.

SOLVE

Rewrite $d = rt$ to express t in terms of the other variables.

$d = rt$ Divide both sides of the equation by r.

$d \text{_____} = t$ Reverse the equation.

$t = \dfrac{d}{r}$

Substitute the given information into the new formula. Let $d = 250$ and $r = 50$.

$t = \dfrac{d}{r}$

$t = \text{_____}$

$t = \text{_____}$

It will take _____ hours of driving at 50 mph for James to travel from Savannah to Atlanta.

CHECK

Substitute $d = \text{_____}$, $r = \text{_____}$, and $t = \text{_____}$ into the distance formula. Verify that a true statement results.

$$d = rt$$

$$\text{_____} \stackrel{?}{=} (50)(5)$$

$$\text{_____} = 250 \checkmark$$

▶ The solution, _____ hours, is correct.

Practice

Rewrite each equation to isolate the indicated variable.

1. $12ab = c$ for a _____

2. $y = 9x + 2$ for x _____

3. $df = g - 10$ for d _____

4. $\frac{1}{3}s - 8 = t$ for s _____

Choose the best answer.

5. Which of the following is equivalent to the equation $4r + 7s = q$?

    A. $r = 4q - 28s$ **C.** $s = 7q + 28r$

    B. $r = \frac{q - 7s}{4}$ **D.** $s = \frac{q + 4r}{7}$

6. Which of the following is **not** equivalent to the equation $a - 3b = 5c + 9$

    A. $a = 3b + 5c + 9$ **C.** $a - 3b - 5c = 9$

    B. $b = \frac{1}{3}(a - 5c - 9)$ **D.** $c = \frac{a - 3b + 9}{5}$

Write the desired equivalent equations. Then find the desired values.

7. Ohm's law of electricity states that $V = IR$, where V = voltage, I = current, and R = resistance.

    Rewrite the equation to isolate R. _____

    If $V = 9$ volts and $I = 0.5$ amperes, what is the value of R? _____ ohms

    Rewrite the equation to isolate I. _____

    If $V = 110$ volts and $R = 2,200$ ohms, what is the value of I? _____ amps

8. A contractor charges \$150 plus \$75 per hour for a job. The equation $c = 75h + 150$ describes the cost, c, for a job that takes h hours.

    Rewrite the equation to isolate h. _____

    If a job cost \$825, how many hours did it take? _____

9. At a baseball game, hot dogs cost \$2.25 and sodas cost \$1.75. The total cost, t, for h hot dogs and s sodas can be described by the equation $t = 2.25h + 1.75s$.

    Rewrite the equation to isolate s. _____

    If Costas spent \$18.25 and bought 5 hot dogs, how many sodas did he buy? _____

Write the desired equivalent equations. Then find the desired values.

10. The weight, in newtons, of an object in a particular location is equal to its mass, in kilograms, times the gravitational acceleration in that location. As a formula, this is written $w = mg$, where w = weight, m = mass, and g = the gravitational acceleration.

    An astronaut has a mass of 80 kg on Earth. On Earth's surface, the gravitational acceleration is $g = 10$ newtons per kilogram. What is the astronaut's weight on Earth? _____ newtons

    Rewrite the equation to isolate g. _____

    On the surface of the moon, the astronaut's weight is 128 newtons. What is the gravitational acceleration on the moon? _____ newtons per kilogram

11. Recall the distance formula $d = rt$, where d = distance, r = rate, and t = time.

    Rewrite the equation to isolate r. _____

    Dana drove from Atlanta to Athens, 70 miles away, in 1 hour 15 minutes. What was her rate of speed in miles per hour? _____

12. **DEMONSTRATE** Solve the equation $\frac{1}{4}p - 5n = 12$ for n. Then choose values for p and n, and show that the equations are equivalent.

    _____

13. **APPLY** A hairdresser charges $25 for a man's haircut, $35 for a woman's haircut, and $15 for a child's haircut. Her total income, t, can be described by the following equation, where m = the number of men's haircuts, w = the number of women's haircuts, and c = the number of children's haircuts.

    $t = 25m + 35w + 15c$

    Last week, the hairdresser's total income was $385. Her customers included 8 women and 2 children. If she wants to find how many customers were men, which variable should she solve the equation for? Solve the equation for that variable and find the number of men who got haircuts.

    _____

LESSON 7 — Writing Linear Equations in Two Variables

UNDERSTAND Sometimes, the relationship between two quantities (such as distance and time) can be modeled by a linear equation. In such an equation, each quantity is represented by a different variable. Linear equations in two variables have the same characteristics as linear equations with one variable.

Consider the simple situation of filling a pool with water. Suppose that water pours into the pool at a rate of 50 gallons per hour. The equation below describes the relationship between the total number of gallons of water in the pool (y) and the number of hours (x) since filling began.

$$y = 50x$$

This equation relates two variables, y and x, and it is linear because both variables are to the first power.

UNDERSTAND A linear equation in two variables can be written in **slope-intercept form**, $y = mx + b$, where:

- y and x are variables

- m is the **slope** of the equation's graph, or its rate of change

- b is the **y-intercept**, or the y-coordinate where the graph intersects the y-axis

In the situation described above, the equation $y = 50x$ is in slope-intercept form. The graph of the equation will have a slope (m) of 50, the coefficient of x. Rewriting the equation as $y = 50x + 0$ shows that the graph has a y-intercept at (0, 0).

UNDERSTAND A linear equation in two variables can be graphed on a coordinate plane. Each axis of the plane represents one variable. The graph of a linear equation in two variables will be a straight line.

To graph an equation in slope-intercept form, first plot a point at the y-intercept, (0, b). Then use the slope to find a second point. Finish by drawing a line through the two points.

To graph $y = 50x$, first plot a point at (0, 0). Using the slope of 50, or $\frac{50}{1}$, move 50 units up and 1 unit to the right to plot a second point at (1, 50). The line drawn through these points is the graph of the equation.

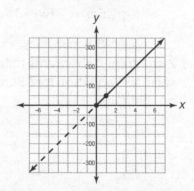

◁ Connect

A botanist transplanted a plant that was 3 centimeters (cm) tall into an experimental soil. He then took measurements once a week and found an average growth rate of 0.5 cm per week. Write a linear equation in two variables to describe the height of the plant over time. Then graph the equation.

1

Examine the given information.

The two variables are the time since the plant was transplanted and the height of the plant. Time is the independent variable, and the height of the plant is the dependent variable, since the height of the plant depends on how much time has passed.

The plant grows an average of 0.5 cm each week. This is the rate of change, or slope.

At the start, when time equals 0, the plant is 3 cm tall. This is the *y*-intercept.

2

Define variables and write an equation.

Since time is the independent variable, let *x* be the number of weeks since the experiment began.

For the dependent variable, let *y* be the height of the plant in centimeters.

Write a linear equation with a slope of 0.5, or $\frac{1}{2}$, and a *y*-intercept of 3.

▶ $y = \frac{1}{2}x + 3$

3

Graph the equation.

Plot a point at the *y*-intercept, (0, 3). Then, using the slope of $\frac{1}{2}$, move two units to the right and one unit up to plot a second point at (2, 4). Draw a line through the points.

▶

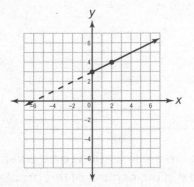

DISCUSS

The points (−4, 1) and (1,000, 503) are on the graph of the equation. Are these solutions to the problem?

EXAMPLE A Tommy has 200 flyers to hand out. He hands out an average of 15 fliers each hour. Write and graph an equation to model the situation.

1

Examine the given information.

The two variables are the time since Tommy started handing out fliers and the number of fliers remaining. Time is the independent variable, and the number of fliers is the dependent variable, since the number of fliers remaining depends on how much time has passed.

Tommy starts with 200 fliers, so this is the *y*-intercept.

He hands out 15 per hour, which is the rate of change. But the number of flyers remaining is decreasing, so the slope should be negative. The slope is −15.

2

Define variables and write an equation.

Let *x* be the amount of time that has passed in hours. Let *y* be the number of fliers that Tommy has. Write an equation in slope-intercept form with slope $m = -15$ and *y*-intercept $b = 200$.

▶ $y = -15x + 200$

3

Graph the equation.

Plot a point at the *y*-intercept, (0, 200). Then, use the slope of −15 to plot a second point. From (0, 200), move 1 unit to the right and 15 units down, and plot a point at (1, 185). Draw a line through the two points.

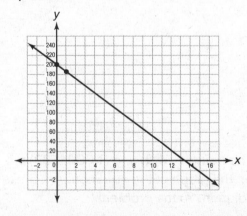

DISCUSS

What are the limitations on the variables *x* and *y* in the context of this problem?

EXAMPLE B A Web site sells MP3 downloads of music albums for $10 and Blu-ray discs of movies for $30. Fiona wants to buy some albums and some movies. She plans to spend a total of $150. Write and graph an equation to represent the situation.

1

Review the given information.

The variables in this situation are the number of albums to be bought and the number of movies to be bought. There is no clear dependent or independent variable, so you can assign the variables either way.

2

Define the variables and write an equation.

Let x be the number of albums to be bought, and let y be the number of movies to be bought.

The amount to be spent on albums is $10x$. The amount to be spent on movies is $30y$. The total to be spent must equal 150.

▶ $10x + 30y = 150$

Notice that this equation is not in slope-intercept form.

3

Find two points on the line.

Choose a value to substitute for x in order to find a point on the line. Let's choose 0.

$$10(0) + 30y = 150$$
$$30y = 150$$
$$y = 5$$

The point $(0, 5)$ lies on the line.

You can also choose a number to substitute for y in order to find a point.

$$10x + 30(0) = 150$$
$$10x = 150$$
$$x = 15$$

The point $(15, 0)$ lies on the line.

4

Graph the line.

Plot the points $(0, 5)$ and $(15, 0)$ and connect them with a line.

▶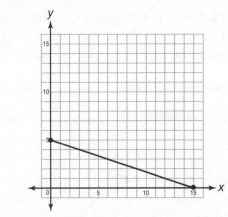

DISCUSS

What are the limitations on the variables x and y in the context of this problem?

Practice

Write an equation to describe each situation.

1. A number y is 6 less than twice a number x. _____

2. Dorothy's age, d, is 1 more than half of Matthew's age, m. _____

3. The number of boys, b, in the class is 3 times the number of girls, g, in the class. _____

Choose the best answer.

4. A beekeeper pays \$30 to rent a booth at a farmers' market. She charges \$5 for each jar of honey. The graph shows this situation, which is modeled by the equation $y = 5x - 30$. Which of the following is true?

    A. The value of x can be negative.

    B. The value of y can be negative.

    C. The value of x can be fractional.

    D. The value of y cannot be zero.

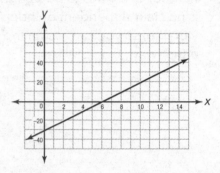

Identify the dependent and independent variables and the y-intercept. Write and graph an equation for the situation, providing labels for the axes of the graph.

5. A baker sells cupcakes at a local festival. He pays \$50 to rent a booth, and he charges \$2.50 for each cupcake. Graph his profit or loss, in dollars, against the number of cupcakes he sells.

    independent variable: _____

    dependent variable: _____

    y-intercept: (_____, _____)

    equation: _____

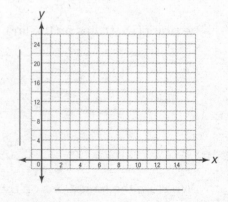

6. A cookie jar contains two dozen cookies. Every day, Nikki eats 2 cookies. Graph the number of cookies in the jar against the number of days since it was filled.

    independent variable: _____

    dependent variable: _____

    y-intercept: (_____, _____)

    equation: _____

Solve.

7. **COMPARE** Ling's bank account has a balance of $55. Every week, she adds $20 to it. Bei Bei's bank account has a balance of $120. Every week, she withdraws $10 from it. Write and graph an equation to describe each girl's bank account. Compare the equations and their graphs.

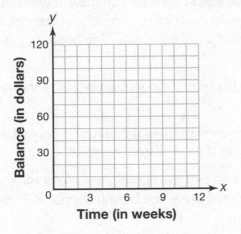

_____

_____

_____

8. **DESCRIBE** A puppy weighed 5 ounces (oz) at birth and gained 3 oz each week for the first 10 weeks. The equation that describes the puppy's weight after x weeks is $y = 3x + 5$, as graphed below.

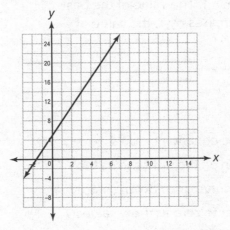

Describe the limitations of the variable x in this situation. Which points on the graph are **not** solutions for the given situation?

_____

_____

_____

Writing Exponential Equations in Two Variables

LESSON 8

UNDERSTAND An **exponential equation** is an equation in which the independent variable is an exponent. In the exponential equation $y = a \cdot b^x$: y is the dependent variable, x is the independent variable, and a and b are constants. The **base**, b, can be any positive real number other than 1.

The equation $y = 3^{2x}$ is an exponential equation because the variable, x, is in the exponent.

The equation $y = 7x^3$ is not an exponential equation because the variable, x, is the base and the exponent is the constant number 3.

In $y = a \cdot b^x$, the constant a represents the starting value of a quantity being measured, such as the number of living things in an area. The base b shows how that quantity changes as the variable x changes.

UNDERSTAND The graph of an exponential equation is not a straight line. It is a curve that is either always increasing or always decreasing.

For the equation $y = a \cdot b^x$, when the base $b > 1$ and $a > 0$, the equation models **exponential growth**. The graph on the right shows the equation $y = 2^x$. At first, the curve rises slowly above the x-axis, but it goes up sharply as the x-values increase. The equation models exponential growth because the base is greater than 1. The value of the base, 2, means that every time x increases by 1, the value of y doubles, or is multiplied by 2.

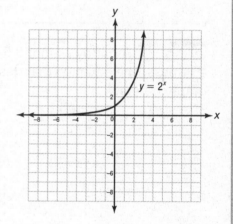

When $a > 0$ and $0 < b < 1$, the equation models **exponential decay**. The graph on the right shows the equation $y = \left(\frac{1}{3}\right)^x$. At first, the curve goes down sharply and then gets closer and closer to zero as the x-values increase. The equation models exponential decay because the base, $\frac{1}{3}$, is less than 1. The base tells us that every time x increases by 1, the value of y is multiplied by $\frac{1}{3}$.

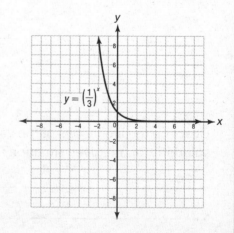

⊏ Connect

A colony of bacteria starts out with 150 cells and triples in population every hour. Write an equation that models the number of cells, y, after x hours. Then, graph the equation.

1

Determine the values of a and b.

The initial population of bacteria is 150, so $a = 150$. Every hour, the population is tripling, which is the same as being multiplied by 3. This means that the base, b, is 3.

2

Write the equation by substituting for a and b in $y = a \cdot b^x$.

▶ The equation that gives the number of bacteria cells, y, after x hours is $y = 150 \cdot 3^x$.

3

Use the equation to make a table of values.

x	$y = 150 \cdot 3^x$	y
0	$y = 150 \cdot 3^0 = 150 \cdot 1 = 150$	150
1	$y = 150 \cdot 3^1 = 150 \cdot 3 = 450$	450
2	$y = 150 \cdot 3^2 = 150 \cdot 9 = 1350$	1350

4

Graph the equation.

Plot the points from the table and connect them with a smooth curve.

▶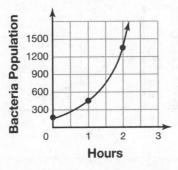

DISCUSS

Is this model an example of exponential growth or exponential decay? How can you tell?

EXAMPLE A The half-life of a substance is the time it takes for half of that substance to break down or decay. The half-life of fermium-253 is 3 days. Write an equation for the amount remaining from a sample of 700 grams of fermium-253 after x days. Make a graph that models the decay of fermium-253.

1

Determine the values of a and b in the equation $y = a \cdot b^x$.

The initial amount of the sample is 700 grams. So, $a = 700$.

After 3 days, there will be half as much fermium, or 350 grams.

$$350 = 700 \cdot b^3$$

$$\frac{1}{2} = b^3$$

$$\sqrt[3]{\frac{1}{2}} = b$$

$$0.79 \approx b$$

2

Write the equation.

▶ $y = 700 \cdot (0.79)^x$

3

Plot points and connect them to graph the equation.

Use the equation to find the value of y at several times.

▶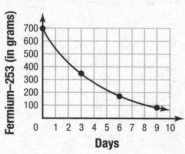

CHECK

Every three days, the amount of fermium is cut in half. Use this information to complete the table below and then compare it to your graph.

Days	0	3	6	9
Fermium-253 (in grams)				

EXAMPLE B Compound interest is calculated by using the exponential function $A = P\left(1 + \frac{r}{n}\right)^{nt}$, where A is the accumulated amount after t years, P is the principal (the amount invested), r is the annual interest rate expressed as a decimal, and n is the number of times that the interest is compounded per year. Write an equation to find the amount that is accumulated when $500 is invested in an account with a 3% annual interest rate, compounded monthly. Make a graph that shows how the account grows over time.

1

Identify the values of P, r, and n.

The principal, P, is the original amount that is invested, $500. So, $P = 500$.

The annual interest rate is 3%. Expressed as a decimal, $r = 0.03$.

The interest for this account is compounded monthly, and there are 12 months in a year. So, $n = 12$.

2

Substitute the values of P, r, and n into the compound interest equation and simplify.

$$A = P\left(1 + \frac{r}{n}\right)^{nt}$$

$$A = 500\left(1 + \frac{0.03}{12}\right)^{12t}$$

▶ $A = 500(1.0025)^{12t}$

3

Plot points and connect them to graph the equation.

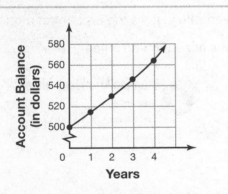

DISCUSS

How could you determine how much money would be in the account after 18 months?

Practice

Determine whether each equation is an exponential equation.

1. $y = 6 \cdot \left(\frac{1}{8}\right)^x$ _____

2. $y = \pi^x$ _____

3. $y = -12 \cdot x^{10}$ _____

Graph the following exponential equations.

4. $y = \frac{1}{6} \cdot 3^x$

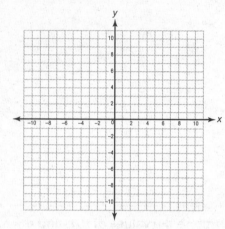

5. $y = 6 \cdot \left(\frac{1}{4}\right)^x$

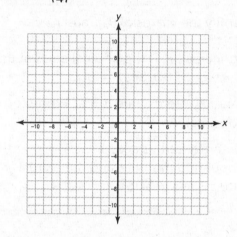

Find the base, _b_, for the exponential equation of the form $y = a \cdot b^x$ that describes each situation.

6. A colony of fruit flies doubles in population every day. The variable _y_ gives the number of fruit flies after _x_ days. _b_ = _____

7. Enrollment at a preschool has dropped by 4.5% each year. The variable _y_ gives the number of students at the school after _x_ years. _b_ = _____

   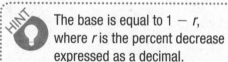 The base is equal to 1 − _r_, where _r_ is the percent decrease expressed as a decimal.

8. A savings account earns 3% annual interest, compounded annually. The variable _y_ gives the amount of money in the account after _x_ years. _b_ = _____

   HINT "Annually" means once per year.

Write an equation for each situation.

9. Sanjay bought a car for $18,500. According to his insurance company, the value of the car depreciates 5% each year. What will the value of the car be _x_ years after Sanjay purchased it?

   _____

10. A colony of bacteria doubles in population every 24 hours. If there were 20 cells initially, how many cells will there be after _x_ days?

    _____

Graph the relationship in each situation.

11. Membership in the Parents' Association at an elementary school has increased each year for the past 5 years by an average of 6%. This year, there were 211 members. Make a graph to represent the number of people in the Parents' Association over the next 10 years, assuming this trend continues.

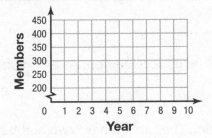

12. A scientist has a sample of 1,500 grams of flerovium-289, a radioisotope with a half-life of 30 seconds. Graph the amount of flerovium-289 in the sample over the next 3 minutes.

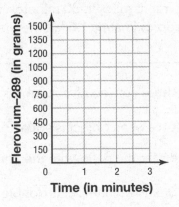

Solve.

13. **PREDICT** When a coffee shop opened at 6 A.M., there were 4 customers. At 7 A.M. there were 6 customers, and at 8 A.M. there were 9 customers. The number of customers continues to increase exponentially. Graph the number of customers in the coffee shop from 6 A.M. to noon. When will there be more than 30 customers in the coffee shop?

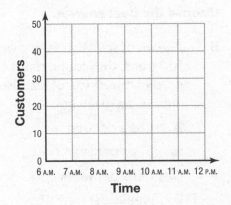

_____

14. **COMPARE** Javier plans to invest $2,000 in a certificate of deposit, or CD, for a period of 10 years. His bank offers two types of CDs. The Super Saver has an annual interest rate of 4% compounded quarterly. The Thrifty Thriver has an annual interest rate of 4.5% compounded annually. Graph the amount of money that would be in each account for the next 10 years. Which option will give Javier more for his investment?

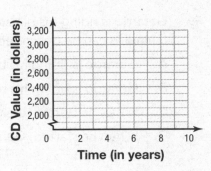

_____

Solve.

1. To qualify for a race, a runner must be able to run at a pace of at least 15 kilometers per hour. Noah ran 5 miles in 30 minutes. Does he qualify for the race? Explain your answer. (Note: There are approximately 1.6 kilometers in a mile.)

_____

2. Find three consecutive numbers whose sum is 156. _____

3. The force of an object is equal to the product of its mass and its acceleration. As a formula, this is

   written $f = m \cdot a$. Rewrite the equation by solving for m. _____

4. One unknown number is double another unknown number. The sum of these two numbers is

   less than 58. Find the largest two integers that fit this description. _____

Choose the best answer.

5. A team of scientists is studying the effects of a plant disease on a forest. In a population of 100 trees, they found that 12 of the trees contracted the disease in one month. They need to predict the effects of the disease over the next decade. Which of the following units should the answer be given in?

   A. years per tree

   B. trees per year

   C. trees per week

   D. weeks per tree

6. Gerardo is riding his bike to the movie theater. His distance in miles from the theater after t minutes can be described by the equation $9 - 0.2t$. Which of the following is true?

   A. Gerardo is riding his bike at a rate of 0.2 miles per hour.

   B. Gerardo is riding his bike at a rate of 9 miles per minute.

   C. When he started, Gerardo was 0.2 mile from the theater.

   D. When he started, Gerardo was 9 miles from the theater.

For questions 7 and 8, interpret parts of the expressions given.

7. A population of wild hares doubles in size each month. The number of hares after m months can be described by the expression $23 \cdot 2^m$. Interpret the meaning of the constant 23.

_____

8. Jean is opening a bank account with money that she got for her birthday. She will deposit money into the account each month. Her bank balance can be described by the expression $250 + 35m$. Explain what the quantities 250, 35, and m represent in the expression. Then explain what the quantity $35m$ represents.

_____

_____

_____

Describe any constraints on the variable.

9. A carpenter charges $120 per job plus $60 for each hour or portion of an hour. His fee for a job lasting h hours can be described by the equation $f = 120 + 60h$. What are the constraints on the variable h?

_____

_____

Choose the best answer.

10. The graph on the right shows the costs and revenues for a small quilting business.

    The x-values represent the number of quilts sold. The y-values represent the amount of money collected or spent, in dollars. The point of intersection is $(-1, 20)$.

    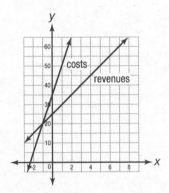

    Which of the following is true?

    A. If the business sells 1 quilt, it will break even.

    B. If the business sells 20 quilts, it will break even.

    C. The point of intersection is not a solution because the value of x cannot be negative. The costs are always higher than the revenues, so the business will never break even.

    D. The point of intersection is not a solution because the value of x cannot be negative. The revenues are always higher than the costs, so the business will always make a profit.

11. Gina is adding a lace border to a circular pillow. The radius of the pillow is approximately 8 inches, and she needs to decide how much lace to buy. Which length should she buy?

    A. 16π inches

    B. 50 inches

    C. 51 inches

    D. 100 inches

Write an equation to model each situation.

12. The number of cells in a sample quadruples every 24 hours. There were 20 bacteria in the sample initially. Write an equation to find b, the number of bacteria in the sample after d days.

_____

13. A bathtub holds 40 gallons of water and is draining at a rate of 4 gallons per minute. Write an equation that gives the amount of water in gallons, w, after m minutes.

_____

Describe the constraints on variables in the equations.

14. Padma works as a babysitter. She charges a $10 fee to cover her transportation costs plus

$13 per hour to watch one child. Write an equation that gives her total pay, y, for a job lasting

x hours. _____

Graph your equation on the coordinate grid below. Be sure to label the axes.

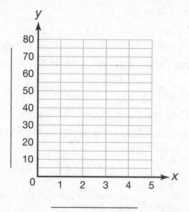

_____

15. As a grocery packer, Jason makes $8 per hour. He also gets occasional tips from customers. After working a shift of h hours, Jason's pay, P, is described by the inequality $P \geq 8h$. What are the constraints of the variable P?

_____

_____

16. Purple pens come in small packages and large packages. Tabitha bought 1 small package and 3 large packages, and she now has a total of 85 pens. Rob bought 2 large packages and 6 small packages, and he now has a total of 110 pens. The following set of equations describes this situation.

$$s + 3l = 85$$
$$6s + 2l = 110$$

What are the constraints on s and l? _____

Solve.

17. Atsuo works as a salesman. He makes $550 per week plus a commission of 10% on anything he sells. His pay each week, P, can be described by the equation $P = 550 + 0.1S$, where S is the total amount of his sales. He wants to figure out how much he needs to sell in order to make $1,000 next week. Rewrite the equation to isolate S. Then, find the amount of sales he needs.

_____

18. **PLAN** Mrs. Chu owns a used car dealership. For the past 2 years, she has kept track of the number of cars sold during each quarter. She needs to create a bar graph for the following information.

Quarter	Number of Cars Sold
1	131
2	112
3	87
4	95
5	109
6	145
7	102
8	97

What variable should go on each axis? What scale should she use?

_____

_____

19. **APPLY** A kitten was born weighing 90 grams and gained 10 grams each day during the first week.

Define variables and write an equation to describe the kitten's weight over time.

_____

Graph your equation on the coordinate grid.

Do all of the points on your graph apply to the situation? Explain.

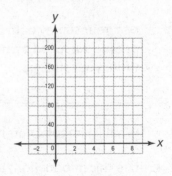

_____

_____

_____

GATHER
DATA AND MAKE PREDICTIONS

For this activity, you will work in teams and survey your fellow classmates, and then use the data to make predictions about all of the students in the school.

Use the tally chart below and survey every student in your class or in your group about something in their lives. For example, you can ask if they own a cat or dog, if they have a brother or a sister, or if they have ever been to a particular place or eaten at a certain restaurant. First, write down your survey question—it should be a "yes" or "no" question.

_____

Now, conduct your survey and fill in the tally chart below.

Yes	No

Review your results and make some calculations.

Total who answered "Yes": _____

Total who answered "No": _____

Total number of people surveyed: _____

Percent surveyed who answered "Yes" _____

Use your survey data to write a statistic, and present the statistic as a rate. For example, if 23% of people surveyed own a dog, then there are 23 dogs per 100 people, or 0.23 dogs per person. Write your statistic.

_____

What is the total number of students enrolled in your school? _____

Use this information, along with your statistic, to make a prediction about the students in your school.

_____

Finally, use your data to write and graph an equation. The equation should allow you to predict something about a group of any number of students, such as how many students in a class of 20 would have a dog. Be sure to choose a scale that makes sense for each axis and give your graph a title.

Equation: _____

Describe the constraints on the variables in your equation and on the points on your graph.

_____

_____

_____

Grade 8

Coordinate Algebra

Analytic Geometry

Expressions & Equations

Understand the connections between proportional relationships, lines, and linear equations.

Analyze and solve linear equations and pairs of simultaneous linear equations.

Functions

Define, evaluate, and compare functions.

Use functions to model relationships between quantities.

Algebra

Reasoning with Equations & Inequalities

Understand solving equations as a process of reasoning and explain the reasoning.

Solve equations and inequalities in one variable.

Solve systems of equations.

Represent and solve equations and inequalities graphically.

Number & Quantity

The Complex Number System

Use complex numbers in polynomial identities and equations.

Algebra

Reasoning with Equations & Inequalities

Solve equations and inequalities in one variable.

Solve systems of equations.

Geometry

Similarity, Right Triangles, and Trigonometry

Define trigonometric ratios and solve problems involving right triangles.

Circles

Find arc lengths and areas of sectors of circles.

Expressing Geometric Properties with Equations

Translate between the geometric description and the equation for a conic section.

Geometric Measurement and Dimension

Explain volume formulas and use them to solve problems.

Unit 2
Reasoning with Equations and Inequalities

LESSON 9

Working with Properties

UNDERSTAND Whenever you simplify or evaluate an expression, you use properties of real numbers. You probably use these properties without even realizing it. They are what justify many of the steps you take when working with expressions and equations.

Some important properties of real numbers are listed in the table below.

Associative property of addition	$(a + b) + c = a + (b + c)$
Commutative property of addition	$a + b = b + a$
Additive identity property	The number 0 is the **additive identity** for the set of real numbers. $a + 0 = 0 + a = a$
Additive inverse property	For every a, there exists an **additive inverse**, $-a$, so that $a + (-a) = (-a) + a = 0$.
Associative property of multiplication	$(a \times b) \times c = a \times (b \times c)$
Commutative property of multiplication	$a \times b = b \times a$
Multiplicative identity property	The number 1 is the **multiplicative identity** for the set of real numbers. $a \times 1 = 1 \times a = a$
Multiplicative inverse property	For every $a \neq 0$, there exists a **multiplicative inverse**, $\frac{1}{a}$, so that $a \times \frac{1}{a} = \frac{1}{a} \times a = 1$.
Distributive property of multiplication over addition and subtraction	$a \times (b + c) = a \times b + a \times c$ $a \times (b - c) = a \times b - a \times c$

Note that the multiplicative inverse of a number is also called its **reciprocal**.

UNDERSTAND Properties are also useful for manipulating equations in order to find solutions.

The properties of equality listed below can be used to isolate variables and find their values.

Reflexive property of equality	$a = a$
Symmetric property of equality	If $a = b$, then $b = a$.
Transitive property of equality	If $a = b$ and $b = c$, then $a = c$.
Addition property of equality	If $a = b$, then $a + c = b + c$.
Subtraction property of equality	If $a = b$, then $a - c = b - c$.
Multiplication property of equality	If $a = b$, then $a \times c = b \times c$.
Division property of equality	If $a = b$ and $c \neq 0$, then $a \div c = b \div c$.
Substitution property of equality	If $a = b$, then b may be substituted for a in any expression containing a.

⊏ Connect

Felix wrote the steps shown below while solving the equation $\frac{1}{2}(4 + x) = -3$.

$$\frac{1}{2}(4 + x) = -3$$

Step 1: $2 + \frac{1}{2}x = -3$ Step 3: $\frac{1}{2}x = -5$

Step 2: $\frac{1}{2}x + 2 = -3$ Step 4: $x = -10$

Use properties of real numbers and of equality to justify each step in Felix's solution.

1

Examine the first step.

In Step 1, Felix distributed $\frac{1}{2}$ to each term in the parentheses. If he had written it out, the step would look like this:

$$\frac{1}{2}(4 + x) = -3$$

$$\frac{1}{2}(4) + \frac{1}{2}(x) = -3$$

Step 1 uses the distributive property of multiplication over addition.

2

Examine the second step.

In Step 2, Felix changed the order of the addends 2 and $\frac{1}{2}x$, but the value of the expression on the left side of the equation remains the same.

Step 2 uses the commutative property of addition.

3

Examine the third step.

In Step 3, Felix subtracted 2 from (or added -2 to) both sides of the equation. If he had written it out, the step would look like this:

$$\frac{1}{2}x + 2 = -3$$

$$\frac{1}{2}x + 2 - 2 = -3 - 2$$

Step 3 uses the subtraction property of equality and the additive inverse property.

4

Examine the final step.

In Step 4, Felix multiplied both sides of the equation by 2. If he had written it out, the step would look like this:

$$\frac{1}{2}x = -5$$

$$2 \cdot \frac{1}{2}x = -5 \cdot 2$$

Step 4 uses the multiplication property of equality and the multiplicative inverse property, because 2 is the multiplicative inverse of $\frac{1}{2}$.

CHECK

Substitute $x = -10$ into the original equation to verify the solution.

EXAMPLE A Carolina was given the equation $36 = 5x + (3y - 7x)$ and was asked to write it in slope-intercept form. The steps Carolina took are shown below.

$$36 = 5x + (3y - 7x)$$

Step 1: $36 = 5x + (-7x + 3y)$ Step 4: $2x + 36 = 3y$

Step 2: $36 = [5x + (-7x)] + 3y$ Step 5: $\frac{2}{3}x + 12 = y$

Step 3: $36 = -2x + 3y$ Step 6: $y = \frac{2}{3}x + 12$

Use properties to justify each step in Carolina's solution.

1

Examine the first step.

Carolina changed the order of the addends $3y$ and $-7x$. Step 1 demonstrates the commutative property of addition.

2

Examine the second and third steps.

In Step 2, Carolina changed the grouping of the terms. Step 2 demonstrates the associative property of addition.

In Step 3, she combined like terms using the distributive property.

3

Examine the fourth step.

Carolina added $2x$ to both sides of the equation. Step 4 demonstrates the addition property of equality.

4

Examine the fifth and sixth steps.

In Step 5, Carolina divided both sides of the equation by 3. Step 5 demonstrates the division property of equality.

In Step 6, the left and right sides of the equation have been switched. Step 6 demonstrates the symmetric property of equality.

DISCUSS

How does simplifying $5x - 7x$ to $-2x$ in Step 3 show the distributive property of multiplication?

EXAMPLE B Hakeem was given the equations $3x + 5y = 12$ and $y = 2 - x$. He used the following steps to find the x-value of the coordinate pair that satisfies both equations.

$$3x + 5y = 12$$

Step 1: $3x + 5(2 - x) = 12$

Step 2: $3x + 10 - 5x = 12$

Step 3: $-2x + 10 = 12$

Step 4: $-2x = 2$

Step 5: $x = -1$

Use properties to justify each step in Hakeem's solution.

1

Examine the first step.

The second equation tells us that $y = 2 - x$. In Step 1, Hakeem substituted the expression $2 - x$ for y in the first equation. This results in an equivalent equation. Step 1 shows the substitution property of equality.

2

Examine the second and third steps.

In Step 2, Hakeem distributed 5 over each term within the parentheses. In Step 3, he combined like terms. Both steps required the distributive property.

3

Examine the fourth step.

In Step 4, Hakeem subtracted 10 from (or added -10 to) both sides of the equation. Step 4 shows the subtraction property of equality and the additive inverse property.

4

Examine the fifth step.

Hakeem divided both sides of the equation by -2. Step 5 shows the division property of equality.

TRY

To find the y-value, Hakeem took the following steps.

$$y = 2 - x$$

Step 1: $y = 2 - (-1)$

Step 2: $y = 3$

Which property justifies Step 1?

Practice

Identify the property of real numbers that is demonstrated by the equation.

1. $12 + 0 = 12$ _____

2. $9 + d = d + 9$ _____

3. $7(2 - p) = 14 - 7p$ _____

4. $6p = 1 \cdot 6p$ _____

Identify the property of equality that is demonstrated.

5. $13q^7 = 13q^7$ _____

6. If $z = 12$ and $12 = 3 \cdot 4$, then $z = 3 \cdot 4$. _____

7. If $12t = 5s$, then $5s = 12t$. _____

8. If $n = 0.25p$ and $3p + 2n = 14$, then $3.5p = 14$. _____

Use the following information for questions 9 and 10. Choose the best answer.

Sarah used the steps shown below to solve the equation $\frac{3}{4} \cdot 7a \cdot \frac{4}{3} = 49$.

$$\frac{3}{4} \cdot 7a \cdot \frac{4}{3} = 49$$

Step 1: $\frac{3}{4} \cdot \frac{4}{3} \cdot 7a = 49$

Step 2: $1 \cdot 7a = 49$

Step 3: $7a = 49$

Step 4: $a = 7$

9. Which step can be justified by the commutative property of multiplication?
    A. Step 1
    B. Step 2
    C. Step 3
    D. Step 4

10. Which step can be justified by the multiplicative identity property?
    A. Step 1
    B. Step 2
    C. Step 3
    D. Step 4

Use properties to justify each step taken to solve the equations.

11. $8 + 7x - 8 = 49$

    $8 - 8 + 7x = 49$ _____

    $0 + 7x = 49$ Additive inverse property.

    $7x = 49$ _____

    $x = 7$ _____

12. $\frac{1}{4}(x - 20) = -2$

    $\frac{1}{4}x - 5 = -2$ _____

    $\frac{1}{4}x = 3$ _____

    $x = 12$ _____

Solve for x in questions 13 and 14. Use properties to justify the steps you use.

13. $x + 6 = 8$

    _____

    Property: _____

14. $y = -5$
    $x = y$

    _____

    Property: _____

15. **RESTATE** The associative property of multiplication states that $(a \times b) \times c = a \times (b \times c)$. How would you express this property in words?

    _____

    _____

16. **EXPLAIN** Alexa solved the equation $5x = 4$ in the two ways shown below.

    Method 1

    $5x = 4$

    $5x \div 5 = 4 \div 5$

    $x = \frac{4}{5}$

    Method 2

    $5x = 4$

    $\frac{1}{5} \cdot 5x = 4 \cdot \frac{1}{5}$

    $x = \frac{4}{5}$

    Use properties to justify the steps in each of Alexa's solution methods. What do Alexa's methods tell you about the relationship between the properties she used?

    _____

    _____

LESSON 10 — Solving Equations and Inequalities

UNDERSTAND When solving an equation in one variable, the goal is to isolate the variable on one side of the equation. Properties of real numbers and properties of equality allow you to manipulate the equation to find the solution.

Manipulating the equation $7x - 3 = 18$ by using properties of equality makes its solution obvious.

$7x - 3 = 18$ Add 3 to both sides (addition property of equality).

$7x = 21$ Divide both sides by 7 (division property of equality).

$x = 3$

Because the original equation was transformed by using properties of equality, the result, $x = 3$, is equivalent to the original equation, $7x - 3 = 18$. Both equations have the same solution, but the solution is much more obvious in $x = 3$ than in $7x - 3 = 18$.

UNDERSTAND Inequalities can be solved in much the same way as equations. The properties of real numbers apply to expressions in both equations and inequalities. The properties of equality have corresponding properties of inequality. For example, according to the addition property of inequality, if $a > b$, then $a + c > b + c$.

The multiplication and division properties of inequality are slightly more complicated than their equality property counterparts. When multiplying or dividing by a negative number, you must reverse the inequality sign.

Usually, the solution to an inequality in one variable is not a single value, but a range of values. This solution can be represented on a number line. The inequality $7x - 3 < 18$ has the solution $x < 3$. This solution is graphed on the number line below.

UNDERSTAND These same properties apply to nonlinear equations and inequalities, too. For some simple exponential equations, you can isolate the exponential expression, and then use mental math to solve the equation. Look at the example below.

$4 \cdot 2^x + 1 = 17$ Subtract 1 from both sides (subtraction property of equality).

$4 \cdot 2^x = 16$ Divide both sides by 4 (division property of equality).

$2^x = 4$

What power of 2 is equal to 4? Since $2^2 = 4$, the value of x in these equations is 2.

⊏ Connect

Solve the equation $\frac{7}{2}p - 2 = 2p - 17$.

1

Get all variable terms on one side of the equation.

Use the subtraction property of equality to subtract $2p$ from both sides.

$$\frac{7}{2}p - 2 = 2p - 17$$

$$\frac{7}{2}p - 2 - 2p = 2p - 17 - 2p$$

$$\frac{7}{2}p - 2p - 2 = -17$$

To simplify the left side, rewrite the coefficient of $2p$ as a fraction with a denominator of 2.

$$\frac{7}{2}p - 2p - 2 = -17$$

$$\frac{7}{2}p - \frac{4}{2}p - 2 = -17$$

$$\frac{3}{2}p - 2 = -17$$

Note that, in order to calculate $\frac{7}{2}p - \frac{4}{2}p = \frac{3}{2}p$, you must use the distributive property.

2

Isolate the variable term.

Use the addition property of equality to add 2 to both sides of the equation.

$$\frac{3}{2}p - 2 = -17$$

$$\frac{3}{2}p - 2 + 2 = -17 + 2$$

$$\frac{3}{2}p = -15$$

3

Isolate the variable.

Use the multiplication property of equality. Multiply both sides of the equation by the reciprocal, or multiplicative inverse, of the coefficient of the variable.

The coefficient of p is $\frac{3}{2}$. The reciprocal of $\frac{3}{2}$ is $\frac{2}{3}$.

$$\frac{3}{2}p = -15$$

$$\frac{2}{3} \cdot \frac{3}{2}p = \frac{2}{3} \cdot -15$$

▶ $p = -10$

CHECK

Substitute $p = -10$ into the original equation and verify the solution.

EXAMPLE A Solve the inequality $8 - 7x \leq -2x - 12$. Then graph the solution on a number line.

1

Move all variable terms to one side of the inequality and all constant terms to the other.

Use the addition and subtraction properties of inequality to isolate the variable terms.

$8 - 7x \leq -2x - 12$	
$8 - 7x - 8 \leq -2x - 12 - 8$	Subtract 8 from both sides.
$-7x \leq -2x - 20$	Simplify.
$-7x + 2x \leq -2x - 20 + 2x$	Add 2x to both sides.
$-5x \leq -20$	Simplify.

2

Isolate the variable.

Divide both sides of the inequality by -5 to isolate x. According to the division property of inequality, when dividing by a negative number, reverse the inequality sign.

$$-5x \leq -20$$
$$\frac{-5x}{-5} \geq \frac{-20}{-5}$$
▶ $$x \geq 4$$

3

Graph the solution set.

First determine whether 4 is part of the solution set. Because x can be greater than or equal to 4, 4 is included in the set. This means that if you substituted 4 for x in the equation, the result would be a true statement.

Place a closed dot at 4. Since all numbers greater than 4 are included, draw an arrow to the right, toward the larger numbers.

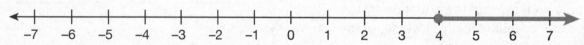

CHECK

Choose two values, one greater than 4 and one less than 4. Substitute each into the original inequality to test the solution you found.

EXAMPLE B Solve the equation $54 \cdot 3^{-n} - 1 = 5$.

1

Isolate the exponential term.

Use the addition property of equality to add 1 to both sides of the equation.

$$54 \cdot 3^{-n} - 1 = 5$$
$$54 \cdot 3^{-n} - 1 + 1 = 5 + 1$$
$$54 \cdot 3^{-n} = 6$$

Use the division property of equality to divide both sides by 54.

$$54 \cdot 3^{-n} = 6$$
$$\frac{(54 \cdot 3^{-n})}{54} = \frac{6}{54}$$
$$3^{-n} = \frac{1}{9}$$

2

Use properties of exponents to rewrite the expression with a positive exponent.

According to the property of negative exponents:

$$a^{-x} = \frac{1}{a^x}.$$

So, $3^{-n} = \frac{1}{3^n}$. Use this to write an equivalent equation.

$$3^{-n} = \frac{1}{9}$$
$$\frac{1}{3^n} = \frac{1}{9}$$

3

Solve for n.

Use the multiplication property of equality to multiply both sides by 3^n and by 9. The multiplicative inverses will cancel out.

$$\frac{1}{3^n} \cdot 3^n \cdot 9 = \frac{1}{9} \cdot 3^n \cdot 9$$
$$9 = 3^n$$

Since $9 = 3^2$, $n = 2$.

▶ The solution to the equation is $n = 2$.

TRY

Solve for a: $(3^a)^2 - 1 = 80$

Practice

Solve each linear inequality.

1. $5a + 5 \leq 3a + 9$

_____

2. $7t + 2 > 6t - 7$

_____

3. $6s + 15 \leq 9s + 16$

_____

Choose the best answer.

4. Which graph shows the solution to the inequality $17 - x > 4x + 12$?

A.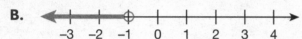

B.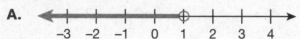

C.

D.

5. Which is the solution to the equation $8 \cdot 2^{-n} + 1 = 1\frac{1}{2}$?

A. $n = -4$

B. $n = -2$

C. $n = 2$

D. $n = 4$

Graph the solution to each linear inequality.

6. $10x - 4 \geq 20 - 2x$

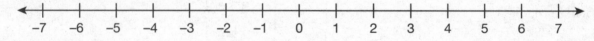

7. $-2x + 9 > -3$

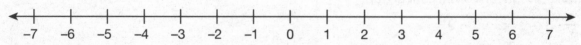

8. $4(5x + 1) \leq 19x + 4$

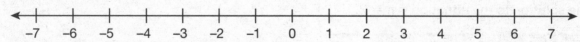

Solve each exponential equation.

9. $\frac{1}{2}(2^x) + 4 = 20$

10. $4 \cdot 5^{3n} = 500$

11. $32 \cdot 4^{-r} = \frac{1}{2}$

_____ _____ _____

Solve each linear equation. List the properties that allow you to carry out each step.

12. $5x - 7 = x - 4$ Properties:

13. $2y + 20 = 2 - y$ Properties:

14. $\frac{1}{2}(z + 2) = 4$ Properties:

15. $13 = 5t - 2$ Properties:

16. RELATE The symmetric property of equality states that if $a = b$ then $b = a$. How would this property relate to the inequality $a < b$?

_____

_____

17. CONSTRUCT Write an inequality with the solution $x \geq 1$.

_____

Solving Systems of Linear Equations

UNDERSTAND A **system of linear equations** consists of two or more linear equations that use the same variables.

Recall that a linear equation in two variables generally has an infinite number of solutions: all of the (x, y) pairs that make the equation true. The solution to a system of equations is the point or points that make both or all of the equations true. Typically, a system of linear equations has one solution. If there is no coordinate pair that satisfies every equation in the system, then the system has no solution. When the equations have the same graph (because they are equivalent equations), the system has an infinite number of solutions: every (x, y) pair on that graph.

You can use graphs to approximate the solution to a system of equations. To solve a system of equations graphically, graph each equation on the same coordinate plane. The solution is the point or points where the graphs of the equations intersect. Because those points are solutions to every equation in the system, they are the solutions for the system. The system shown on the graph on the right has one solution: (3, 2).

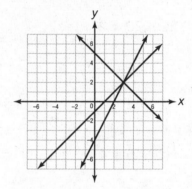

UNDERSTAND One way to solve a system of equations algebraically is to use the **elimination method**. In this method, equations are added and subtracted in order to eliminate all but one variable. This results in an equation in one variable, which can be solved. The value for that variable is then used to solve for the other variables.

Knowing the properties of equality is crucial to understanding how the elimination method works. For example, one step involves multiplying both sides of an equation by a constant factor. The multiplication property of equality assures that doing that will not change the solution of that equation.

Another way to solve a system algebraically is the **substitution method**. In this method, a variable in one equation is replaced by an equivalent expression from another equation. This results in a new equation that has fewer variables. This can be repeated until only one variable remains in the equation. The value of the variable can be found from that equation and then used to find the values of the other variables.

The substitution method is especially useful when a system of equations includes an equation with an isolated variable, such as $y = 3x + 7$. If the system does not include an equation in this form, you can take the necessary steps to isolate a variable in one of the system's equations.

⟜€ Connect

Solve the system of equations by graphing.

$$\begin{cases} y = 2x - 6 \\ x - 2y = 6 \end{cases}$$

1

Write the equations in slope-intercept form.

The first equation is already in slope-intercept form.

Isolate y in the second equation.

$$x - 2y = 6$$
$$-2y = -x + 6$$
$$y = \frac{1}{2}x - 3$$

2

Graph the first equation.

Plot a point at the y-intercept, $(0, -6)$. Then use the slope, 2, to plot a second point at $(1, -4)$. Draw a line to connect the points.

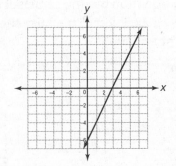

3

Graph the second equation.

Plot a point at the y-intercept, $(0, -3)$. Then use the slope, $\frac{1}{2}$, to plot a second point at $(2, -2)$. Draw a line to connect the points.

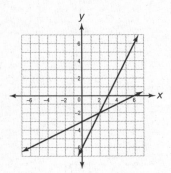

4

Find the solution.

To find the solution to the system, find the point where the lines intersect.

▶ The point of intersection appears to be $(2, -2)$.

CHECK

Substitute $x = 2$ and $y = -2$ into both equations in the system and confirm that true statements result.

EXAMPLE A Solve the system by using the elimination method.

$$\begin{cases} -3x - 2y = -10 \\ 2x + y = 7 \end{cases}$$

1

Choose which variable to eliminate.

Look at the coefficients of the y-terms. The y-term in the first equation has a coefficient of -2, and the y-term in the second equation has a coefficient of 1.

Use the multiplication property of equality to multiply both sides of the second equation by 2.

$$2(2x + y) = 2(7)$$
$$4x + 2y = 14$$

This new equation has the same set of solutions as $2x + y = 7$, because they are equivalent equations.

2

Combine equations to eliminate one variable.

The addition property of equality allows you to add equivalent values to both sides of an equation. Add the new equation to the first equation from the original system to eliminate y.

$$\begin{array}{rcr} -3x - 2y & = & -10 \\ + \quad 4x + 2y & = & 14 \\ \hline x + 0 & = & 4 \\ x & = & 4 \end{array}$$

3

Use the value of x to solve for y.

The substitution property of equality allows you to substitute 4 for x in the original second equation in order to solve for y.

$$2x + y = 7$$

$2(4) + y = 7$ Substitute $x = 4$ into the equation.

$8 + y = 7$ Simplify.

$y = -1$ Subtract 8 from both sides of the equation.

▶ The solution to the system is the ordered pair $(4, -1)$.

 CHECK

Substitute the x- and y-values of $(4, -1)$ into both equations in the system and verify that the solution is correct.

EXAMPLE B A system of equations and its graph are shown.

$$\begin{cases} x + 2y = 3 \\ x + y = 2 \end{cases}$$

Use elimination to find the solution to the system. Show that the elimination method produces a new and simpler system of equations with the same solution as the original system.

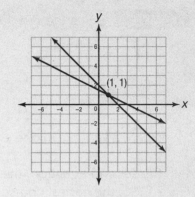

1

Replace the first equation in the system.

Multiply both sides of the second equation by -1, and then add the result to the first equation.

$$\begin{array}{r} x + 2y = 3 \\ + \ -x - y = -2 \\ \hline y = 1 \end{array}$$

Replace the first equation with this equation to produce a new system.

$$\begin{cases} y = 1 \\ x + y = 2 \end{cases}$$

2

Replace the second equation in the new system.

Multiply both sides of the new first equation by -1, and then add the result to the second equation.

$$\begin{array}{r} x + y = 2 \\ + -y = -1 \\ \hline x = 1 \end{array}$$

Replace the second equation with this equation to produce a new system.

$$\begin{cases} y = 1 \\ x = 1 \end{cases}$$

3

Graph this new system.

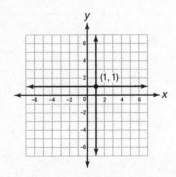

The systems have the same solution, (1, 1).

▶ Combining one equation in a system with a multiple of another equation yields a different system of equations with the same solution as the original system.

 DISCUSS

Compare the original system of equations to the final system of equations. In which system is the answer more obvious?

EXAMPLE C Solve the system by using the substitution method.

$$\begin{cases} 2y - 3x = 19 \\ x + 4y = -4 \end{cases}$$

1

Isolate a variable in one equation.

In the second equation, the coefficient of x is 1. So, the easiest course of action is to solve the second equation for x. Subtract $4y$ from both sides of the equation.

$$x + 4y = -4$$
$$x = -4 - 4y$$

2

Perform the substitution and solve for the other variable.

The substitution property of equality allows you to replace x with the expression $-4 - 4y$ in the first equation from the system. Doing so allows you to solve for y.

$$2y - 3x = 19$$
$$2y - 3(-4 - 4y) = 19$$
$$2y + 12 + 12y = 19$$
$$14y + 12 = 19$$
$$14y = 7$$
$$y = \frac{1}{2}$$

3

Use the value of one variable to solve for the other variable.

Apply the substitution property of equality again. Substitute $\frac{1}{2}$ for y in one of the equations and solve for x.

$$x + 4y = -4$$
$$x + 4\left(\frac{1}{2}\right) = -4$$
$$x + 2 = -4$$
$$x = -6$$

▶ The solution to the system is $\left(-6, \frac{1}{2}\right)$.

 TRY

Solve the system by substitution.

$$\begin{cases} 4x - 3y = -1 \\ 3x + y = 9 \end{cases}$$

Problem Solving

READ

Bonnie has a jewelry-making business. She rents a studio space for $400 per month, and each necklace she makes costs her $15 in materials. She sells the necklaces for $55 each. How many necklaces must she sell in a month to make twice as much money as she spends? How much will she spend and how much will she make?

PLAN

Write and solve a system of equations.

Let n be the number of necklaces that Bonnie makes and sells in a month.
Let m be the amount of money Bonnie spends on the business that month.

Write an equation to represent the amount Bonnie spends for the month if she makes n necklaces at her studio.

$m =$ _____ + _____

Write another equation showing that the amount she makes by selling n necklaces is twice as much as she spends.

$2m =$ _____

SOLVE

Solve the system by using substitution.
The first equation has m isolated on the left side. So, substitute the expression on the right side for m in the second equation.

$2m =$ _____

$2(\underline{\hspace{3cm}}) = \underline{\hspace{3cm}}$

Now, solve the resulting equation for n.

$n =$ _____

Now, substitute the value of n into either of the original equations to find the value of m.

$m =$ _____

$2m =$ _____

CHECK

Substitute the values of n and m into the original equations.

Do the substitutions result in true equations? _____

▶ If Bonnie makes _____ necklaces, she will spend $_____ and she will make $_____.

Practice

Determine if the given ordered pair is a solution to the given system.

1. $\begin{cases} 3x + 7y = 12 \\ 6x - y = -4 \end{cases}$

   $(-3, 3)$

   _____

2. $\begin{cases} 2x - 7 = -y \\ -5x + 13 = y \end{cases}$

   $(2, 3)$

   _____

3. $\begin{cases} \frac{1}{2}x + \frac{2}{3}y = -2 \\ -\frac{3}{4}x - 2y = 9 \end{cases}$

   $(4, -6)$

   _____

Choose the best answer.

4. A system of three equations is shown on the graph below.

   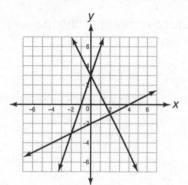

   What is the solution to the system?

   A. $(2, -1)$

   B. $(-2, -3)$

   C. $(0, 3)$

   D. The system has no solution.

5. A baker rents space in a commercial kitchen for $210 per week. For each pie he bakes, he spends $4 on materials. He charges $7.50 per pie. The graph below shows the baker's costs and revenues for a week in which he sells p pies.

   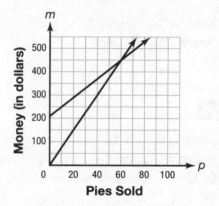

   How many pies must he sell in a week in order to break even?

   A. 20

   B. 40

   C. 60

   D. He will never break even.

Solve each system of equations by using the method suggested.

6. $\begin{cases} 3x - 5y = 13 \\ 2x - y = -3 \end{cases}$

   elimination

   _____

7. $\begin{cases} y - 2x = 5 \\ -2y + 7x = -4 \end{cases}$

   substitution

   _____

Solve.

8. Sanjit has a collection of quarters and dimes worth $3.70. He has a total of 19 coins. How many quarters and how many dimes does Sanjit have?

_____

9. Sonya opened a savings account with $200 and deposits $10 each week. Brad opened a savings account with $140 and contributes $40 each week. After how many weeks will Brad's account balance be twice as much as Sonya's? What will the balance be in each account then?

_____

Solve each system of equations by graphing on the coordinate grid.

10. $\begin{cases} y = -x - 4 \\ y = 2x + 5 \end{cases}$

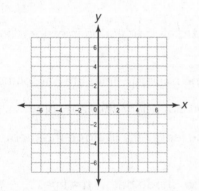

Solution: _____

11. $\begin{cases} 2x - y = 4 \\ \frac{1}{2}x + 10 = 3y \end{cases}$

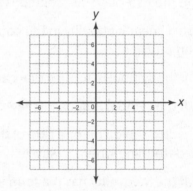

Solution: _____

Answer the questions below.

12. **EXPLAIN** How many solutions does the following system of equations have? How do you know?

$\begin{cases} 2x + 6y = 18 \\ 3x + 9y = 27 \end{cases}$

_____

_____

_____

LESSON 12 Graphing Inequalities

Graphing an Inequality

UNDERSTAND A linear inequality looks like a linear equation. However, instead of the equal sign, an inequality contains one of four inequality symbols: $<$, $>$, $\leq$, or $\geq$.

If you replace the inequality symbol in a linear inequality with an equal sign, you get a related equation.

$y > 3x + 2$ is a linear inequality.

$y = 3x + 2$ is its related linear equation.

The solutions to a linear equation in two variables can be represented by a line. Every point on that line is a solution to the equation. The solution to a linear inequality is a **half-plane**, the portion of the coordinate plane that lies on one side of a line called the boundary. All of the points in the half-plane are solutions to the inequality.

To graph a linear inequality in the coordinate plane, graph its related equation in order to find the boundary line.

- If the symbol is $<$ or $>$, draw a dashed line. Points on the boundary lines are not solutions.

- If the symbol is $\leq$ or $\geq$, draw a solid line. Points on the boundary lines are solutions.

Then shade a region on one side of the boundary line. Put the inequality in slope-intercept form to determine where to shade.

- If the inequality has the form $y < mx + b$ or $y \leq mx + b$, shade below the line.

- If the inequality has the form $y > mx + b$ or $y \geq mx + b$, shade above the line.

You can also find the correct region to shade by choosing a test point and substituting its x- and y-values into the inequality. If the result is a true number sentence, such as $0 = 0$, then shade the region that contains the test point. Otherwise, shade the other region.

The graph shows the inequality $y < \frac{1}{3}x + 4$. The dashed boundary line means that points on the line are not solutions of the inequality. Any point that lies below the line, in the shaded half-plane, is a solution of the inequality.

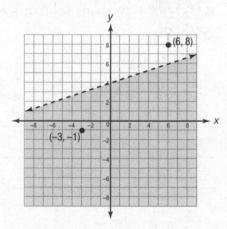

The point $(-3, -1)$ is a solution because it lies in the half-plane that shows all solutions to the inequality. The point $(6, 8)$ is not a solution because it does not lie in the half-plane.

⌐ Connect

Graph the inequality $y \geq 2x - 5$.

1

Find the line for the related equation.

To find the related equation, replace the inequality symbol $\geq$ with an equal sign. The related equation is $y = 2x - 5$. The line $y = 2x - 5$ passes through the points $(0, -5)$ and $(1, -3)$.

2

Determine whether the line is solid or dashed.

The inequality symbol is $\geq$. So, the line is solid. Points on the line and points in one half-plane are solutions of the inequality.

3

Determine which half-plane to shade.

The inequality is already in slope-intercept form. The inequality symbol is $\geq$. So, shade the half-plane above the line.

4

Graph the inequality on a coordinate plane.

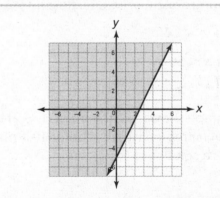

CHECK

The point $(-1, 1)$ is in the half-plane. Substitute these values of x and y into the inequality to confirm that this coordinate pair is a solution.

Graphing a System

UNDERSTAND The solution to a system of linear inequalities is also a portion of the coordinate plane. It consists of the points that are solutions for every inequality in the system. This is the part of the coordinate plane where all of the shaded regions overlap.

In a system of two inequalities, the solution to the system is the intersection of the two half-planes that are solutions to the individual inequalities. All the points that lie in that intersection are solutions for both inequalities.

The graph on the right shows the solutions to the system of inequalities:

$$\begin{cases} y \geq \frac{1}{2}x - 1 \\ y > -\frac{3}{2}x + 4 \end{cases}$$

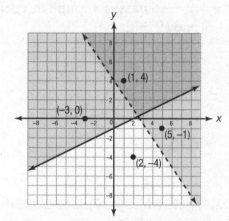

The point $(2, -4)$ is not a solution to either inequality.

The point $(-3, 0)$ is a solution to the first inequality, but not the second.

The point $(5, -1)$ is a solution to the second inequality, but not the first.

The point $(1, 4)$ is a solution to both inequalities, and thus it is a solution to the system.

In a system of more than two inequalities, the solution is the intersection of all the half-planes that are solutions to the individual inequalities.

The graph on the right shows the solutions to the following system of inequalities:

$$\begin{cases} y > -4 \\ x < 5 \\ y < x \end{cases}$$

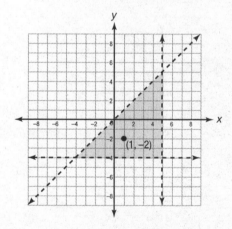

The graph shows that the point $(1, -2)$ lies in the triangular region where all three half-planes intersect, so it is a solution to the system.

⟻ Connect

Graph the solution for the following system of inequalities.

$$\begin{cases} y < 3x - 3 \\ y < -\frac{1}{2}x + 1 \end{cases}$$

1

Graph the first inequality.

The related equation, $y = 3x - 3$, is represented by the line through $(0, -3)$ and $(1, 0)$.

Since the inequality symbol is $<$, use a dashed line and shade below the line.

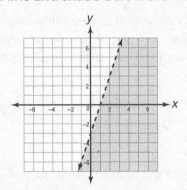

2

Graph the second inequality on the same coordinate plane.

The related equation, $y = -\frac{1}{2}x + 1$, is represented by the line through $(0, 1)$ and $(2, 0)$.

Since the inequality symbol is $<$, use a dashed line and shade below the line.

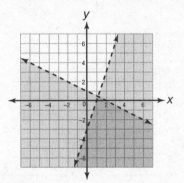

3

Identify the solution.

▶ The darker region, the quadrilateral region below both lines, represents the solution set for the system of inequalities.

DISCUSS

Is the point $(4, -1)$ a solution to the system of inequalities $y < 3x - 3$ and $y < -\frac{1}{2}x + 1$?

EXAMPLE Graph the solution to the following system of inequalities.

$$\begin{cases} y \geq 2x + 3 \\ -2y - 2 \geq -4x \end{cases}$$

1

Graph the first inequality.

The related equation, $y = 2x + 3$, is represented by the line through $(0, 3)$ and $(-1, 1)$.

Since the inequality symbol is $\geq$, use a solid line and shade above the line.

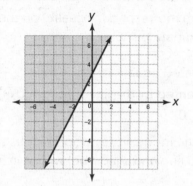

2

Graph the second inequality on the same coordinate plane.

Begin by solving the inequality for y. Remember to reverse the inequality sign when dividing both sides by a negative number.

$$-2y - 2 \geq -4x$$
$$-2y \geq -4x + 2$$
$$y \leq 2x - 1$$

The line for the related equation, $y = 2x - 1$, passes through $(0, -1)$ and $(1, 1)$. Since the inequality symbol is $\leq$, use a solid line and shade below.

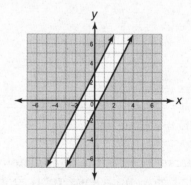

3

Identify the solution.

▶ The two lines are parallel, which means that they will never intersect. Since the two regions have no points in common, the system of inequalities has no solution.

Can a system of inequalities whose graph consists of parallel boundaries have a solution? If so, draw a graph to support your answer.

Problem Solving

READ

A jewelry maker is creating a line of bracelets and necklaces with a new type of chain. The bracelets are 8 inches long, and the necklaces are 14 inches long. She has 280 inches of the chain. It takes her 4 hours to make a bracelet and 3 hours to make a necklace, and she can work no more than 120 hours this month.

Write a system of inequalities to model the number of bracelets and the number of necklaces that can be made with her existing materials this month. Determine how many necklaces and bracelets she can possibly produce.

PLAN

Write a system of inequalities to describe the situation.

Let x be the number of bracelets and y be the number of necklaces she can make.

Since these are numbers of real objects, they cannot be negative numbers.

So, $x \geq$ _____ and $y \geq$ _____.

It takes 8 inches of chain to make a bracelet and 14 inches to make a necklace. The total amount of chain used must be less than or equal to the total amount available, 280 inches.

So, _____ $x +$ _____ $y \leq 280$.

It takes 4 hours to make a bracelet and 3 hours to make a necklace. The total amount of time spent making the jewelry this month must be no more than 120 hours.

So, $4x + 3y$ _____ 120.

SOLVE

The boundary lines for the system of inequalities are graphed on the coordinate plane to the right. Shade the region that represents the solution.

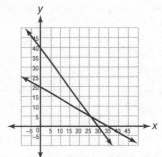

CHECK

The point (15, ___) lies within the solution region. Show that it satisfies all 4 inequalities.

$15 \geq 0$ ✓

___ ≥ 0

$8(15) + 14(\_\_\_) \leq 280 \rightarrow$ _____ ≤ 280

$4(15) + 3(\_\_\_)$ ___ $120 \rightarrow$ _____

Practice

Determine whether each point is a solution to the inequality graphed below.

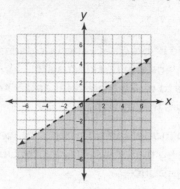

1. $(-3, -1)$

_____

2. $(2, 0)$

_____

3. $(6, 4)$

_____

 Points on a dashed boundary line are not included in a solution set. Points on a solid boundary line are included in a solution set.

Determine whether each point is a solution to the system of inequalities graphed below.

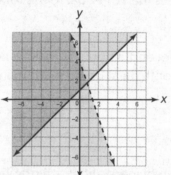

4. $(-5, 0)$

_____

5. $(1, -4)$

_____

6. $(-2, -1)$

_____

7. $(0, 4)$

_____

REMEMBER A solution to a system of inequalities must be a solution for each inequality in the system.

Use the graph below to answer questions 8 and 9. Choose the best answer.

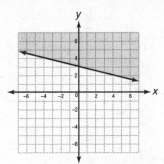

8. Which point is **not** part of the solution set for this inequality?

   A. (0, 3)

   B. (3, 3)

   C. (4, 0)

   D. (−4, 6)

9. Which inequality is represented by the graph?

   A. $y > -\frac{1}{4}x + 3$

   B. $y < -\frac{1}{4}x + 3$

   C. $y \le -\frac{1}{4}x + 3$

   D. $y \ge -\frac{1}{4}x + 3$

Use the graph below to answer questions 10 and 11. Choose the best answer.

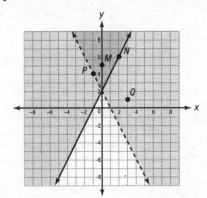

10. Which points are included in the solution set for this system of inequalities?

    A. *M* only

    B. *M* and *N*

    C. *M*, *N*, and *P*

    D. *M* and *Q*

11. Which system of inequalities is represented by this graph?

    A. $\begin{cases} y \ge 2x + 2 \\ y < -2x + 2 \end{cases}$

    B. $\begin{cases} y \ge 2x + 2 \\ y > -2x + 2 \end{cases}$

    C. $\begin{cases} y > 2x + 2 \\ y > -2x + 2 \end{cases}$

    D. $\begin{cases} y \le 2x + 2 \\ y < -2x + 2 \end{cases}$

Use the graph below to answer questions 12–14.

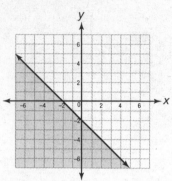

12. Name a point that is part of the solution set. _____

13. Name a point that is **not** part of the solution set. _____

14. Write the inequality represented by the graph.

_____

Use the graph below to answer questions 15–17.

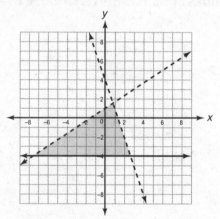

15. Name a point that is part of the solution set. _____

16. Name a point that is **not** part of the solution set. _____

17. Write the system of inequalities represented by the graph.

_____

_____

_____

Graph each inequality.

18. $y \le \frac{4}{5}x - 1$

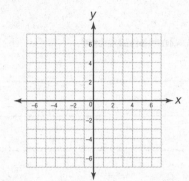

19. $6x - 2y < 8$

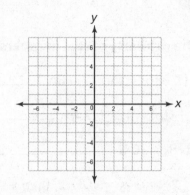

20. **SHOW** A farmer will plant corn and soy on his farm this year. He has a total of 25 acres available for planting. Each acre of corn costs $350 to plant, and each acre of soy costs $150 to plant. His costs must be no more than $5,250.

Let x = the number of acres of corn to be planted and let y = the number of acres of soy to be planted. Write a system of 4 inequalities to describe the situation. Then, graph the system.

_____

_____

_____

_____

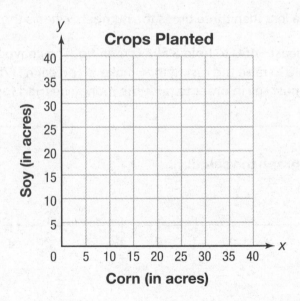

UNIT 2 Review

Identify the property of real numbers or property of equality demonstrated.

1. $6a \cdot (7 \cdot 3b) = (6a \cdot 7) \cdot 3b$ _____

2. $12(s + 2p) = 12s + 24p$ _____

3. $364t \cdot 1 = 364t$ _____

4. If $x = 2y$ and $2y = 10 + z$, then $x = 10 + z$. _____

Solve.

5. $6x + 5 = 47$

_____

6. $2y + 29 = 8 - 5y$

_____

7. $6z + 1 = 9 - 10z$

_____

8. $2 \cdot 3^n - 12 = 150$

_____

9. At a football game, Jim spent $9 for a ticket and bought hot dogs for his friends and himself for $1.50 each. He spent a total of $19.50. How many hot dogs did Jim buy? _____

10. Twice a number is three less than three times the number. What is the number? _____

11. The film club needs at least $450 to hold a film screening. They have $225, and they are holding a used DVD sale to raise the rest. If they make $5 on each DVD, what is the minimum number of DVDs they must sell in order to raise the money needed for the screening?

_____

Solve each inequality and graph the solution.

12. $9x + 6 > 7x - 2$

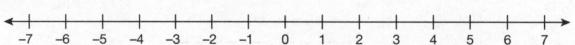

13. $5x + 2 \le 5 - x$

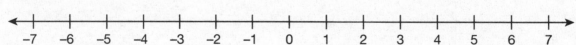

The following problems show solutions to linear equations. Justify each step with a property of equality or a property of real numbers.

14. $8x - 1 = 5x - 13$

$3x - 1 = -13$ Subtraction property of equality

$3x = -12$ _____

$x = -4$ _____

15. $-30 = 3(6 - 2x) - 18$

$-30 = 18 - 6x - 18$ _____

$-30 = 18 - 18 - 6x$ _____

$-30 = 0 - 6x$ Additive inverse property

$-30 = -6x$ _____

$5 = x$ Division property of equality

$x = 5$ _____

Choose the best answer.

16. A system of equations is shown below.

$$\begin{cases} 2x + 5y = 4 \\ x + y = 1 \end{cases}$$

Which of the following systems of equations has the same solution as the system given above?

A. $\begin{cases} 2x + 5y = 4 \\ (2x + 5y) + (x + y) = 4 + 1 \end{cases}$

B. $\begin{cases} 2x + 5y = 4 \\ (2x + 5y) + (x + y) = 1 \end{cases}$

C. $\begin{cases} 2x + 5y = 4 \\ (2x + 5y) - (x + y) = 4 + 1 \end{cases}$

D. $\begin{cases} 2x + 5y = 4 \\ (2x + 5y) + 2(x + y) = 4 + 1 \end{cases}$

17. The equations from a system of linear equations are graphed below.

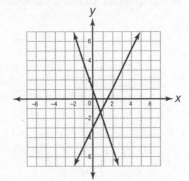

Which of the following is the best approximation of the solution of that system of equations?

A. $\left(\frac{1}{3}, 0\right)$

B. $\left(\frac{3}{4}, -1\frac{1}{2}\right)$

C. $(0, -3)$

D. $(-1, 1)$

Solve each system of equations algebraically.

18. $\begin{cases} x - 2y = 11 \\ 2x + 5y = 4 \end{cases}$

19. $\begin{cases} 2x - 5y = 40 \\ -4x + 3y = -10 \end{cases}$

_____

_____

Solve each system of equations by graphing on the coordinate grid.

20. $\begin{cases} y = 2x \\ y = -\frac{1}{2}x - 5 \end{cases}$

21. $\begin{cases} y - x = -6 \\ y + 2x = 3 \end{cases}$

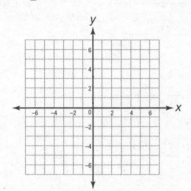

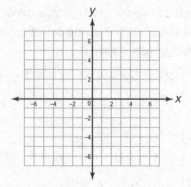

Solution: _____

Solution: _____

Graph each inequality on the coordinate plane.

22. $y \leq 4x - 1$

23. $2y - 3x > 4$

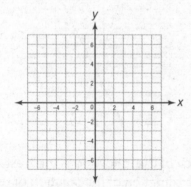

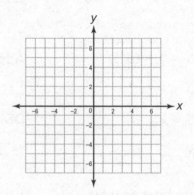

Graph the system of inequalities and shade the portion of the plane that represents the solution.

24. $\begin{cases} y < \frac{2}{3}x - 2 \\ y \geq -x \end{cases}$

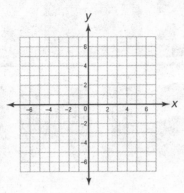

Solve.

25. Ginny has $1.60 made up of quarters and nickels. She has a total of 12 coins. How many of each coin does she have?

_____

26. At a food truck, Mr. Hoffman bought 3 tacos and a bottle of juice for $5.50. At the same food truck, Mr. Kim bought 5 tacos and 2 bottles of juice for $9.75. What is the price of a taco, and what is the price of a bottle of juice?

_____

Use the situation below to answer questions 27 and 28.

While shopping at the mall, Juan will spend $10 on lunch and buy some shirts for $25 each. He will spend no more than $150. He wants to know how many shirts he can buy.

27. **EXAMINE** What is the variable in the situation? What possible values can that variable have, given the situation?

_____

_____

28. **IDENTIFY** Write an inequality to describe this situation and solve it. List the property of equality that justifies each step of your work. What are the possible solutions to this problem?

Property of Equality:

Solution set: {_____}

USING MATH in BUSINE$$

Solve the problems to find out how a business can maximize its profits.

Leon has a small pottery business, making vases and serving bowls to sell at a store. It takes him an hour to make each item, and he can work no more than 15 hours per week. The store will buy at most 10 vases and at most 7 bowls each week. Leon makes a $20 profit on each vase and a $30 profit on each bowl.

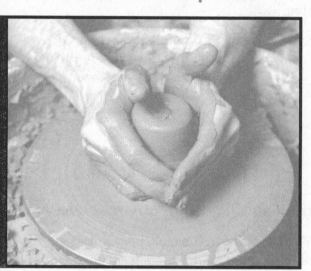

1 Write a system of inequalities to describe the situation.

Let *v* be the number of vases Leon makes each week.

Let *b* be the number of bowls he makes each week.

Write an inequality to model each constraint.

The number of vases cannot be negative: _____

The number of bowls cannot be negative: _____

The store will buy no more than 10 vases: _____

The store will buy no more than 7 bowls: _____

It takes him an hour to make each item, and he can work no more than 15 hours per week: _____

2 Graph the system on the coordinate grid below.

Use the horizontal axis to represent the number of vases and the vertical axis to represent the number of serving bowls. Shade only the area that contains the solutions to the system.

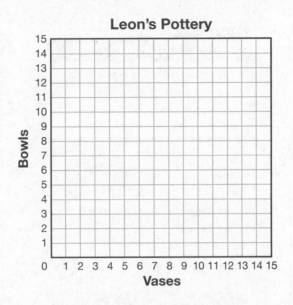

3 Is every point in the shaded region a solution to the problem? Explain your answer.

_____

_____

4 Recall that Leon makes a $20 profit on each vase and a $30 profit on each bowl. Write an equation to describe the amount of profit, P, he makes by selling v vases and b bowls.

_____

5 Identify the coordinates of the five points where the boundary lines of the solution set intersect. Substitute the coordinates of each intersection point to find the amount of profit if Leon sells those numbers of vases and bowls. Which point yields the highest value of P?

_____

_____

_____

_____

_____

6 How many vases and bowls should Leon make each week in order to earn the greatest possible profit?

_____

Grade 8 → Coordinate Algebra → Analytic Geometry

Grade 8

Expressions & Equations

Work with radicals and integer exponents.

Understand the connections between proportional relationships, lines, and linear equations.

Analyze and solve linear equations and pairs of simultaneous linear equations.

Functions

Define, evaluate, and compare functions.

Use functions to model relationships between quantities.

Geometry

Understand congruence and similarity using physical models, transparencies, or geometry software.

Coordinate Algebra

Algebra

Reasoning with Equations & Inequalities

Represent and solve equations and inequalities graphically.

Functions

Interpreting Functions

Understand the concept of a function and use function notation.

Interpret functions that arise in applications in terms of the context.

Analyze functions using different representations.

Building Functions

Build a function that models a relationship between two quantities.

Build new functions from existing functions.

Linear, Quadratic, and Exponential Models

Construct and compare linear, quadratic, and exponential models and solve problems.

Interpret expressions for functions in terms of the situation they model.

Analytic Geometry

Algebra

Creating Equations

Create equations that describe numbers or relationships.

Reasoning with Equations & Inequalities

Solve systems of equations.

Functions

Interpreting Functions

Interpret functions that arise in applications in terms of the context.

Analyze functions using different representations.

Linear, Quadratic, and Exponential Models

Construct and compare linear, quadratic, and exponential models and solve problems.

Building Functions

Build a function that models a relationship between two quantities.

Build new functions from existing functions.

Statistics & Probability

Interpreting Categorical & Quantitative Data

Summarize, represent, and interpret data on two categorical and quantitative variables.

Unit 3
Linear and Exponential Functions

LESSON 13 Functions

UNDERSTAND A **relation** is a set of ordered pairs of the form (x, y). The equation $y = x + 4$ describes a relation. It relates the value of y to the value of x. A relation can be represented as an equation, a graph, a table, a mapping diagram, or a list of ordered pairs.

A **function** is a special kind of relation in which each **input**, the first value in the ordered pair, is mapped to one and only one **output**, the second value in the ordered pair.

This relation is not a function:

(1, 6), **(3**, 8), **(3**, 9)

The input 3 is assigned to two different outputs.

This relation is a function:

(1, 6), **(3**, 8), **(5**, 10)

Each input is assigned to only one output.

The set of all possible inputs for a function is called the function's **domain**. The set of all possible outputs for a function is called its **range**. The domain and range are sets that consist of values called **elements**. Look at the function shown in the mapping diagram. The domain for that function is the numbers $-4, -3, -2, -1$, and 0, or the set $\{-4, -3, -2, -1, 0\}$. The range is $\{-5, -4, -3, 2\}$.

Input	Output
-4	-5
-3	-4
-2	-3
-1	2
0	

A function can be written as an equation by using functional notation. In the equation $f(x) = 2^x + 1$, the notation $f(x)$ is read as "f of x." It takes the place of y and stands for the output of the function for the input x. So, when $x = 2$, $f(2) = 2^2 + 1 = 5$. This means that the function f includes the ordered pair $(2, 5)$.

This same function can be represented by a graph. By replacing $f(x)$ with y, the equation can be graphed on the xy-coordinate plane. The set of all the points on that graph is the function.

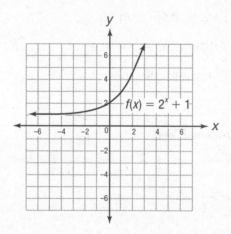

$f(x) = 2^x + 1$

Most often, a function is named by the letter f and has input x, but a function can be named by almost any letter or symbol. For example, a function might be named $g(x)$ or $a(x)$. A function in another situation might be named $h(t)$, so that the variable representing the input is t.

⊏ Connect

Does this graph represent a function?

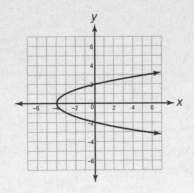

1

Perform the **vertical line test** by drawing a vertical line through the graph at $x = 5$.

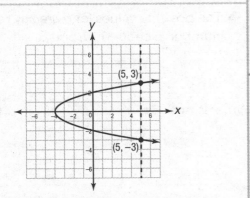

2

Determine if the graph represents a function.

If any vertical line drawn through a graph passes through more than one point, the graph does not represent a function. The vertical line passes through two points: $(5, 3)$ and $(5, -3)$. This means that the input value of 5 maps to two different outputs, 3 and -3, so the graph does not show a function.

▶ The graph does not pass the vertical line test. It does not represent a function.

Does this table represent a function?

x	−2	−1	0	1	2	3
f(x)	$-2\frac{3}{4}$	$-2\frac{1}{2}$	-2	$-2\frac{1}{2}$	$-2\frac{3}{4}$	-3

Look at the input values in the table.

No input, or *x*-value, appears in the table more than once, so each input corresponds to only one output. This means that the table represents a function.

MODEL

Construct a mapping diagram by using the elements in the table. How can a mapping diagram help you determine if the relation is a function?

EXAMPLE A If the table at the right represents a function, what are the possible values for a?

x	$f(x)$
-1	-1.5
3	6
a	14
6	17

1

Think of the definition of a function.

Recall that a function is a relation in which every input, or x-value, maps to only one output, or $f(x)$-value.

So, if the table at the right represents a function, no x-value can map to more than one $f(x)$-value.

2

Find possible values for a.

If $a = -1$, 3, or 6, then an x-value would map to more than one $f(x)$-value. For example, if $a = -1$, then -1 would map to both -1.5 and 14. In those cases, the relation would no longer be a function.

▶ The possible values for a are any real number except -1, 3, and 6.

EXAMPLE B If the table at the right represents a relation that is **not** a function, what are the possible values for b?

x	$f(x)$
-1	-1.5
3	6
6	14
6	b

1

Think of the definition of a function.

If the table at the right represents a relation that is not a function, at least one x-value must map to more than one $f(x)$-value.

2

Find possible values for b.

The table shows that the x-value 6 is repeated. In the first instance, 6 maps to the $f(x)$-value 14.

If $b = 14$, then the relation is a function because every x-value maps to only one $f(x)$-value.

For the relation not to be a function, b can be any number except 14.

▶ The possible values for b are all real numbers except 14.

TRY

Write two ordered pairs, each with the same x-coordinate. Could these two ordered pairs belong to the same function?

A function in which the input variable is an exponent is an **exponential function**.

EXAMPLE C Evaluate the exponential function $h(t) = 3^t + 1$ for $t = 4$.

1

Substitute 4 for t in the equation.

Evaluating a function means finding the output for a given input. In this case, the input is 4, so find the value of $h(4)$.

$h(t) = 3^t + 1$

$h(4) = 3^4 + 1$

2

Perform the calculations to find the output.

$h(4) = 3^4 + 1$

$h(4) = 81 + 1$

▶ $h(4) = 82$

A function in which the input variable is raised to the first power is a **linear function**.

EXAMPLE D The linear function $g(x) = 3x + 4$ has the domain $\{-2, -1, 0, 1, 2\}$. Find the range of $g(x)$.

1

Create a table of values to find all the elements in the range.

In order to find the elements of the range, evaluate the function at each value in the domain.

x	$g(x) = 3x + 4$	$g(x)$
-2	$g(-2) = 3(-2) + 4 = -2$	-2
-1	$g(-1) = 3(-1) + 4 = 1$	1
0	$g(0) = 3(0) + 4 = 4$	4
1	$g(1) = 3(1) + 4 = 7$	7
2	$g(2) = 3(2) + 4 = 10$	10

2

Collect the values of $g(x)$ into a set.

The values of $g(x)$ are $-2, 1, 4, 7$, and 10.

▶ The range of $g(x)$ is $\{-2, 1, 4, 7, 10\}$.

TRY

The function $P(t) = 10 \cdot 2^t$ can be used to represent the population of bacteria in a Petri dish after t hours. What are the values of $P(0)$ and $P(4)$? What do these values represent?

Practice

Determine whether each relation is a function.

1.

Input	Output
0	2
1	6
2	18
3	54

_____

2.

Input	Output
1	10
3	30
5	50
7	70

_____

3.

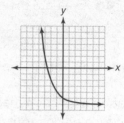

_____

> **HINT** Does a vertical line pass through more than one point?

Write *true* or *false* for each statement. If false, rewrite the statement so it is true.

4. Every relation is a function.

_____

5. The range of a function is the set of all of its inputs.

_____

6. To graph the function $f(x) = x + 2$, you can draw the graph of $y = x + 2$ because the graph of f is the graph of the equation $y = f(x)$.

_____

Choose the best answer.

7. Which value could **not** be substituted for a in the table if the table represents a function?

x	g(x)
−3	24
a	4
1	4
2	−1

A. 1

B. 0

C. −1

D. −3

8. Which value or values could be substituted for b in the table to ensure that the table represents a function?

x	h(x)
−1	$2\frac{1}{4}$
0	3
1	b
4	258

A. 1 only

B. $3\frac{1}{4}$ only

C. 18 only

D. any real number

Evaluate the functions for the inputs given. Show your work in the tables.

9.

x	$d(x) = \frac{x}{2} - 1$	d(x)
−4	$d(-4) =$	
−2	$d(-2) =$	
0	$d(0) =$	
2	$d(2) =$	
4	$d(4) =$	

10.

x	$f(x) = 10^x + 5$	f(x)
0	$f(0) =$	
1	$f(1) =$	
2	$f(2) =$	
3	$f(3) =$	
4	$f(4) =$	

Solve.

11. A ball dropped onto a hard floor from a height of 16 inches bounces back up to $\frac{1}{2}$ its previous height on each successive bounce. The function $h(b) = 16 \cdot \left(\frac{1}{2}\right)^b$ can be used to represent this situation. To what height, in inches, will the ball rise on its third bounce? (Hint: Evaluate $h(b) = 16 \cdot \left(\frac{1}{2}\right)^b$ for $b = 3$.)

_____

_____

12. **EVALUATE** The total charge for a babysitting job that lasts *t* hours can be represented by the function $c(t) = 2 + 9t$. Evaluate this function for the domain {1, 2, 3}. Briefly explain what each pair of values means in this problem situation.

_____

_____

13. **JUSTIFY** If you switch the domain and range of a function, will the relation that results sometimes be a function? Will it always be a function? Give examples to justify your answer.

_____

_____

Key Features of Functions

LESSON 14

Intercepts and End Behavior

UNDERSTAND The graphs and tables of functions contain various key features. These key features are often important for understanding functions and using them to solve problems.

The **x-intercept** of a function is the point $(a, 0)$ at which the graph intersects the x-axis. The **y-intercept** is the point $(0, b)$ at which the graph intersects the y-axis. In the graph of $f(x) = 3^x - 3$ shown, the x-intercept is $(1, 0)$ and the y-intercept is $(0, -2)$.

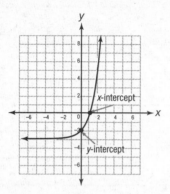

x	f(x)	
−2	$-2\frac{8}{9}$	
−1	$-2\frac{2}{3}$	
0	−2	← y-intercept
1	0	← x-intercept
2	6	

You can locate the x-intercept in a table by finding the row whose y-value is 0. The y-intercept is in the row whose x-value is 0.

Functions can also be described in terms of their **end behavior**. In the graph of $f(x) = 3^x - 3$, look at the arrows on each end of the graph. The arrow on the right end of the curve shows that as x increases, y also continuously increases. Since the value of y is continuously increasing, this function has no **maximum** value. The arrow on the left end of the curve shows that as x decreases (becomes more negative), y approaches but never reaches −3. This line that the graph approaches but never touches is called the **asymptote** of the function. Since the graph asymptotically approaches the line $y = -3$ but never intersects it, the function has no **minimum** value.

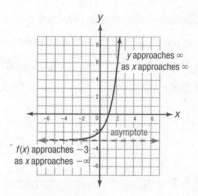

If enough values are listed in a table, you can estimate end behavior based on the values of $f(x)$. Starting from the top of the second column and moving down, notice that the value of $f(x)$ gets larger and larger. Starting from the bottom of the column and moving up, notice that $f(x)$ gets smaller (more negative) but never passes −3.

x	f(x)	
−3	$-2\frac{26}{27}$	f(x) decreases toward −3
−2	$-2\frac{8}{9}$	
−1	$-2\frac{2}{3}$	
0	−2	
1	0	f(x) increases without bound
2	6	
3	24	

⫷ Connect

The function $f(x) = \left(\frac{1}{2}\right)^x + 2$ is graphed below.

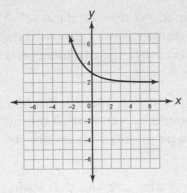

Identify the function's intercepts and describe its end behavior.

1

Find the *x*- and *y*-intercepts of the function.

Where does the graph intersect the *x*-axis?

The graph never intersects the *x*-axis, so the function does not have an *x*-intercept.

Where does the graph intersect the *y*-axis?

The graph intersects the *y*-axis at (0, 3). The function's *y*-intercept is (0, 3).

2

Describe the end behavior of the function.

What happens to the graph as *x* values approach $-\infty$?

As *x* values approach $-\infty$, *y* values increase toward ∞.

What happens to the graph as *x* values approach ∞?

As *x* values approach ∞, *y* values decrease toward 2.

This means that the function has an asymptote of $y = 2$.

TRY

Does the function have a minimum and a maximum? If so, what are they? If not, why not?

UNDERSTAND Remember that a function's domain is the set of all possible inputs. For a function such as $f(x) = 3^x - 3$, the domain is the interval on the x-axis on which the function is defined, in which the graph exists. The range of a function is the interval on the y-axis containing all possible outputs.

Interval notation can be used to represent an interval. In interval notation, the end values of an interval are listed as a pair separated by a comma. A bracket beside the value means that it is included in the interval, while a parenthesis means that it is not. For example, the domain [0, 5) is equivalent to $0 \leq x < 5$.

The domain can be broken up into smaller intervals that share a certain characteristic. For example, it can be useful to divide the domain into sections in which the value of $f(x)$ is positive and sections where it is negative.

Look again at a graph of the function $f(x) = 3^x - 3$. Determine the intervals where y is positive and where y is negative. The value of y is negative when $x < 1$. The value of y is positive when $x > 1$. Using interval notation, y is negative on the interval $(-\infty, 1)$ and positive on the interval $(1, \infty)$.

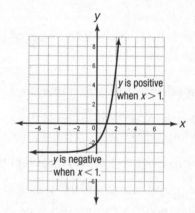

The domain can also be divided into sections where the value of $f(x)$ is increasing from left to right and where it is decreasing from left to right.

Look at the graph. From left to right, the graph is always curving upward. The value of y is always increasing as the value of x increases. This is true across the entire domain, from negative infinity $(-\infty)$ to positive infinity (∞). The function is always increasing. In other words, the interval of increase is $(-\infty, \infty)$.

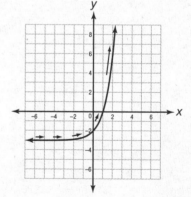

Usually, these intervals can also be determined from tables by looking at the values in the $f(x)$ column.

Connect

The graph below represents an exponential function *f*. The table below represents a linear function *g*.

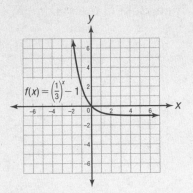

$$f(x) = \left(\frac{1}{3}\right)^x - 1$$

$g(x) = -\frac{1}{3}x$	
x	**g(x)**
−6	2
−3	1
0	0
3	−1
6	−2

Compare and contrast functions *f* and *g* by using these key features: domain; range; intervals of increase and decrease; and positive and negative intervals.

1 Identify the domain and range.

The end behavior of the graph of *f* shows that it extends indefinitely both left and right. Thus, its domain is all real numbers, or the interval $(-\infty, \infty)$.

Since *f* has an asymptote of $y = -1$, its range is $y > -1$, or the interval $(-1, \infty)$.

The table for function *g* does not list all values of *x* or *g*(*x*), but it also does not give evidence of any boundaries (such as an asymptote). Since *g* is a linear function, without other information, you may assume that the domain and range are all real numbers.

2 Compare the intervals of increase and decrease.

The graph of *f* continuously curves downward. So, *f* is always decreasing.

The table for function *g* shows that as *x*-values increase, *g*(*x*)-values decrease, so *g* is also a decreasing function.

Both functions are decreasing across their entire domains. The interval of decrease is $(-\infty, \infty)$ for both functions.

3 Compare positive intervals and negative intervals for the functions.

The graph of *f* intercepts the *x*-axis at (0, 0). The third row of values in the table shows that *g* also has an *x*-intercept of (0, 0). The functions are always decreasing.

Functions *f* and *g* are both positive when $x < 0$, on the interval $(-\infty, 0)$, and negative when $x > 0$, on the interval $(0, \infty)$.

CHECK Graph function *g* on the same grid as *f*. Compare and contrast the two graphs to check the answers on this page.

EXAMPLE A The domain of a linear function is $\{-1 \leq x \leq 2\}$. The function has an *x*-intercept at (1, 0) and a *y*-intercept at (0, −3). Graph the function. Then identify the maximum, minimum, range, and intervals of increase and decrease for the function.

1

Graph the function, paying attention to the restricted domain.

Plot the intercepts. Draw a line through the intercepts, but do not extend it to the left of −1 or to the right of 2 on the *x*-axis.

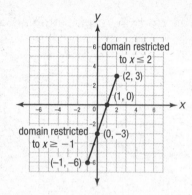

2

Describe the function's minimum, maximum, and range.

When the domain is restricted to $\{-1 \leq x \leq 2\}$, the lowest point on the graph is at (−1, −6). Thus, the minimum *y*-value is −6.

The highest point on the graph is at (2, 3). Thus, the maximum *y*-value is 3.

The range is all values of *y* greater than or equal to the minimum, −6, and less than or equal to the maximum, 3. This can be represented as $\{-6 \leq y \leq 3\}$.

3

Identify intervals of increase or decrease.

The line segment slants up from left to right, so the function is always increasing.

The value of *y* increases across the entire domain. The function increases on the interval $\{-1 \leq x \leq 2\}$.

TRY

Identify intervals where the linear function graphed above is positive and where it is negative.

EXAMPLE B A piano is being lowered from an apartment that is 18 feet above the sidewalk. The piano descends at a constant rate. The piano's elevation over time is represented by the linear function graphed below. Identify and interpret the key features of the graph.

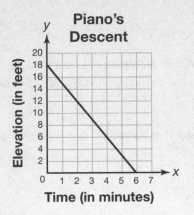

1

Identify and interpret the domain.

The graph is shown to exist on the domain [0, 6]. This domain contains the minutes over which the piano is being lowered.

2

Identify and interpret intervals of increase and decrease.

The function is decreasing for the entire domain. This means that the piano's elevation is always decreasing.

The function has no interval of increase. This makes sense because the piano is always being lowered and never being raised.

3

Identify and interpret the intercepts.

The *y*-intercept, (0, 18), represents the piano's initial elevation of 18 feet.

The *x*-intercept, (6, 0), shows that it takes 6 minutes for the piano to reach the sidewalk, at an elevation of 0 feet.

TRY

What is the range for this function? What does it represent in the problem?

Practice

Rewrite each domain in interval notation.

1. $\{5 < x < 100\}$

2. $\{x \geq 0\}$

3. {all real numbers}

_____

_____

_____

> **REMEMBER** A bracket means include the value, and a parenthesis means exclude the value.

For each graph, determine whether the function is increasing or decreasing. Identify the interval of increase or decrease.

4.

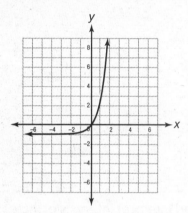

_____

_____

5.

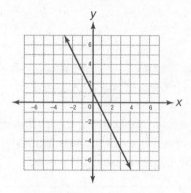

_____

_____

 HINT Does the graph curve (or slant) upward or downward?

Identify the intercepts of the given function.

6.

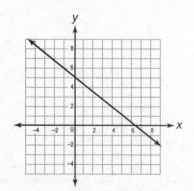

x-intercept: _____

y-intercept: _____

7.

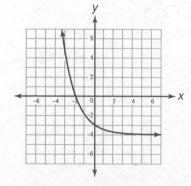

x-intercept: _____

y-intercept: _____

Identify the intercepts of the given function.

8.

x	−24	−12	0	12	24
f(x)	−8	−6	−4	−2	0

x-intercept: _____

y-intercept: _____

9.

x	−2	−1	0	1	2
g(x)	−9.99	−9.9	−9	0	90

x-intercept: _____

y-intercept: _____

Fill in each blank with an appropriate word or words.

10. A point at which a graph crosses the y-axis is a(n) _____.

11. A function's _____ is a line that the graph of the function approaches but never intersects.

12. The _____ of a function describes how its f(x)-values change as x approaches positive infinity or negative infinity.

13. The greatest y-value on the graph of a function is the function's _____.

Choose the best answer.

14. Which statement about this function is **not** true?

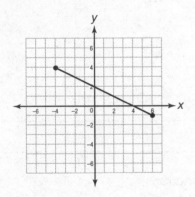

A. Its domain is $\{-4 \leq x \leq 6\}$.

B. Its range is $\{-1 \leq y \leq 4\}$.

C. It has a y-intercept at (0, 2).

D. It has a maximum of 6.

15. The table below shows some ordered pairs for an exponential function.

x	f(x)
−1	$-\frac{5}{6}$
0	0
1	5
2	35
3	215

Which statement about this function is **not** true?

A. Its x-intercept is the same as its y-intercept.

B. It is positive on the interval $(0, \infty)$.

C. It is increasing on the interval $(-\infty, \infty)$.

D. As x approaches $-\infty$, f(x) approaches ∞.

Describe the end behavior of each function.

16.

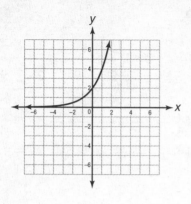

17.

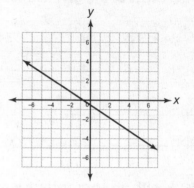

_____

_____

_____

_____

Use the graph and table below for questions 18–20. The graph represents exponential function _f_. The table represents some ordered pairs for linear function _g_.

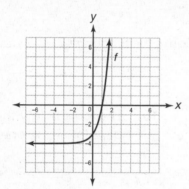

x	g(x)
−1	−8
0	−4
1	0
2	4
3	8

18. Compare and contrast the intercepts of the functions.

_____

_____

19. Compare the increasing and decreasing intervals of the functions.

_____

_____

20. Compare the intervals on which the functions are positive and those on which they are negative.

_____

_____

For each graph, describe the intervals where the function is positive and where it is negative.

21.

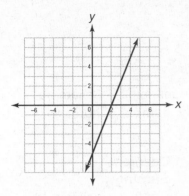

_____

_____

22.

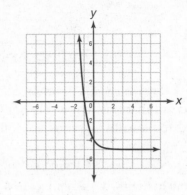

_____

_____

Solve.

23. `INTERPRET` A cylinder contains 20 milliliters of water. The water begins to leak out as represented by the linear function graphed on the right. Identify the intercepts and interpret what they mean in this situation.

_____

_____

_____

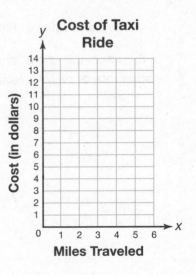

24. `CREATE` The cost of a taxi ride includes a $3 fee plus $2 for each mile traveled. So, a 1-mile ride costs $5 and a 2-mile ride costs $7. Create a graph to represent this linear function. Identify the domain for your graph and explain why you chose it.

_____

_____

LESSON 15 Average Rate of Change

Finding Average Rate of Change

UNDERSTAND Rates allow us to relate quantities measured in different units. For example, the table and graph below show a linear function that compares the number of hours a cashier works to his total earnings, in dollars.

Cashier's Earnings	
Time in hours, x	Earnings in \$, y
0	0
2	15
4	30

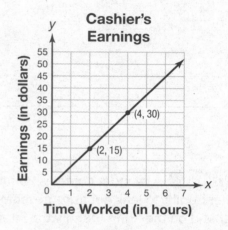

The cashier's earnings change, depending on the number of hours he works. His pay rate is an example of a **rate of change**. A rate of change shows how one quantity changes relative to another quantity. To calculate the average rate of change between two ordered pairs (x_1, y_1) and (x_2, y_2), use this formula:

$$\text{average rate of change} = \frac{\text{change in } y}{\text{change in } x} = \frac{y_2 - y_1}{x_2 - x_1}$$

For the function describing the cashier's earnings, choose two ordered pairs, such as (2, 15) and (4, 30).

$$\text{average rate of change} = \frac{30 - 15}{4 - 2} = \frac{15}{2} = 7.50$$

In this case, the rate of change compares dollars earned to hours worked. So, the cashier's hourly rate of pay is \$7.50 per hour.

⊏ Connect

A basketball championship begins with 64 teams. Every time a team wins a game, it goes on to the next round. Once a team loses a game, it is eliminated from competition and does not play any more games. The number of teams in each round of the championship is a function of the round. That function is represented on the graph to the right. Compare the rate of change between rounds 1 and 2 to the rate of change between rounds 2 and 3.

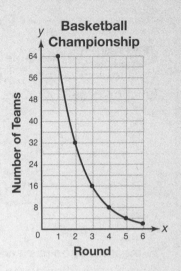

1

Calculate the average rate of change between rounds 1 and 2.

Find the rate of change from (1, 64) to (2, 32).

$$\frac{32 - 64}{2 - 1} = \frac{-32}{1} = -32 \text{ teams per round}$$

Between rounds 1 and 2, the number of teams decreases at a rate of 32 teams per round.

2

Calculate the average rate of change between rounds 2 and 3.

Find the rate of change from (2, 32) to (3, 16).

$$\frac{16 - 32}{3 - 2} = \frac{-16}{1} = -16 \text{ teams per round}$$

Between rounds 2 and 3, the number of teams decreases at a rate of 16 teams per round.

3

Compare the rates of change.

▶ The rate of change is different between rounds 1 and 2 than it is between rounds 2 and 3. The rate between rounds 2 and 3 is half what it was between rounds 1 and 2.

TRY

Choose a pair of points on the graph below and find the average rate of change between them. Compare your result with those of other students. Did they use the same two points?

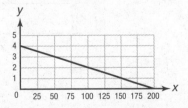

Comparing Average Rates of Change

UNDERSTAND The table below represents the linear function $f(x) = 2x + 1$. Notice that as x-values increase by 1, $f(x)$-values increase by a constant amount, 2. In other words, the function grows by an equal amount, 2, in each unit interval.

	+1	+1	+1	+1	+1
x	0	1	2	3	4	5
f(x)	1	3	5	7	9	11
	+2	+2	+2	+2	+2

A linear function has a constant rate of change. Its average rate of change is the same no matter what interval you are observing. The constant rate of change of a linear function is its **slope**.

An exponential function has a graph that is a curve. An exponential growth function is always increasing, while an exponential decay function is always decreasing. The table below represents an exponential growth function.

	+1	+1	+1	+1	+1
x	0	1	2	3	4	5
f(x)	1	2	4	8	16	32
	×2	×2	×2	×2	×2

Notice that as each x-value increases by 1, each $f(x)$-value is multiplied by 2. The value of the function, $f(x)$, does not grow by constant amounts over equal intervals, so it does not have a constant rate of change. However, $f(x)$ does grow by the same factor over equal intervals. This function increases by a factor of 2, or doubles, over each unit interval.

The value of an exponential function grows by equal factors over equal intervals. If the factor by which the function changes is greater than 1, then the function represents exponential growth. If the factor is less than 1, then the function represents exponential decay.

The average rates of change for an exponential function grow by the same factor as the values of the function. For the table above, the average rate of change doubled over each unit interval.

	+1	+1	+1	+1	+1
x	0	1	2	3	4	5
f(x)	1	2	4	8	16	32
	+1	+2	+4	+8	+16
	×2	×2	×2	×2	

⊏ Connect

Find and describe the average rate of change for four consecutive pairs of values in the table. What type of function is this?

x	−3	−2	−1	0	1
f(x)	64	16	4	1	$\frac{1}{4}$

1

Determine the average rate of change for consecutive pairs of values $(x, f(x))$.

Be sure that the intervals are the same between each pair of points. The difference between each pair of x-values in the table is 1 unit, so the intervals are the same.

between $(−3, 64)$ and $(−2, 16)$:

$$\frac{16 − 64}{−2 − (−3)} = \frac{−48}{1} = −48$$

between $(−2, 16)$ and $(−1, 4)$:

$$\frac{4 − 16}{−1 − (−2)} = \frac{−12}{1} = −12$$

between $(−1, 4)$ and $(0, 1)$:

$$\frac{1 − 4}{0 − (−1)} = \frac{−3}{1} = −3$$

between $(0, 1)$ and $\left(1, \frac{1}{4}\right)$:

$$\frac{\frac{1}{4} − 1}{1 − 0} = \frac{−\frac{3}{4}}{1} = −\frac{3}{4}$$

2

Compare the average rates of change in order to classify the function.

The average rates of change for the first four consecutive pairs of points are:

$−48, −12, −3, −\frac{3}{4}$.

These rates are different. The rate of change is not constant, so this is not a linear function.

The value of $f(x)$ decreases by a common factor over each interval.

between $(−3, 64)$ and $(−2, 16)$:

$$\frac{16}{64} = \frac{1}{4}$$

between $(−2, 16)$ and $(−1, 4)$:

$$\frac{4}{16} = \frac{1}{4}$$

between $(−1, 4)$ and $(0, 1)$:

$$\frac{1}{4} = \frac{1}{4}$$

between $(0, 1)$ and $\left(1, \frac{1}{4}\right)$:

$$\frac{\frac{1}{4}}{1} = \frac{1}{4}$$

▶ Since the values of $f(x)$ change by an equal factor over equal intervals and that factor is $\frac{1}{4}$, this is an example of an exponential decay function.

DISCUSS

Why is it important to keep the intervals between each pair of values $(x, f(x))$ the same when comparing average rates of change?

EXAMPLE A Determine the average rate of change between several consecutive pairs of points for the function $f(x) = -3x + 2$. Describe how the function is changing and classify it.

1

Create a table of ordered pairs for the function.

x	$f(x) = -3x + 2$	$f(x)$
−2	$f(-2) = -3(-2) + 2 = 6 + 2 = 8$	8
−1	$f(-1) = -3(-1) + 2 = 3 + 2 = 5$	5
0	$f(0) = -3(0) + 2 = 0 + 2 = 2$	2
1	$f(1) = -3(1) + 2 = -3 + 2 = -1$	−1
2	$f(2) = -3(2) + 2 = -6 + 2 = -4$	−4

2

Determine the average rate of change for four consecutive pairs of values $(x, f(x))$.

Be sure that the intervals are the same between each pair of points.

between $(-2, 8)$ and $(-1, 5)$:
$\frac{5 - 8}{-1 - (-2)} = \frac{-3}{1} = -3$

between $(-1, 5)$ and $(0, 2)$:
$\frac{2 - 5}{0 - (-1)} = \frac{-3}{1} = -3$

between $(0, 2)$ and $(1, -1)$:
$\frac{-1 - 2}{1 - 0} = \frac{-3}{1} = -3$

between $(1, -1)$ and $(2, -4)$:
$\frac{-4 - (-1)}{2 - 1} = \frac{-3}{1} = -3$

3

Compare the average rates of change.

The average rates of change are all the same, −3.

Since the rate of change is constant, $f(x) = -3x + 2$ must be a linear function.

▶ The rate of change, or slope, is −3 for all pairs of values. The function is linear.

DISCUSS

Does the equation $y = -3x + 5$ provide any clues about what the rate of change for the linear function is? Explain.

EXAMPLE B Compare the rates of change for $f(x) = 10^x$ and function g, which is represented in the table.

x	g(x)
−1	$\frac{1}{8}$
0	1
1	8
2	64
3	512

1

Create a table of values for f.

x	$f(x) = 10^x$	f(x)
−1	$f(-1) = 10^{-1} = \frac{1}{10}$	$\frac{1}{10}$
0	$f(0) = 10^0 = 1$	1
1	$f(1) = 10^1 = 10$	10
2	$f(2) = 10^2 = 100$	100
3	$f(3) = 10^3 = 1,000$	1,000

2

Find the average rate of change for three consecutive intervals for function f.

between (0, 1) and (1, 10): $\frac{10 - 1}{1 - 0} = \frac{9}{1} = 9$

between (1, 10) and (2, 100):

$\frac{100 - 10}{2 - 1} = \frac{90}{1} = 90$

between (2, 100) and (3, 1,000):

$\frac{1,000 - 100}{3 - 2} = \frac{900}{1} = 900$

The rate of change of the function f is not constant. Each average rate of change is 10 times the previous rate of change.

3

Find the average rate of change for three consecutive points for function g.

between (0, 1) and (1, 8): $\frac{8 - 1}{1 - 0} = \frac{7}{1} = 7$

between (1, 8) and (2, 64):

$\frac{64 - 8}{2 - 1} = \frac{56}{1} = 56$

between (2, 64) and (3, 512):

$\frac{512 - 64}{3 - 2} = \frac{448}{1} = 448$

The rate of change of the function g is not constant. Each average rate of change is 8 times the previous average rate of change.

▶ The average rates of change for function f are growing more rapidly than the average rates of change for function g.

DISCUSS

By what factor are the values of function $f(x)$ growing? Does the equation $f(x) = 10^x$ help you determine that factor? How could you write an explicit expression for $g(x)$?

Practice

Fill in the blanks by writing an operation sign and a number to show how the *f(x)*-values are changing in each unit interval. Then classify each function as linear or exponential.

1.

	+1	+1	+1	+1	+1
x	−1	0	1	2	3	4
f(x)	$\frac{1}{6}$	1	6	36	216	1,296

_____

> **HINT**
> Over each interval, does *f(x)* change by an equal amount or an equal factor?

2.

	+1	+1	+1	+1	+1
x	−3	−2	−1	0	1	2
f(x)	11	7	3	−1	−5	−9

_____

Fill in the blanks with an appropriate word or phrase.

3. The average _____ between two ordered pairs (*x*, *y*) is the ratio $\frac{\text{change in } y}{\text{change in } x}$.

4. In a linear function, the rate of change is also known as the _____.

5. The average rate of change for a _____ function is constant.

6. The average rate of change for an exponential function grows by equal _____ per unit interval.

Use the graph for questions 7–10.

7. Determine the average rate of change between $\left(-1, \frac{4}{3}\right)$ and (0, 2).

_____

8. Determine the average rate of change between (0, 2) and (1, 4).

_____

9. Determine the average rate of change between (1, 4) and (2, 10).

_____

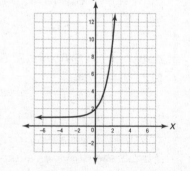

10. Write a sentence or two comparing the average rates of change you found. (If they vary, describe how they vary.)

_____

_____

Use the information about function $f(x)$, given as a table below, and function $g(x) = 5^x$ for questions 11–14.

11. Using the table on the right, find the average rate of change for three unit intervals for function f.

x	f(x)
−1	$\frac{1}{4}$
0	1
1	4
2	16

_____

_____

_____

12. Complete the table to find four consecutive ordered pairs for the function $g(x) = 5^x$.

x	$g(x) = 5^x$	g(x)
−1	$g(-1) =$	
0	$g(0) =$	
1	$g(1) =$	
2	$g(2) =$	

13. Find the average rate of change for three unit intervals for function g.

_____

_____

_____

14. Compare the changes in the values of functions f and g.

_____

_____

_____

15. (INTERPRET) The graph shows how the total amount that a landscaper charges for a job changes depending on the number of hours she works. Identify the slope of the graph. Then interpret what this slope represents in this problem situation.

_____

_____

_____

Graphing Functions

Graphing Linear Functions

UNDERSTAND The various representations of a function give different details about the function. An equation in function notation explains the rule for generating an output from any given input. A table can list many, but usually not all, input/output pairs for the function. A graph is a visual representation of all the input/output pairs of the function.

The graph of a function is the graph of $y = f(x)$, so y takes on the value of the output. If you choose any point (x, y) on the graph of a function, the y-coordinate is the output of the function when the x-coordinate is the input. Every point on the graph is a solution to the equation $y = f(x)$.

To understand the most about a function, it is often helpful to translate from one form to another. By examining the equation of the function, you can often identify key features that will help you construct the graph of the function.

Examine the linear function represented symbolically as $f(x) = \frac{3}{2}x + 1$. Its graph on the xy-coordinate plane is $y = f(x)$ or $y = \frac{3}{2}x + 1$. The equation is in **slope-intercept form**, $y = mx + b$, where m represents the slope and b represents the y-intercept. For $y = \frac{3}{2}x + 1$, the slope or rate of change, m, is $\frac{3}{2}$, and the y-intercept, b, is 1.

This is enough information to graph the function. The y-intercept of a linear equation $y = mx + b$ is at $(0, b)$. For $y = \frac{3}{2}x + 1$, the y-intercept is at $(0, 1)$. Plotting this point starts your graph. Now you can use the slope to find another point on the graph. The slope is a rate of change that tells how to move from one point on the graph to another. It is the ratio $\frac{\text{change in } y}{\text{change in } x}$. Place your finger at the y-intercept and count 3 units up and 2 units to the right to find another point, (2, 4). Draw a straight line through those points. Every point on the line is a solution for $y = \frac{3}{2}x + 1$. So, $(-4, -5)$, $(-2, -2)$, $(0, 1)$, and $(2, 4)$ are all solutions.

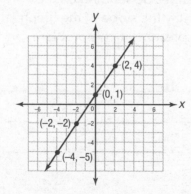

Sometimes, a linear equation will not be in slope-intercept form. In that case, you may need to put it in that form yourself before graphing it.

⊂ Connect

Graph the linear equation $6x + 3y = 12$ on a coordinate plane. Identify at least three ordered pairs that are solutions for the equation.

1

Rewrite the equation in slope-intercept form and identify the *y*-intercept and the slope.

$6x + 3y = 12$	Subtract $6x$ from both sides.
$3y = -6x + 12$	Divide both sides by 3.
$y = -2x + 4$	

2

Plot the *y*-intercept and use the slope to find a second point on the line.

After plotting (0, 4), count down 2 units and 1 unit to the right. Plot a point there at (1, 2).

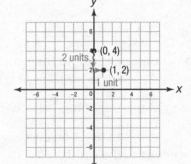

3

Draw a line through the points. Locate a third point on the line.

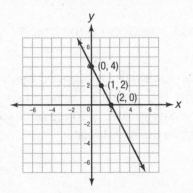

You can "eyeball" another point on your line, or you can use the slope to find a third point.

▶ The ordered pairs (0, 4), (1, 2), and (2, 0) are solutions for $6x + 3y = 12$.

CHECK

Use a graphing calculator to check your work. Press `Y=`. Enter $Y_1 = -2X+4$. Press `GRAPH`.

Does the graph on your calculator screen look like the graph drawn on the left? If you press `2nd` `GRAPH`, do the data in the table match the graph on the left?

Graphing Exponential Functions

UNDERSTAND You can also use key features to help you graph an exponential function. A general exponential function has the form $f(x) = a \cdot b^x + c$, where $a \neq 0$, $b > 0$ and $b \neq 1$, and c is a real number.

Examine the exponential function $f(x) = 3 \cdot 2^x - 4$. In this function, $a = 3$, $b = 2$, and $c = -4$. To graph this function on the xy-coordinate plane, graph $y = 3 \cdot 2^x - 4$.

The simplest key feature to find from the graph is the horizontal asymptote. No matter what input x is entered, the term $a \cdot b^x$ can never equal 0, so $f(x)$ can never equal c. So the line $y = c$ is a horizontal asymptote. Thus, the given function has a horizontal asymptote at $y = -4$.

The parameter a tells where the graph lies in relation to the asymptote.

- If $a > 0$, then the graph lies entirely above the asymptote.

- If $a < 0$, then the graph lies entirely below the asymptote.

The y-intercept, $(0, f(0))$, of an exponential function is located at the point $(0, a + c)$.

$$f(0) = a \cdot b^0 + c$$

simplifies to

$$f(0) = a \cdot 1 + c = a + c$$

since any number raised to the power of 0 is equal to 1.
For $y = 3 \cdot 2^x - 4$, the y-intercept is $(0, -1)$.

The parameter b describes how to move from one point to another on the graph.

- If $b > 1$, the function curves away from the asymptote as x increases (as the graph moves to the right).

- If $0 < b < 1$, the function approaches the asymptote as x increases (as the graph moves to the right).

For the example function, $b = 2$. This means the value of y will double (be multiplied by 2) as the graph moves 1 unit to the right. At $x = 0$ (the y-intercept), the graph is 3 units above the asymptote. At $x = 1$, the graph will be twice as far from the asymptote, 6 units above it. At $x = 2$, the graph will be twice that distance, or 12 units, above the asymptote.

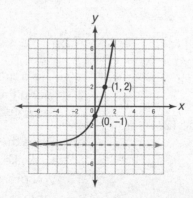

⊏ Connect

Use what you know about key features to graph $f(x) = 3\left(\frac{1}{2}\right)^x$.

1

Identify the parameters.

An exponential function has the form
$f(x) = a \cdot b^x + c$.
In $y = 3\left(\frac{1}{2}\right)^x$, $a = 3$, $b = \frac{1}{2}$, and $c = 0$.

2

Identify the asymptote.

The asymptote is the line $y = c$, in this case, $y = 0$, or the x-axis.

3

Identify the y-intercept.

Any number raised to the power of 0 equals 1.

So, when $x = 0$, $y = 3\left(\frac{1}{2}\right)^0 = 3(1) = 3$.

The y-intercept will be at $(0, 3)$.

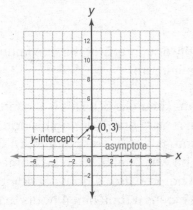

4

Use b as a factor to find additional points on the graph.

Since $b = \frac{1}{2}$, moving along the x-axis 1 unit means dropping half the distance to the asymptote. Since the y-intercept is 3 units above the asymptote, at $x = 1$, the graph will be 1.5 units above the asymptote, and at $x = 2$, the graph will be 0.75 unit above it.

Since $0 < b < 1$, connect these points with a smooth curve that approaches the asymptote.

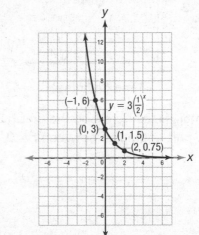

DISCUSS

How could you use the value of b to find points to the left of the y-intercept?

EXAMPLE A Sean is at his grandmother's house, which is 60 miles from his home. He starts riding home at time $t = 0$. His distance from his home, $d(t)$, after t hours can be modeled by the function $d(t) = 60 - 15t$. Graph the function for the domain $0 \leq t \leq 4$. Explain why the domain must be restricted in that way and what the maximum and minimum values mean in this situation.

1

Identify the type of function.

Is the function linear or exponential? The equation $d(t) = 60 - 15t$ has a variable, t, raised to the power of 1. So, the function is linear.

2

Identify the slope and y-intercept from the equation.

The graph of the function is the graph of the equation $d(t) = 60 - 15t$, or $d(t) = -15t + 60$, for all values of t between 0 and 4, inclusive. The slope, m, of the line is -15, and its y-intercept, $(0, b)$, is $(0, 60)$.

3

Graph the function, choosing an appropriate scale and label for each axis.

Plot the y-intercept. According to the slope, another point is 15 units down and 1 unit to the right, at $(1, 45)$. Draw a line through those points.

▶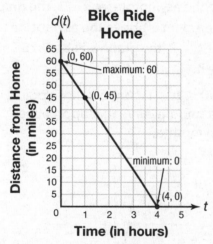

The domain is restricted, so the graph is only the part of the line between $t = 0$ and $t = 4$.

4

Identify and interpret the maximum and minimum.

▶ The maximum is 60. This is the farthest Sean is from home during his ride. The minimum is at 0. The point $(4, 0)$ shows that he was 0 miles from his home—or at home—after 4 hours of riding. That means it took him 4 hours to reach his home.

DISCUSS

Why is the graph a line segment instead of an entire line? Do values outside the domain make sense?

EXAMPLE B The equation $f(x) = 3x + 1$ represents a linear function f. The table of values on the right represents an exponential function g.

Graph functions f and g on the same coordinate plane. Then compare their properties.

x	g(x)
−1	$\frac{1}{3}$
0	1
1	3
2	9
3	27

1

Graph the functions.

To plot $f(x) = 3x + 1$, notice that it is in slope-intercept form. So, plot the y-intercept at (0, 1) and then count 3 units up and 1 unit to the right. Draw a straight line through the points.

To graph function g, plot and connect the coordinate pairs from the table.

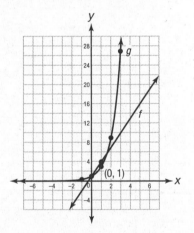

2

Use the graphs to compare the functions.

▶ Both functions have the same domain: the set of all real numbers.

Function f has a range that includes all real numbers. Function g approaches but never touches the x-axis (the line $y = 0$), so its range is $y > 0$.

Both functions have the same y-intercept at (0, 1).

Both are increasing functions. However, shortly after $x = 1$, the graph of function g starts to increase at a much more rapid rate than the graph of function f, which continues to increase at a constant rate. Notice that around $x = 1.5$, the graph of function g overtakes the graph of function f.

DISCUSS

Will an exponential function always overtake a linear function? Explain and give or sketch an example.

Practice

Circle the ordered pairs that are solutions for the graphed function.

1.

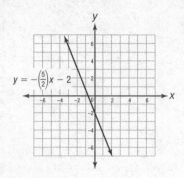

$y = -\left(\dfrac{5}{2}\right)x - 2$

(−2, 3)

(0, −2)

(1, −3)

2.

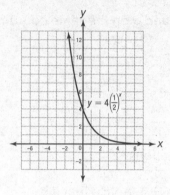

$y = 4\left(\dfrac{1}{2}\right)^x$

(1, 2)

(2, 1)

(4, 0)

> **REMEMBER** Each point on the graph is a solution for the equation.

Choose the best answer.

3. Which graph represents the function $f(x) = 2(3^x)$?

A.

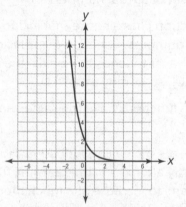

C.

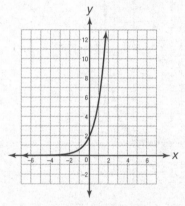

B.

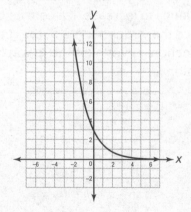

D.

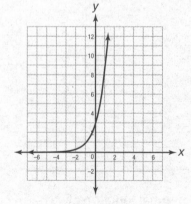

Graph each function.

4. $f(x) = -3x + 5$

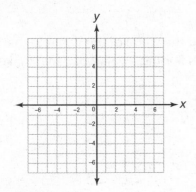

5. $f(x) = 4\left(\frac{1}{3}\right)^x$

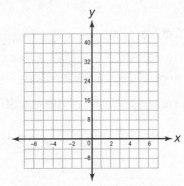

6. COMPARE The graph of $f(x) = 2\left(\frac{1}{5}\right)^x$ is shown on the coordinate plane. Graph $g(x) = 2(5^x)$ on the same coordinate plane. Then compare the end behavior of the two functions.

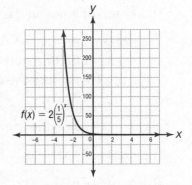

_____

_____

_____

7. EXPLAIN A hurricane is located off the coast when scientists begin tracking its distance from land. Its distance from land, $d(t)$, after t hours can be modeled by the function $d(t) = 120 - 20t$. Graph the function for the domain $0 \leq t \leq 6$. Identify the maximum and minimum values and explain what each represents in this situation.

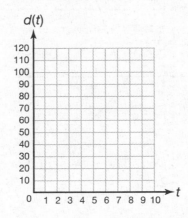

_____

_____

_____

17 Using Functions to Solve Equations

UNDERSTAND Solving a one-variable equation means finding the value of the variable that makes the equation true. So, solving $3x + 5 = -x - 3$ means finding a value of x that makes the left side of the equation equal to the right side.

You can treat each side of the equation as a function, like this:

$f(x) = 3x + 5$

$g(x) = -x - 3$

The graph of function f is the graph of $y = f(x)$.

The graph of function g is the graph of $y = g(x)$.

The point where these two graphs intersect is the point at which one input, x, produces the same output for both functions. At this point $f(x) = g(x)$, so the x-value for that point is the value of x that makes the original equation true.

You can find the value of x that makes $3x + 5 = -x - 3$ true by graphing $f(x) = 3x + 5$ and $g(x) = -x - 3$ on the same coordinate plane.

The graph of $f(x) = 3x + 5$ has a y-intercept at $(0, 5)$ and a slope of 3.

The graph of $g(x) = -x - 3$ has a y-intercept at $(0, -3)$ and a slope of -1.

Graph and label the two functions. Then find their point of intersection.

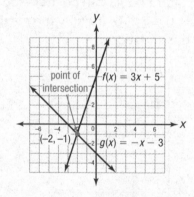

The graphs of f and g intersect at $(-2, -1)$. The x-value of that ordered pair is -2, so the solution of $3x + 5 = -x - 3$ is $x = -2$.

⇇ Connect

Solve for x by graphing: $4x + 1 = 2x + 3$.

1

Treat the expression on each side of the equation as a function.

Let $f(x) = 4x + 1$.

Let $g(x) = 2x + 3$.

2

Graph each function on the same coordinate plane.

The graph of *f* is the graph of $y = f(x)$, or $y = 4x + 1$. This graph is a line with a *y*-intercept at (0, 1) and a slope of 4.

The graph of *g* is the graph of $y = g(x)$, or $y = 2x + 3$. This graph is a line with a *y*-intercept at (0, 3) and a slope of 2.

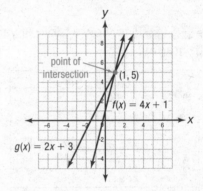

3

Find the *x*-coordinates of any points of intersection.

The graphs intersect at (1, 5).

The *x*-coordinate of that ordered pair is 1.

▶ The solution is $x = 1$.

CHECK

Solve $4x + 1 = 2x + 3$ algebraically and compare the solution to the solution found above.

EXAMPLE Use a graphing calculator to solve for x: $2^{x-1} = 4$.

1

Treat the expression on each side of the equation as a function.

Let $f(x) = 2^{x-1}$.

Let $g(x) = 4$.

2

Graph the functions on your graphing calculator and find the point of intersection.

Press Y= .

For Y_1 enter 2^(X−1).

For Y_2 enter 4.

Press GRAPH.

Your screen should show the following:

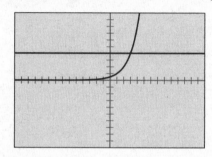

The point of intersection appears to be at $x = 3$.

3

Look at tables of values on your calculator to verify the point of intersection.

Press 2nd GRAPH to view a table of values for both graphs.

X	Y_1	Y_2
−2	.125	4
−1	.25	4
0	.5	4
1	1	4
2	2	4
3	4	4
4	8	4
X= −2		

The tables show that when X is 3, both Y_1 and Y_2 are equal to 4.

▶ The solution is $x = 3$.

 CHECK

Using pencil and paper (not a calculator), complete the table of values below for these functions. Use the table to check that $x = 3$ is the solution for $2^{x-1} = 4$.

x	$f(x) = 2^{x-1}$	$g(x) = 4$
0		
1		
2		
3		
4		

Problem Solving

READ

Cara and Cami are twins. They came up with a math puzzle. Cara says she is $(-2x + 3)$ years old, and Cami says she is $\left(-\frac{5}{2}x + 1\right)$ years old. What is the value of x? What are their ages?

PLAN

Since Cara and Cami are twins, you can set their ages equal and solve for x.

$$-2x + 3 = -\frac{5}{2}x + 1$$

Then evaluate _____ to determine their ages.

SOLVE

Use graphing to solve for x.

Let $f(x) =$ _____.

Let $g(x) =$ _____.

Graph each function on the coordinate plane on the right.

The point of intersection is (_____, _____).

So, $x =$ _____. The y-value, _____, shows

_____.

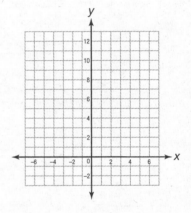

CHECK

Substitute that value of x into the original equation to verify that the two ages are the same and that their age is the one that you found.

$$-2x + 3 = -\frac{5}{2}x + 1$$

$$-2(\underline{}) + 3 \overset{?}{=} -\frac{5}{2}(\underline{}) + 1$$

$$\underline{} + 3 \overset{?}{=} \underline{} + 1$$

_____

▶ The value of x is _____. Each girl is _____ years old.

Practice

Write two functions f and g that could be graphed in order to solve the equation.

1. $7x + 11 = 8x - 1$

_____

_____

2. $\frac{2}{3}x + 12 = -2x - 4$

_____

_____

3. $3^t = 27$

_____

_____

 HINT Assign each side to a function.

Solve each equation by using the given graph.

4. $x + 2 = \frac{1}{3}x$

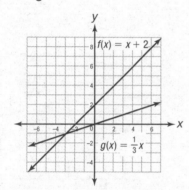

$x =$ _____

5. $-\frac{3}{2}x - 5 = -5x + 2$

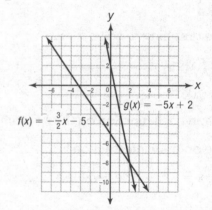

$x =$ _____

REMEMBER Look for the point of intersection.

6. $-x + 9 = \frac{3}{5}x + 1$

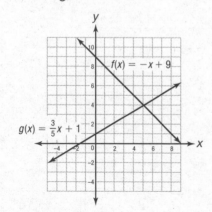

$x =$ _____

7. $\left(\frac{1}{2}\right)^x - 5 = -3$

$x =$ _____

Solve each equation for x by using the given table.

8. $5^{x-2} = 25$

x	$f(x) = 5^{x-2}$	$g(x) = 25$
2	1	25
3	5	25
4	25	25
5	125	25
6	625	25

$x =$ _____

9. $\frac{1}{2}x + 1 = \frac{3}{2}x - \frac{1}{2}$

x	$f(x) = \frac{1}{2}x + 1$	$g(x) = \frac{3}{2}x - \frac{1}{2}$
0	1	$-\frac{1}{2}$
$\frac{1}{2}$	$\frac{5}{4}$	$\frac{1}{4}$
1	$\frac{3}{2}$	1
$\frac{3}{2}$	$\frac{7}{4}$	$\frac{7}{4}$
2	2	$\frac{5}{2}$

$x =$ _____

Complete the tables to solve each equation for x. Show your work.

10. $\left(\frac{1}{3}\right)^x = 3^x$

x	$f(x) = \left(\frac{1}{3}\right)^x$	$g(x) = 3^x$
−2	$f(-2) =$	$g(-2) =$
−1	$f(-1) =$	$g(-1) =$
0	$f(0) =$	$g(0) =$
1	$f(1) =$	$g(1) =$
2	$f(2) =$	$g(2) =$

$x =$ _____

11. $-x + 5 = 2x - 1$

x	$f(x) =$ _____	$g(x) =$ _____
−2	$f(-2) =$	$g(-2) =$
−1	$f(-1) =$	$g(-1) =$
0	$f(0) =$	$g(0) =$
1	$f(1) =$	$g(1) =$
2	$f(2) =$	$g(2) =$

$x =$ _____

Define two functions and graph them on the coordinate plane to solve for x.

12. $x - 3 = -2x + 6$

$f(x) =$ _____ $g(x) =$ _____

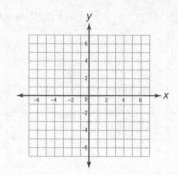

$x =$ _____

13. $-x + 2 = -3x - 4$

$f(x) =$ _____ $g(x) =$ _____

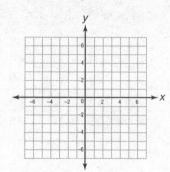

$x =$ _____

14. $4x + 5 = 0.5x - 2$

$f(x) =$ _____ $g(x) =$ _____

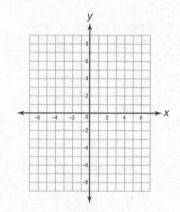

$x =$ _____

15. $-\frac{1}{4}x + 6 = 3x - 7$

$f(x) =$ _____ $g(x) =$ _____

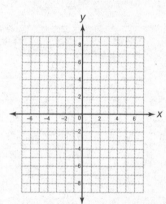

$x =$ _____

16. $2^{x+2} = 8$

$f(x) =$ _____ $g(x) =$ _____

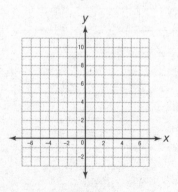

$x =$ _____

17. $\left(\frac{1}{2}\right)^x - 3 = 2^x - 3$

$f(x) =$ _____ $g(x) =$ _____

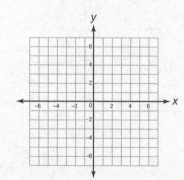

$x =$ _____

Choose the best answer.

18. Lucia correctly used a graphing calculator to solve an equation for x. Her screen is shown below. The solution was $x = 2$.

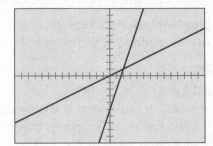

Which could be the equation she solved?

A. $\frac{1}{2}x = 3x - 5$

B. $\frac{1}{2}x = -3x - 5$

C. $\frac{1}{2}x - 5 = 3x$

D. $\frac{1}{2}x - 5 = -3x$

19. Adler correctly used a graphing calculator to solve an equation for x. His screen is shown below. The solution was $x = -1$.

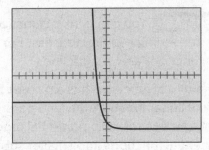

Which could be the equation he solved?

A. $\left(\frac{1}{4}\right)^x - 8 = -7$

B. $\left(\frac{1}{4}\right)^x - 8 = -4$

C. $\left(\frac{1}{4}\right)^x + 8 = 4$

D. $\left(\frac{1}{4}\right)^x + 8 = 8$

Solve.

20. **SHOW** Ling decided to sell cupcakes at the county fair. Her ingredients cost her about 25 cents per cupcake. Renting a booth costs \$30 per day. She sells each cupcake for \$1. Ling's expenses can be modeled by the function $c(x) = 0.25x + 30.00$. Her income can be modeled by the function $p(x) = 1.00x$. How many cupcakes must she sell before she turns a profit?

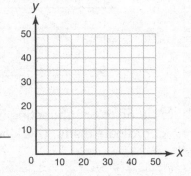

_____

21. **JUSTIFY** Is there a value of x that makes $2^x = -2$ true? Use the equation to write two functions and graph them. Justify your answer using information from the graph.

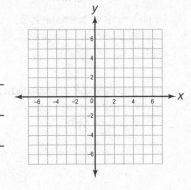

_____

_____

_____

Translating Functions

LESSON 18

UNDERSTAND You can think of functions as being grouped into families. All functions in a family have similar characteristics. For example, the graphs of all functions in the family of linear functions are straight lines.

Each family of functions has a **parent function**, the most basic function in the family. The family of linear functions has the parent function $f(x) = x$. The function $f(x) = e^x$ is the general parent function for all exponential functions. However, it can often be easier to group the exponential functions into smaller subfamilies that have the same base, such as $f(x) = 2^x$ and $f(x) = 23.5^x$.

If you change the parent function by adding, subtracting, multiplying, or dividing by a constant, you transform the function and make a new function from the same family. For example, the function $g(x) = x - 3$ is different from the parent function $f(x) = x$, but it is still in the linear function family. Changing the equation of the function also changes the graph of the function. This change to the graph is called a **transformation**.

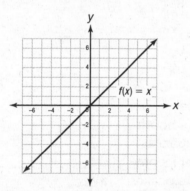
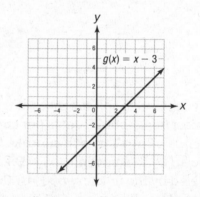

Adding to or subtracting from a function moves its graph up, down, left, or right on the coordinate plane. This kind of transformation is called a **translation**.

Translation	Algebraic Notation	Change to Graph
In a **vertical translation**, every point on the graph shifts up or down.	$g(x) = f(x) + k$ A real number, k, is added to the output, $f(x)$.	If $k > 0$, shift the graph $\|k\|$ units up. If $k < 0$, shift the graph $\|k\|$ units down.
In a **horizontal translation**, every point on the graph shifts left or right.	$g(x) = f(x + k)$ A real number, k, is added to the input, x.	If $k < 0$, shift the graph $\|k\|$ units right. If $k > 0$, shift the graph $\|k\|$ units left.

⊏ Connect

The exponential function $f(x) = 3^x$ is graphed on the coordinate plane below. Make a table of values for the function $g(x) = 3^x + 2$. Then graph function g on the same coordinate plane. Describe how function f could be translated to form function g and how translating a function affects its size and shape.

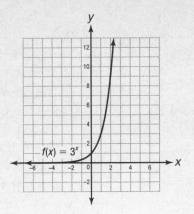

1

Create a table of values for $g(x) = 3^x + 2$.

x	$g(x) = 3^x + 2$	g(x)
−2	$g(-2) = 3^{-2} + 2 = \frac{1}{9} + 2 = \frac{19}{9}$	$\frac{19}{9}$
−1	$g(-1) = 3^{-1} + 2 = \frac{1}{3} + 2 = \frac{7}{3}$	$\frac{7}{3}$
0	$g(0) = 3^0 + 2 = 1 + 2 = 3$	3
1	$g(1) = 3^1 + 2 = 3 + 2 = 5$	5
2	$g(2) = 3^2 + 2 = 9 + 2 = 11$	11

2

Plot the ordered pairs for function g and connect them with a curve.

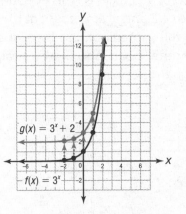

3

Compare the graphs.

▶ Each point on the graph of function g is 2 units above its corresponding point on function f. So, function g is the result of a vertical translation of function f 2 units up.

Since all we are doing is sliding the graph in the coordinate plane, the size and shape of the graph have not changed.

DISCUSS

Since you were given the graph of $f(x) = 3^x$, could you have graphed $g(x) = 3^x + 2$ without creating a table of values first? Explain.

EXAMPLE A Let $f(x) = 2x$ and define a function g such that $g(x) = f(x + 3)$. Graph both functions, f and g, on the same coordinate plane. Compare the two graphs and identify how function f could be translated to form function g.

1

Write function g in terms of x by using functional notation.

For the function g, use the expression for $f(x)$ and replace x with $(x + 3)$.

$g(x) = f(x + 3)$

$g(x) = 2(x + 3)$

$g(x) = 2x + 6$

2

Graph function f.

The graph of f is the graph of the equation $y = f(x)$ or $y = 2x$. This equation has a slope of 2 and a y-intercept at $(0, 0)$. Graph the y-intercept, use the slope to find another point, and draw a straight line through those points.

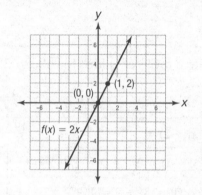

3

Graph function g.

The graph of g is the graph of the equation $y = g(x)$ or $y = 2x + 6$. This equation has a slope of 2 and a y-intercept at $(0, 6)$. Graph the y-intercept, use the slope to find another point, and draw a straight line through those points.

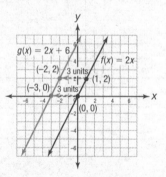

4

Compare the graphs.

▶ Each point on function g is 3 units to the left of the corresponding point on function f.

This makes sense. When 3 is added to the input, as it was in $g(x) = f(x + 3)$, the result is a translation of 3 units to the left.

Notice that both lines have the same slope, 2. So, translating a line horizontally does not change its slope.

TRY

On the grid shown in Step 3 above, graph $h(x) = f(x - 3)$. Describe how function f could be translated to form function h.

EXAMPLE B A linear function *f* is graphed below. On the same coordinate plane, graph the function $g(x) = f(x) - 5$. Identify the transformation.

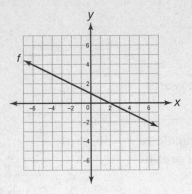

1

Describe the translation.

$g(x) = f(x) - 5$ is in the form $g(x) = f(x) + k$, where $k = -5$.

When a numerical value, *k*, is added to an output, *f(x)*, the result is a vertical shift.

Since *k* is the negative number -5, shift the graph 5 units down.

2

Graph the function *g*.

Shift two points on the graph of function *f* down 5 units. Then draw a line through them.

$(0, 1)$ is translated 5 units down to $(0, -4)$.

$(2, 0)$ is translated 5 units down to $(2, -5)$.

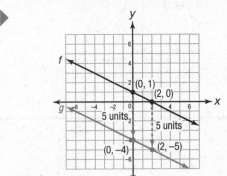

The transformation is a vertical translation 5 units down.

DISCUSS

The equations for functions *f* and *g* are not given. Can you determine if their slopes are the same? Explain how.

EXAMPLE C The graph of $f(x) = \left(\frac{1}{2}\right)^x$ is shown. Translate function f to form the function $h(x) = f(x - 4) + 2$. Graph h and write its explicit equation.

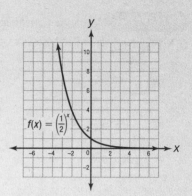

1

Describe the translation by using words and symbols.

Subtracting 4 from the input, x, indicates a horizontal translation. Translate the graph 4 units to the right.

Adding 2 to the output, $f(x - 4)$, indicates a vertical translation. Translate the graph 2 units up.

2

Graph h.

Choose several points on the graph of f and translate each point 4 units to the right and 2 units up.

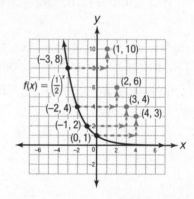

3

Connect the points with a smooth curve.

▶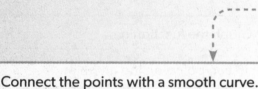

4

Write an equation for h.

The translation involved subtracting 4 from the input and adding 2 to that output. So, subtract 4 from x, the exponent in $\left(\frac{1}{2}\right)^x$, and then add 2 to the resulting expression.

▶ $h(x) = \left(\frac{1}{2}\right)^{x-4} + 2$.

CHECK

Use a graphing calculator to check your work. Press `Y=`.

For Y_1, enter (1/2)^X. For Y_2, enter (1/2)^(X − 4) + 2. Press `2nd` `GRAPH` to bring up a table of values. Press `GRAPH` to view the graph.

EXAMPLE D Functions *f* and *g* are graphed on the right. Using function notation, write an equation describing *g*(*x*) in terms of *f*(*x*). Then use the equation given for *f*(*x*) to write an equation for *g*(*x*) in terms of *x*.

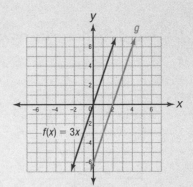

1

Identify how *f* could be translated to form *g*.

Choose a point on *f*, such as (0, 0).

If this point is translated 2 units to the right, it would cover point (2, 0), which is on the graph of *g*.

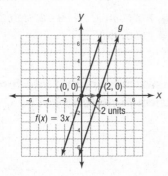

Verify that any point on *f*, if translated 2 units to the right, has a corresponding point on *g*.

2

Write the function *g*(*x*) in terms of *f*(*x*).

To represent a horizontal translation of 2 units to the right, add −2 to the input, *x*.

So $g(x) = f(x - 2)$.

3

Write the function *g*(*x*) in terms of *x*.

To find an explicit expression for *g*(*x*), substitute (*x* − 2) for *x* in the expression for *f*(*x*).

$g(x) = f(x - 2)$

$g(x) = 3(x - 2)$

▶ $g(x) = 3x - 6$

CHECK

Use a graphing calculator to check that $g(x) = 3x - 6$ is the correct equation for function *g*.

Practice

Use words to describe how function _f_ could be translated to form function _g_ in one step.

1.

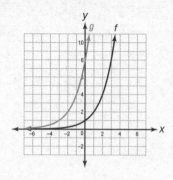

_____

2.

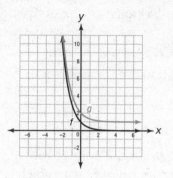

_____

> **HINT** How can (0, 1) be translated to cover (0, 2)?

Use words to describe a horizontal translation that would transform function _f_ into function _g_. Then describe a vertical translation that would transform function _f_ into function _g_.

3.

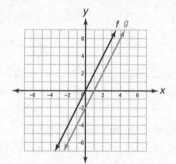

horizontal translation: _____

vertical translation: _____

> **REMEMBER** Horizontal means left and right. Vertical means up and down.

4.

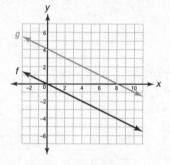

horizontal translation: _____

vertical translation: _____

Write _true_ or _false_ for each statement. If false, rewrite the statement to make it true.

5. A translation is a slide of a graph to a new location on the coordinate plane.

_____

6. If $g(x) = f(x) - k$, then the graph of _f_ is translated _k_ units down to form the graph of _g_.

_____

7. If $g(x) = f(x - k)$, then the graph of _f_ is translated _k_ units left to form the graph of _g_.

_____

Translate the graph of _f_ according to the verbal description to form _g_ and draw the graph for _g_ on the same coordinate plane. Then write an equation for _g(x)_ in terms of _x_.

8. Translate the graph of _f_ 5 units up to form _g_.

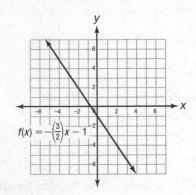

$f(x) = -\left(\frac{3}{2}\right)x - 1$

$g(x) = $ _____

9. Translate the graph of _f_ 3 units to the right to form _g_.

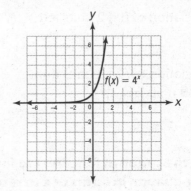

$f(x) = 4^x$

$g(x) = $ _____

Choose the best answer. Use your graphing calculator to check your answer.

10. The graphing calculator screen below shows the graph of $f(x) = 1.5x$ and the graph of _g_.

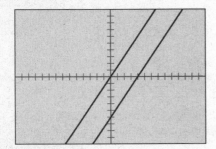

Which equation could represent _g(x)_ in terms of _f(x)_?

A. $g(x) = f(x) + 6$

B. $g(x) = f(x) - 6$

C. $g(x) = f(x + 6)$

D. $g(x) = 6f(x)$

11. The graphing calculator screen below shows the graph of $f(x) = 2^x$ and the graph of _g_.

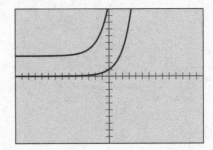

Which equation could represent _g(x)_ in terms of _f(x)_?

A. $g(x) = f(x + 3) + 3$

B. $g(x) = f(x - 3) + 3$

C. $g(x) = f(x + 3) - 3$

D. $g(x) = f(x - 3) - 3$

Write an explicit expression in terms of x for each function g(x) described below.

For questions 12–17, $f(x) = 5^x$.

12. translation of $f(x)$ 2 units up

$g(x) =$ _____

13. translation of $f(x)$ 2 units down

$g(x) =$ _____

14. translation of $f(x)$ 2 units left

$g(x) =$ _____

15. translation of $f(x)$ 2 units right

$g(x) =$ _____

16. translation of $f(x)$ 3 units right
and 3 units up

$g(x) =$ _____

17. translation of $f(x)$ 3 units left
and 3 units down

$g(x) =$ _____

Translate the graph of function f to form the translated function g described algebraically. Write an equation in terms of x to represent the translated image.

18. $g(x) = f(x) + 5$

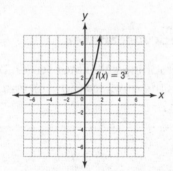

$g(x) =$ _____

19. $g(x) = f(x + 5)$

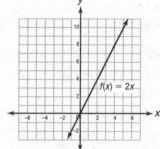

$g(x) =$ _____

20. $g(x) = f(x - 6) - 4$

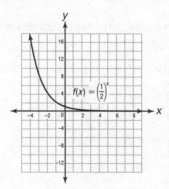

$g(x) =$ _____

21. $g(x) = f(x - 4) - 3$

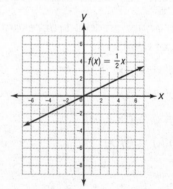

$g(x) =$ _____

Function *f* was translated to form function *g* according to the rule given. For each rule, identify the value of *k*. Include the sign. Briefly explain how you know.

22.

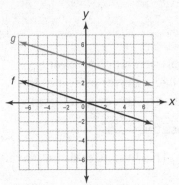

$g(x) = f(x) + k; k =$ _____

_____

_____

23.

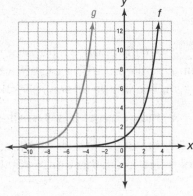

$g(x) = f(x + k); k =$ _____

_____

_____

Solve.

24. **EXPLAIN** Macy graphed $f(x) = -4x$ and parallel line *g*. She believes that since the rule for the translation is $g(x) = f(x + 1)$, the equation for *g* must be $g(x) = -4x + 1$. Explain why Macy's reasoning is flawed. Then identify the correct equation for *g*.

_____

_____

_____

25. **DESCRIBE** Zack used to charge only an hourly rate to mow lawns, as shown by the graph of function *p*. Because of rising costs, he now charges a set fee for each job in addition to his hourly rate, as shown by the graph of function *n*. Use algebraic notation to describe how *p* could be translated to form *n*. Use what you know about translations to explain how the new costs differ from the old costs.

_____

_____

_____

19 Reflecting Functions

UNDERSTAND A **reflection** is a transformation that can flip the graph of a function over a line. That line is called the **line of reflection**. The new graph looks like a mirror image of the original graph. The image after a reflection is the same size and shape as the original graph.

If $g(x) = f(-x)$, the graph of g is the reflection of the graph of f across the y-axis.

Changing the sign of the input, x, reflects the graph over the y-axis. This means that the y-axis is the line of reflection in this transformation.

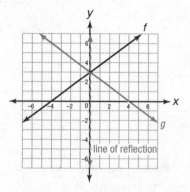

Compare the two lines. The point $(4, 6)$ is found on the graph of f. The corresponding point $(-4, 6)$ is found on the graph of g. The point $(-4, 6)$ is the reflection of $(4, 6)$ across the y-axis.

If $h(x) = -f(x)$, the graph of h is the reflection of the graph of f across the x-axis.

Changing the sign of the output, $f(x)$, reflects the graph over the x-axis. This means that the x-axis is the line of reflection in this transformation.

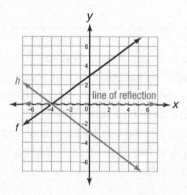

Compare the two lines. The point $(4, 6)$ is found on the graph of f. The corresponding point $(4, -6)$ is found on the graph of h. The point $(4, -6)$ is the reflection of $(4, 6)$ across the x-axis.

⊏ Connect

The graph of the exponential function $f(x) = 3^x$ is shown. On the same coordinate plane, graph function $g(x) = -f(x)$.

Compare the graphs and describe the reflection.

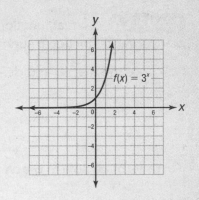

1

Write the equation for g.

We know that $f(x) = 3^x$ and that the reflected image is equal to $g(x) = -f(x)$.

Substitute the expression for $f(x)$ to find an expression for $g(x)$.

$$g(x) = -f(x) = -(3^x)$$

2

Create a table of values for function g.

x	$g(x) = -(3^x)$	$g(x)$
-2	$g(-2) = -(3^{-2}) = -\left(\dfrac{1}{3^2}\right)$ $= -\dfrac{1}{9}$	$-\dfrac{1}{9}$
-1	$g(-1) = -(3^{-1}) = -\left(\dfrac{1}{3^1}\right)$ $= -\dfrac{1}{3}$	$-\dfrac{1}{3}$
0	$g(0) = -(3^0) = -(1) = -1$	-1
1	$g(1) = -(3^1) = -(3) = -3$	-3
2	$g(2) = -(3^2) = -(9) = -9$	-9

3

Graph $g(x)$ and compare it to $f(x)$.

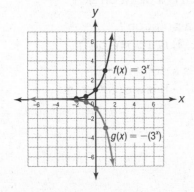

Consider $(1, 3)$ and $(1, -3)$. Each has the same input, x, but the outputs have opposite signs.

Also, notice that $(1, 3)$ and $(1, -3)$ are the same distance from the x-axis but lie on different sides of it.

This is true for every pair of corresponding points on the two functions.

▶ The graph of g is the result of a reflection of the graph of f across the x-axis.

CHECK

Use a graphing calculator to check your work.

Press [Y=]. Enter $Y_1 = 3\wedge X$.

Enter $Y_2 = -3\wedge X$.

Press [2nd] [GRAPH] to bring up a table of values, and compare them.

Press [GRAPH]. Compare the graphs to the ones shown on the left.

EXAMPLE A A linear function *f* is graphed. On the same coordinate plane, graph function *g* such that $g(x) = f(-x)$.

Compare the graphs and describe the reflection.

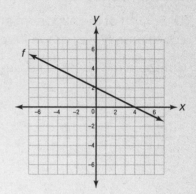

1

Determine how to graph *g*.

No explicit function was given for *f*, but the graph of *g* can be found by using the graph of *f*.

The algebraic notation $g(x) = f(-x)$ means that the opposite value of each input, *x*, will be used.

So, find points on the graph of *f*, change the sign of each *x*-value, and graph the resulting points.

2

Find several points on the graph of *g*.

$(-2, 3)$ is a point on *f*.

Find the opposite of the input (*x*-value) and keep the same output (*y*-value).

$(-2, 3) \rightarrow (2, 3)$
So, $(2, 3)$ is a point on *g*.

$(2, 1)$ is a point on *f*.
So, $(-2, 1)$ is a point on *g*.

$(6, -1)$ is a point on *f*.
So, $(-6, -1)$ is a point on *g*.

3

Graph *g* and describe the reflection.

Plot the points that you found and draw a straight line through them to graph *g*.

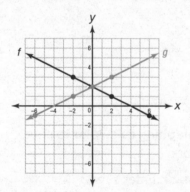

Each point on *f* and its corresponding point on *g* are the same distance from the *y*-axis, but they lie on different sides of it.

▶ The graph of *g* is the result of a reflection of *f* across the *y*-axis.

DISCUSS

Identify key features, such as the intercepts and slopes, of functions *f* and *g*. How are the key features of *f* and its reflected image similar? How are they different?

EXAMPLE B Exponential functions *f* and *g* are graphed. Use function notation to define *g(x)* in terms of *f(x)*.

If the equation for function *f* is $f(x) = 2^x - 2$, write an equation for *g*.

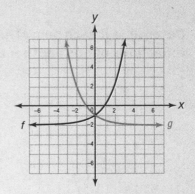

1 Describe the transformation.

The graphs are mirror images of one another. So, this is a reflection.

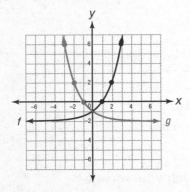

Points $(-2, 2)$ and $(2, 2)$ lie on the same horizontal line, but they are on different sides of the *y*-axis. Each is the same distance from the *y*-axis.

Other pairs of points from *f* and *g* share this characteristic. So, *f* can be reflected across the *y*-axis to form *g*.

2 Use function notation to describe the reflection.

For each pair of corresponding points, the inputs, *x*, are opposites and the outputs are the same.

▶ Each point (x, y) on *f* has a corresponding point $(-x, y)$ on *g*, so this reflection can be described as $g(x) = f(-x)$.

3 Write an explicit equation for *g(x)*.

To write *g(x)*, write the expression for *f(x)* and replace *x* with *−x*.

If $f(x) = 2^x - 2$, then $g(x) = 2^{-x} - 2$.

▶ $g(x) = 2^{-x} - 2$

TRY

Use what you know about negative exponents to express $g(x) = 2^{-x} - 2$ in a different way. (Hint: The number raised to the exponent *x* will be less than 1.)

Practice

Determine if each pair of functions *f* and *g* are reflections of one another across the *x*-axis, reflections of one another across the *y*-axis, or neither.

1.

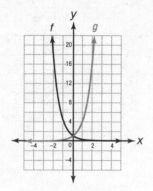

_____

2.

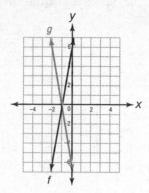

_____

3.

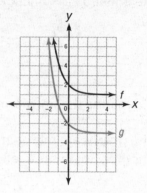

_____

 HINT Find pairs of corresponding points.
Which changed: the input or the output?

Choose the best answer. Use your graphing calculator to check your answer.

4. The graphing calculator screen below shows $f(x) = 2^x$ and its reflection *g*. Which could represent $g(x)$?

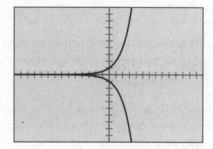

A. $g(x) = 2^x$

B. $g(x) = 2^{-x}$

C. $g(x) = -(2^x)$

D. $g(x) = -(2^{-x})$

5. The graphing calculator screen below shows $f(x) = -3x - 4$ and its reflection *g*. Which is **not** true of the functions?

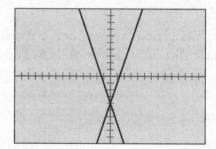

A. $g(x) = f(-x)$

B. Function *f* was reflected across the *y*-axis to form *g*.

C. Both *f* and *g* have the same *y*-intercept.

D. Both *f* and *g* have the same slope.

Graph g. Then write an equation for g(x) in terms of x.

6. $g(x) = f(-x)$

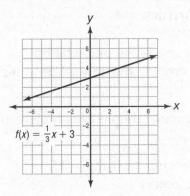

$f(x) = \frac{1}{3}x + 3$

$g(x) = $ _____

7. $g(x) = -f(x)$

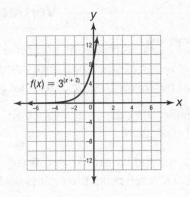

$f(x) = 3^{(x+2)}$

$g(x) = $ _____

Solve.

8. **JUSTIFY** Maggie graphed functions f and g as shown. Maggie says that g is the result of a reflection of f across the x-axis. Jay says that g is actually the result of a reflection of f across the y-axis. Who is correct? Justify your answer.

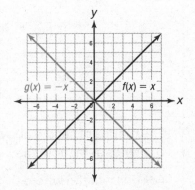

$g(x) = -x$ $f(x) = x$

_____

_____

9. **SEPARATE** A graph can be reflected across a point, such as the origin. If $j(x) = -f(-x)$, then j is the reflection of f across the origin. How could you use two different reflections to produce the same graph of j?

_____

_____

Lesson 20 Stretching and Shrinking Functions

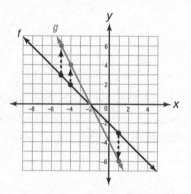

Vertical Stretches and Shrinks

UNDERSTAND Translations and reflections do not change the size of the graph being transformed, but stretches and shrinks do. After a stretch or a shrink, the new graph looks wider or narrower than the original graph.

Multiplying the output of a function, $f(x)$, by a constant stretches or shrinks the graph in the vertical direction.

For $g(x) = kf(x)$ where $|k| > 1$, the graph of g is a **vertical stretch** of the graph of f. A vertical stretch pulls the points on the graph away from the x-axis.

The graphs of f and g above illustrate the vertical stretch $g(x) = 2f(x)$. Notice how each point on g is twice as far from the x-axis as its corresponding point on f.

For $g(x) = kf(x)$ where $0 < |k| < 1$, the graph of g is a **vertical shrink** of the graph of f. A vertical shrink pushes the points of a graph toward the x-axis.

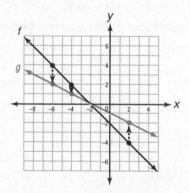

The graphs of f and g above illustrate the vertical shrink $g(x) = \frac{1}{2}f(x)$. Notice how each point on g is half as far from the x-axis as its corresponding point on f.

Notice that, after a vertical stretch or shrink, the new function always has the same x-intercept as the original function. This point cannot be shrunk toward or stretched away from the x-axis because it is on the x-axis.

⊷ Connect

The exponential function $f(x) = 2^x$ is graphed on the right. Graph $g(x) = 4(2^x)$ on the same coordinate plane. Is g the result of a vertical stretch or a vertical shrink of f? by what factor?

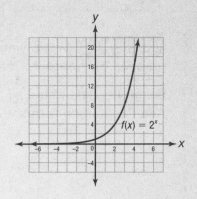

1

Create a table of values for g.

x	$g(x) = 4(2^x)$	$g(x)$
-2	$g(-2) = 4(2^{-2}) = 4\left(\frac{1}{4}\right) = 1$	1
-1	$g(-1) = 4(2^{-1}) = 4\left(\frac{1}{2}\right) = 2$	2
0	$g(0) = 4(2^0) = 4(1) = 4$	4
1	$g(1) = 4(2^1) = 4(2) = 8$	8
2	$g(2) = 4(2^2) = 4(4) = 16$	16

2

Graph g.

Plot those ordered pairs $(x, g(x))$ on the coordinate plane and connect them with a smooth curve.

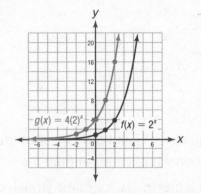

3

Compare the graphs and identify the transformation.

The point $(0, 1)$ on the graph of f is transformed to $(0, 4)$ on the graph of g.

The point $(1, 2)$ is transformed to $(1, 8)$.

The point $(2, 4)$ is transformed to $(2, 16)$.

Notice that for each pair of points, the input is the same, but the output is 4 times as great.

The equation of g also shows that the output, $f(x)$, was multiplied by 4.

▶ The graph of g is the result of a vertical stretch of f by a factor of 4.

TRY

On the coordinate plane above, graph $h(x) = \frac{1}{4}(2^x)$. Is this a vertical stretch or a vertical shrink? by what factor?

UNDERSTAND Multiplying the input of a function, x, by a constant stretches or shrinks the graph in the horizontal direction.

For $g(x) = f(kx)$ where $|k| > 1$, the graph of g is a **horizontal shrink** of the graph of f. A horizontal shrink pushes the points of a graph toward the y-axis.

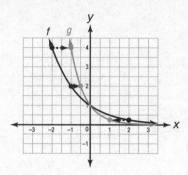

The graphs of f and g above illustrate the horizontal shrink $g(x) = f(2x)$. Notice how each point on g is half as far from the y-axis as its corresponding point on f.

For $g(x) = f(kx)$ where $0 < |k| < 1$, the graph of g is a **horizontal stretch** of the graph of f. A horizontal stretch pulls the points of a graph away from the y-axis.

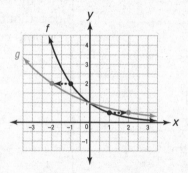

The graphs of f and g above illustrate the horizontal stretch $g(x) = f\left(\frac{1}{2}x\right)$. Notice how each point on g is twice as far from the y-axis as its corresponding point on f.

Notice that the factor of the stretch or shrink is the reciprocal of the constant. In the case of a horizontal stretch or shrink, k is not the factor by which a graph is stretched or shrunk; $\frac{1}{k}$ is.

Notice that, after a horizontal stretch or shrink, the new function always has the same y-intercept as the original function. This point cannot be shrunk toward or stretched away from the y-axis because it is on the y-axis.

ᐊ Connect

Graph the linear function $f(x) = \frac{1}{2}x + 2$. Then graph its image, g, resulting from the transformation described below.

$$g(x) = f(3x)$$

Is this an example of a horizontal stretch or shrink? by what factor?

1

Create a table of values for f.

x	$f(x) = \frac{1}{2}x + 2$	$f(x)$
-6	$f(-6) = \frac{1}{2}(-6) + 2$ $= -3 + 2 = -1$	-1
0	$f(0) = \frac{1}{2}(0) + 2 = 0 + 2 = 2$	2
6	$f(6) = \frac{1}{2}(6) + 2 = 3 + 2 = 5$	5

2

Write an equation and create a table of values for g.

Since $g(x) = f(3x)$, replace x with $3x$ to find the equation for g.

$$g(x) = f(3x) = \frac{1}{2}(3x) + 2 = \frac{3}{2}x + 2.$$

x	$g(x) = \frac{3}{2}x + 2$	$g(x)$
-2	$g(-2) = \frac{3}{2}(-2) + 2$ $= -3 + 2 = -1$	-1
0	$g(0) = \frac{3}{2}(0) + 2 = 0 + 2 = 2$	2
2	$g(2) = \frac{3}{2}(2) + 2 = 3 + 2 = 5$	5

3

Use those points to graph the functions.

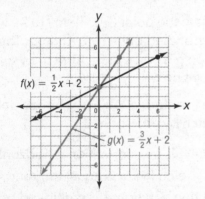

4

Identify the transformation and the factor.

The points on the graph of g are closer to the y-axis than their corresponding points on the graph of f. A horizontal shrink pushes a graph toward the y-axis.

For $g(x) = f(3x)$, $k = 3$. So, the factor is $\frac{1}{k}$ or $\frac{1}{3}$.

▶ The graph of g is the result of a horizontal shrink of f by a factor of $\frac{1}{3}$.

CHECK

Enter the equations for f and g into your graphing calculator, graph them, and call up tables of values for them. Do the graphs and tables match what appears on this page?

EXAMPLE A Graph the linear functions $f(x) = -4x - 3$ and $g(x) = -2x - 3$.

Use words to describe the transformation, including if it is a horizontal stretch or a horizontal shrink, and by what factor. Then write an equation for $g(x)$ in terms of $f(x)$.

1

Use what you know about slope-intercept form to graph each line.

In $f(x) = -4x - 3$, the slope is -4 and the y-intercept is $(0, -3)$.

So, plot the point $(0, -3)$. Then count 4 units down and 1 unit to the right and plot a second point, $(1, -7)$. Draw and label the line for f.

In $g(x) = -2x - 3$, the slope is -2 and the y-intercept is $(0, -3)$.

So, plot the point $(0, -3)$. Then count 2 units down and 1 unit to the right and plot a second point, $(1, -5)$. Draw and label the line for g.

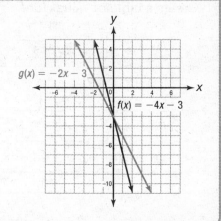

2

Identify the transformation.

The points on the graph of g are farther from the y-axis than their corresponding points on the graph of f. A horizontal stretch pulls a graph away from the y-axis.

3

Describe the transformation in words and as a function.

Compare the point $(-1, 1)$ on f to its corresponding point $(-2, 1)$ on g. The point on g is twice as far from the y-axis as the point on f.

▶ The transformation was a horizontal stretch by a factor of 2.

Since this transformation is horizontal, the stretch factor is equal to $\frac{1}{k}$, and, in function notation, k is multiplied by the input, x.

$2 = \frac{1}{k}$

$k = \frac{1}{2}$

▶ $g(x) = f\left(\frac{1}{2}x\right)$

Does a stretch or shrink of the graph of a line always change its slope? Explain.

EXAMPLE B The graph of function f was transformed to create the graph of function g, as shown. Was f stretched or shrunk, horizontally or vertically, and by what factor? If $f(x) = 4^x + 8$, what is the equation of $g(x)$?

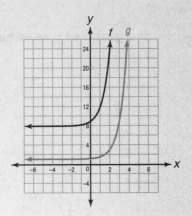

1

Examine the key features to determine how f was transformed.

As you move left on the graph of f, the values of $f(x)$ get very close to 8. So, f appears to have an asymptote at $y = 8$.

Many points on the graph of g lie below that asymptote, so points from the graph of f must have been moved much closer to the x-axis. Thus, g appears to be a vertical shrink of f.

2

Identify the factor of the shrink.

In a vertical shrink, the output is multiplied by a factor, k. So, compare points.

A vertical shrink has the form $g(x) = kf(x)$.

So, $k = \dfrac{g(x)}{f(x)}$ for all x.

The point $(2, 24)$ on the graph of f was shrunk to $(2, 3)$ on the graph of g.

$k = \dfrac{g(2)}{f(2)} = \dfrac{3}{24} = \dfrac{1}{8}$

3

Find the equation for $g(x)$.

$g(x) = \dfrac{1}{8} f(x) = \dfrac{1}{8}(4^x + 8) = \dfrac{1}{8} \cdot 4^x + 1$

DISCUSS

Suppose $f(x) = 4^x + 8$ is shrunk horizontally by a factor of $\dfrac{1}{8}$ to form function h. Will the equation of h be $h(x) = 4^{\frac{1}{8}x} + 8$ or $h(x) = 4^{8x} + 8$? Explain.

Practice

Classify the graph of g as either a vertical stretch or a vertical shrink of the graph of f.

1.

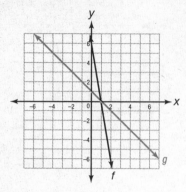

_____

2.

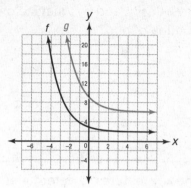

_____

 A vertical shrink draws points closer to the *x*-axis.

Classify the graph of g as each as either a horizontal stretch or a horizontal shrink of the graph of f.

3.

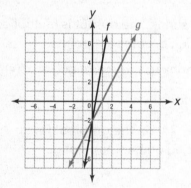

_____

4.

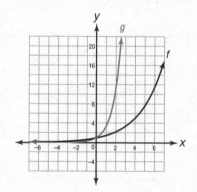

_____

 Is *g* closer to or farther away from the *y*-axis?

Fill in each blank with an appropriate word, phrase, or expression.

5.   A horizontal _____ pushes the points of a graph toward the *y*-axis.

6.   A horizontal _____ pulls the points of a graph away from the *y*-axis.

7.   If $g(x) = k\,f(x)$ and $|k| > 1$, then *g* is the result of a vertical stretch of *g* by a factor of _____.

8.   If $g(x) = f(kx)$ and $|k| > 1$, then *g* is the result of a horizontal shrink of *g* by a factor of _____.

Graph each function g on the coordinate plane below it. Classify each graph of g as either a vertical stretch or a vertical shrink of the graph of f. Then identify the factor.

9. $g(x) = 2x - 6$

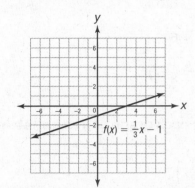

transformation: vertical _____

factor: _____

10. $g(x) = \frac{1}{2}(2^x)$

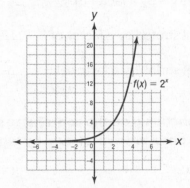

transformation: vertical _____

factor: _____

Graph each function g on the coordinate plane below it. Classify each graph of g as either a horizontal stretch or a horizontal shrink of the graph of f. Then identify the factor.

11. $g(x) = -5x + 1$

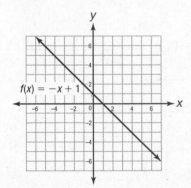

transformation: horizontal _____

factor: _____

12. $g(x) = \left(\frac{1}{3}\right)^{\frac{1}{2}x}$

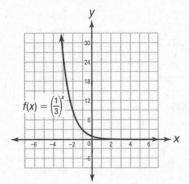

transformation: horizontal _____

factor: _____

Match each verbal description of a translation of $f(x) = 6^x$ with the equation of its transformed image by writing the correct letter next to each description.

13. vertical stretch by a factor of 8 _____

    A. $g(x) = 6^{8x}$

14. vertical shrink by a factor of $\frac{1}{8}$ _____

    B. $g(x) = 8(6^x)$

15. horizontal stretch by a factor of 8 _____

    C. $g(x) = 6^{\frac{1}{8}x}$

16. horizontal shrink by a factor of $\frac{1}{8}$ _____

    D. $g(x) = \frac{1}{8}(6^x)$

Graph each function g on the coordinate plane below it. Classify each graph of g as a stretch or a shrink, horizontal or vertical, and by what factor.

17. $g(x) = \frac{3}{2}f(x)$

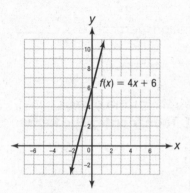

$f(x) = 4x + 6$

transformation: _____

factor: _____

18. $g(x) = f\left(\frac{1}{3}x\right)$

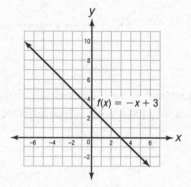

$f(x) = -x + 3$

transformation: _____

factor: _____

19. $g(x) = \frac{1}{2}f(x)$

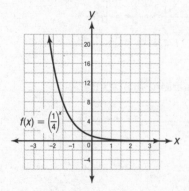

$f(x) = \left(\frac{1}{4}\right)^x$

transformation: _____

factor: _____

20. $g(x) = f(2x)$

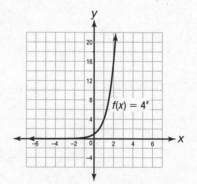

$f(x) = 4^x$

transformation: _____

factor: _____

Solve.

21. **RESTATE** Graph $f(x) = 2x - 2$ and its image, g, after a horizontal stretch by a factor of 4. Write equations for $g(x)$ in terms of $f(x)$ and in terms of x.

$g(x) = $ _____ $f($_____$x)$

$g(x) = $ _____ $x - $ _____

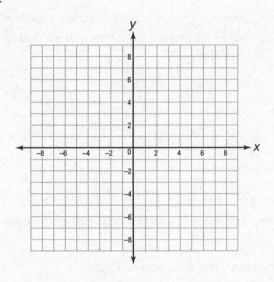

22. **DISTINGUISH** The graph of $f(x) = 3^x$ is shown. Graph $g(x) = -\frac{1}{3}f(x)$. Then describe the two transformations needed to create the image, g, from the graph of f.

_____

_____

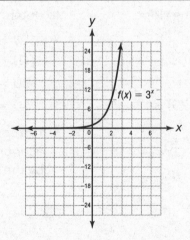

$f(x) = 3^x$

LESSON 21 Functions in Context

People often use functions to model real-world relationships. These functions tell how one quantity changes in relation to another quantity. Representations of these functions, such as tables, graphs, or equations, can be used to answer questions about the relationships or to make predictions.

EXAMPLE A The EZ Car Rental Company charges a set fee plus a daily rate to rent a car. It costs $90 to rent an economy car for 1 day and $170 to rent the same car for 3 days. Write a function to model the cost of renting an economy car for x days.

1

Decide if this relationship is linear or exponential.

The relationship can be represented as:

(total charge) = (set fee) + (cost per day) × (number of days, x)

The variable, x, is multiplied by a constant rate, the cost per day. The set fee is then added to that product.

Since the rate of change is constant, the function is linear.

2

Find the cost per day.

The cost per day is the slope of the linear function. Find two points and use the slope formula to find the cost per day.

A 1-day rental costs $90. So, (1, 90) is a solution for this function.

A 3-day rental costs $170. So, (3, 170) is also a solution.

$$\text{cost per day} = \frac{170 - 90}{3 - 1} = \frac{80}{2} = 40$$

3

Find the set fee and write the function.

We can use an ordered pair, such as (1, 90), to determine the complete equation.

$$f(x) = (\text{set fee}) + 40x$$
$$f(1) = (\text{set fee}) + 40(1)$$
$$90 = (\text{set fee}) + 40$$
$$50 = (\text{set fee})$$

▶ The cost, $f(x)$, in dollars of renting an economy car for x days can be modeled by the equation $f(x) = 50 + 40x$.

CHECK

Substitute 1 day and 3 days into your model function to check that it outputs $90 and $170, respectively.

EXAMPLE B Mr. Vega bought a new car for $20,000. He used a function to estimate how its value will depreciate, or decrease over time.

Age in Years, t	0	1	2	3	4
Value in Thousands of Dollars, $v(t)$	20	16	12.8	10.24	8.192

What type of function did Mr. Vega use to model this relationship? Describe the rate at which the car depreciates. Write an equation for the function.

1

Test to see if the function is linear.

Examine the decrease in value from year to year.

1 year after purchase: $v(0) - v(1) = 20 - 16 = 4$, or $4,000

Between years 1 and 2: $v(1) - v(2) = 16 - 12.8 = 3.2$, or $3,200

Between years 2 and 3: $v(2) - v(3) = 12.8 - 10.24 = 2.56$, or $2,560

The rate of depreciation is not constant, so this model is not a linear function.

2

Test to see if the function is exponential.

Compare the value of the car in successive years.

1 year after purchase: $\dfrac{v(1)}{v(0)} = \dfrac{16}{20} = 0.8$

Between years 1 and 2: $\dfrac{v(2)}{v(1)} = \dfrac{12.8}{16} = 0.8$

Between years 2 and 3: $\dfrac{v(3)}{v(2)} = \dfrac{10.24}{12.8} = 0.8$

Each year, the value of the car is 0.8, or 80%, of its value the previous year. This means the car's value is decreasing at a constant percent rate. Functions that decrease at a constant percent rate are exponential functions.

3

Determine an equation for the function.

The constant percent rate is 80%, or 0.8. This is the factor by which the previous year is multiplied to get the next year.

$v(1) = v(0) \cdot 0.8$

$v(2) = v(1) \cdot 0.8 = (v(0) \cdot 0.8) \cdot 0.8$
$\quad = v(0) \cdot (0.8)^2$

$v(3) = v(2) \cdot 0.8 = (v(0) \cdot (0.8)^2) \cdot 0.8$
$\quad = v(0) \cdot (0.8)^3$

You can see a pattern forming. For any year x after purchase, the car's value is given by $v(x) = v(0) \cdot (0.8)^x$.

Substitute $v(0)$, the initial value, 20.

▶ $v(x) = 20 \cdot (0.8)^x$

MODEL

Make a graph to illustrate the depreciation of the car over time.

EXAMPLE C Leah opened a checking account and bought a certificate of deposit (CD) on the same day. She deposits money into her checking account each month. The amount in her checking account, C, can be modeled by $C(t) = 50(12)t$, or $C(t) = 600t$, where t is the time in years since the account was opened.

Leah's CD has a set annual interest rate, and the interest is compounded monthly. The amount in her CD can be modeled by the function $A(t) = 800\left(1 + \frac{0.03}{12}\right)^{12t}$, where t is the time in years since she deposited the money.

Interpret the parameters of functions C and A in this situation.

1 Interpret the parameters of $C(t)$.

The problem explains that t represents time in years, and there are 12 months in 1 year. The quantity $\frac{12 \text{ months}}{\text{year}} \times t$ years gives a number of months.

Thus, the 50 likely represents the amount deposited each month.

$\frac{\$50}{\text{month}} \times \frac{12 \text{ months}}{\text{year}} \times t \text{ years}$ = the money in the checking account at time t

2 Interpret the parameters of $A(t)$.

The equation for A, an exponential growth function, shows an amount earning compound interest. The formula for calculating this amount, A, is $A = P\left(1 + \frac{r}{n}\right)^{nt}$, where P is the principal, r is the annual interest rate, and n is the number of times the interest is compounded per year.

So, in $A(t) = 800\left(1 + \frac{0.03}{12}\right)^{12t}$, 800 is P, the principal; 0.03 is r, the interest rate; and 12 is n, the number of times the interest is compounded per year. This means that Leah deposited \$800 in a CD at 3% annual interest, compounded monthly.

EXAMPLE D Combine functions C and A above to build a function that shows the total amount of money Leah has in both accounts at any time, t.

Combine both functions by adding them to form a new function, L.

$L(t) = C(t) + A(t)$

$\quad = 50(12)t + 800\left(1 + \frac{0.03}{12}\right)^{12t}$

$\quad = 600t + 800(1.0025)^{12t}$

▶ The total amount in both accounts after t months is: $L(t) = 600t + 800(1.0025)^{12t}$.

TRY

Leah always keeps \$200 hidden at home, which she calls her "emergency fund." Write a function for the total amount of money Leah has in her checking account, CD, and emergency fund at any time t.

Problem Solving

READ

Abdul buys a bus card with a value of $30. Each time he takes a bus ride, $1.50 is deducted from his card. Write a function that can be used to model this situation. Then use the function to determine the value of the bus card after Abdul takes 4 rides.

PLAN

Since the value decreases at a constant rate per ride, model this with a(n) _____ function.

Write an equation and then use the equation to solve the problem.

SOLVE

The initial value of his card is $30. So, when he has taken 0 rides, there is $30 left on his card. The point (0, ____) is an ordered pair for this function. It is also the ____ -intercept.

Each time Abdul takes a bus ride, $1.50 is deducted from his card.

So, the rate of change, or slope, is _____. This rate should be negative because

_____.

Substituting _____ for m, the slope, and _____ for b, the y-intercept, gives the equation:

$$c(x) = \text{\_\_\_\_} x + \text{\_\_\_\_}$$

If Abdul takes 4 rides, the value of his card, in dollars, will be:

$$c(4) = (\text{_____})(4) + \text{_____} = \text{_____}$$

CHECK

The initial value of the card is $30: $c(0) = 30$.

The value decreases by $1.50 each time he rides the bus.

After 1 ride, the value will be: $c(1) = 30.00 - 1.50 = 28.50$

After 2 rides, the value will be: $c(2) = 28.50 - 1.50 =$ _____

After 3 rides, the value will be: $c(3) =$ _____

After 4 rides, the value will be: $c(4) =$ _____

Is this the same value you found for $c(4)$ when you used the equation? _____

▶ This situation can be modeled by the equation $c(x) =$ _____. After taking 4 rides, the value of Abdul's card will be $_____.

Practice

For each situation, identify the type of function (linear or exponential) that could model it. Then write a function to model the relationship.

1. The highest possible grade for a report is 100 points. Each day the report is late, the teacher deducts 10 points.

Days Late, x	0	1	2	3	4
Starting Grade, g(x)	100	90	80	70	60

function type: _____

$g(x) =$ _____

> **REMEMBER** If the rate of change is constant, the function is linear.

2. Sixteen teams are participating in a tournament. Only the winning teams in each round advance to the next round.

Number of Rounds Completed, x	0	1	2	3	4
Teams Remaining, f(x)	16	8	4	2	1

function type: _____

$f(x) =$ _____

3. As soon as a Web site went up, it received 1 hit. After one minute, it had received 4 hits. The number of hits then quadrupled each minute after that.

Time Since Launch, in minutes, x	0	1	2	3	4
Number of Hits, h(x)	1	4	16	64	256

function type: _____

$h(x) =$ _____

4. A cake decorator charges a $30 set fee for each cake plus $20 for each color of icing required.

Colors of Icing Required, x	1	2	3	4	5
Cost of Cake in dollars, c(x)	50	70	90	110	130

function type: _____

$c(x) =$ _____

Choose the best answer.

5. A salesperson earns a weekly salary plus a commission on each appliance he sells. The function $p(x) = 200 + 0.05x$ shows his weekly earnings if x represents his weekly sales, in dollars. Which is also true?

   A. His weekly salary is $205.

   B. He earns $200 for each appliance he sells.

   C. He earns $0.05 for each appliance he sells.

   D. He earns a 5% commission for each appliance he sells.

6. The equation $A(t) = 900(0.85)^t$ represents the value of a motor scooter t years after it was purchased. Which statement is also true of this situation?

   A. When new, the scooter cost $765.

   B. When new, the scooter cost $900.

   C. The scooter's value is decreasing at a rate of 85% each year.

   D. The scooter's value is decreasing at a rate of 0.15% each year.

Use the following information for questions 7–10.

Trini bought a car by using a combination of a private loan from her parents and an auto loan from a bank. For both loans, the amount Trini will have to pay depends on the number of years before she pays it back.

7. The private loan is a simple interest loan. The amount Trini must pay to her parents can be modeled by the function $p(t) = 5,000 + 5,000(0.03)(t)$, where t is the number of years before she repays the loan. What do the values 5,000 and 0.03 represent in this model?

   _____

   _____

8. The bank charges an annual interest rate that is compounded monthly. The amount Trini must pay to the bank can be modeled by the function $c(t) = 10,000\left(1 + \frac{0.06}{12}\right)^{12t}$, where t is the number of years before she repays the loan. What do the values 10,000; 0.06; and 12 represent in this model?

   _____

   _____

9. Combine functions p and c to build a new function, a, which will show the total amount Trini must repay in car loans if she repays them after t years.

   $a(t) = $ _____

10. Use function a to determine the total amount of money she will have to repay if she pays the loan after 5 years.

    _____

Solve.

11. **SHOW** Marcus is buying a plane ticket. If he purchases his ticket on the day of his departure, it will cost $239. The ticket costs less if he buys it earlier. If he purchases it 20 days before his departure, it will cost $189. Model this situation by using a linear function. Then determine the cost of the ticket if Marcus buys it 3 days before his departure.

    _____

    _____

12. **CREATE** A ball is dropped from a height of 50 centimeters onto a hard floor and bounces back up to $\frac{2}{5}$ of its original height. On each successive bounce, it rebounds to $\frac{2}{5}$ of its previous height. Model this situation with a function. List the height to which the ball bounces on its first, second, third, and fourth bounces.

    _____

    _____

    _____

Arithmetic Sequences

LESSON 22

UNDERSTAND A **sequence** is an arrangement of numbers or objects that follows a rule or a pattern. Take a look at the Fibonacci sequence:

1, 1, 2, 3, 5, 8, 13, 21, 34, …

Each number in the sequence is called a **term**. The pattern of the Fibonacci sequence is that each term is equal to the sum of the two previous terms. This rule is an example of using a **recursive process**, because finding a term depends on knowing previous terms. When defining a recursive process, you must define at least one previous term.

The variable a is often used to stand for the terms in a sequence. The first term is a_1, the second is a_2, and so on. The nth term of the sequence is written a_n, where n can be any positive integer. This notation is useful for writing the sequence's rule mathematically. The equations below represent the rule for the Fibonacci sequence.

$$a_1 = 1 \qquad a_2 = 1 \qquad a_n = a_{n-1} + a_{n-2}$$

UNDERSTAND In an **arithmetic sequence**, each term is found by adding a fixed number, called the **common difference (d)**, to the previous term. The arithmetic sequence 3, 5, 7, 9, 11, 13, … has a common difference of 2.

If you know any term in an arithmetic sequence, you can add the common difference to it to find the next term. The following equation is a recursive definition of an arithmetic sequence.

$$a_n = a_{n-1} + d$$

You can derive an explicit equation to find any term in an arithmetic sequence, as long as you know the first term.

$$a_1 = a_1$$
$$a_2 = a_1 + d$$
$$a_3 = a_2 + d = a_1 + d + d = a_1 + 2d$$
$$a_4 = a_3 + d = a_1 + 2d + d = a_1 + 3d$$

Notice the pattern. To find a desired term, add the first term, a_1, to a multiple of the common difference, d. The coefficient of d is 1 less than the number of the desired term.

$$a_n = a_1 + (n - 1)d$$

⊏ Connect

Below are the first four terms in an arithmetic sequence.

25, 22, 19, 16

Use a recursive process to find the next 3 terms in the sequence. Plot the first seven terms on a coordinate plane.

1

Find the common difference.

Solve the recursive equation for d.

$a_n = a_{n-1} + d$

$d = a_n - a_{n-1}$

Find the difference between successive terms.

$d = 22 - 25 = -3$

$d = 19 - 22 = -3$

$d = 16 - 19 = -3$

So, the recursive formula for a_n is $a_n = a_{n-1} - 3$.

2

Find the next three terms.

$a_5 = a_4 - 3 = 16 - 3 = 13$

$a_6 = a_5 - 3 = 13 - 3 = 10$

$a_7 = a_6 - 3 = 10 - 3 = 7$

▶ The next three terms are 13, 10, and 7.

3

Plot a point to represent each term in the sequence.

Plot each point (n, a_n) for the first seven terms.

▶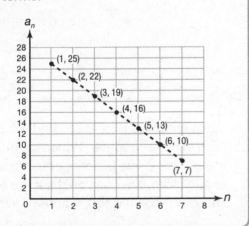

DISCUSS

Based on the graph, what type of relationship exists between the n-values and the a_n-values? Use what you know about functions to help you explain the relationship.

EXAMPLE In a certain arithmetic sequence, each term is found by subtracting 4.5 from the previous term. If the first term in the sequence is 10, what is the 9th term in the sequence?

1 Identify the values of a_1 and d.

You are told that the first term, a_1, is 10.

The next term is found by subtracting 4.5, so the common difference, d, is -4.5.

2 Write an explicit formula to find a_n.

Substitute the values of a_1 and d into the formula.

$a_n = a_1 + (n - 1)d$

$a_n = 10 + (n - 1)(-4.5)$

$a_n = 10 - 4.5n + 4.5$

$a_n = 14.5 - 4.5n$

3 Substitute 9 for n in the formula. Evaluate.

$a_n = 14.5 - 4.5n$

$a_9 = 14.5 - 4.5(9) = 14.5 - 40.5 = -26$

▶ The 9th term in the sequence is -26.

CHECK Use a recursive process to find the 9th term in the sequence. Which method—using a recursive process or using an explicit formula—do you think is a better choice for solving this problem? Why?

Problem Solving

READ

Ami is training for a long-distance race. She ran for 30 minutes per day on three days this week. Each week she will increase her daily running time by 5 minutes. By the 6th week, for how many minutes will she run each day that she trains?

PLAN

She increases her running time by the same number of minutes each week. So, this is an arithmetic sequence.

Write an explicit formula to represent the situation. Then find the _____ term in the sequence.

SOLVE

Her daily running time during the 1st week is 30 minutes, so $a_1 =$ _____.

She will increase her daily running time by 5 minutes each week, so $d =$ _____.

Find a_6, the number of minutes she will run each day during the 6th week.

$$a_n = a_1 + (n - 1)d$$
$$a_6 = 30 + (\underline{} - 1)(\underline{}) = \underline{}$$

CHECK

Use a recursive process to check the answer.

$a_2 = 30 + \underline{} = \underline{}$

$a_3 = \underline{} + \underline{} = \underline{}$

$a_4 = \underline{} + \underline{} = \underline{}$

$a_5 = \underline{} + \underline{} = \underline{}$

$a_6 = \underline{} + \underline{} = \underline{}$

Do you get the same value for a_6? _____

▶ By the sixth week, Ami will be running _____ minutes each day that she trains.

Practice

Determine if each sequence is an arithmetic sequence. If it is, identify the common difference.

1. 5, 3, 1, −1, −3, …

2. 2, 2, 4, 6, 10, …

3. $\frac{3}{2}, \frac{5}{2}, \frac{7}{2}, \frac{9}{2}, \frac{11}{2}, \ldots$

_____   _____   _____

> **HINT** Is the same number added to each term to get the next term?

Write a recursive process for each arithmetic sequence. Then use it to find the specified term.

4. 5, 9, 13, 17, 21, … _____

$a_1 = $ _____

$a_n = $ _____

$a_7 = $ _____

5. 3, $2\frac{3}{4}$, $2\frac{1}{2}$, $2\frac{1}{4}$, 2, …

$a_1 = $ _____

$a_n = $ _____

$a_7 = $ _____

6. 10, 3, −4, −11, −18, …

$a_1 = $ _____

$a_n = $ _____

$a_8 = $ _____

> **REMEMBER** In a recursive process, a_n is defined by using previous terms.

Write an explicit formula for the _n_th term and use it to find the specified term.

7. 11, 15, 19, 23, …

$a_n = $ _____

$a_8 = $ _____

8. 100, 88, 76, 64, …

$a_n = $ _____

$a_{10} = $ _____

9. 1.2, 1.8, 2.4, 3, …

$a_n = $ _____

$a_{12} = $ _____

Use the given information to find the specified term in each arithmetic sequence.

10. $a_1 = 14$, $d = 6$

$a_4 = $ _____

11. $a_1 = 52$, $d = -5$

$a_6 = $ _____

12. $a_1 = 0$, $d = \frac{1}{3}$

$a_{15} = $ _____

Choose the best answer.

13. The formula $a_n = 10 - 4n$ describes an arithmetic sequence. What are the first four terms in the sequence?

  A. 6, 2, −2, −6

  B. 6, 2, 0, −2

  C. 10, 6, 2, −2

  D. 14, 18, 22, 26

14. For an arithmetic sequence, $a_1 = 21$. Its recursive formula is $a_n = a_{n-1} + 11$. Which explicit formula can be used to find the _n_th term in the sequence?

  A. $a_n = 10 - 11n$

  B. $a_n = 10 + 11n$

  C. $a_n = 21 - 11n$

  D. $a_n = 21 + 11n$

Use the arithmetic sequence below for questions 15–17.

$$2, 5, 8, 11, \ldots$$

15. Write an explicit formula in terms of n to show how to find the nth term in this sequence.

_____

16. Plot points (n, a_n) on the grid to represent the first six terms in the sequence.

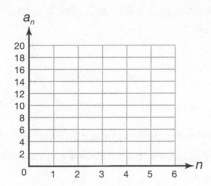

What does the slope of the graph represent?

_____

17. Think of this sequence as a function. What type of function is it? What are its domain and its range? Explain your thinking.

_____

_____

_____

Solve.

18. COMPOSE Steve is buying a new tablet computer on layaway. He makes an initial payment of $50 and will increase the payment each month as shown by the table. Write a recursive formula and an explicit formula to describe this sequence. Explain how you determined the formulas.

Month (n)	Payment in $ (a_n)
1	50
2	60
3	70
4	80
5	90

_____

_____

_____

_____

Geometric Sequences

LESSON 23

UNDERSTAND In a **geometric sequence**, each pair of consecutive terms is related by a **common ratio**, r.

To find a term in the sequence, multiply the previous term by the common ratio. The geometric sequence 1, 3, 9, 27, 81, ... has a common ratio of 3. Each term is multiplied by 3 in order to yield the next term.

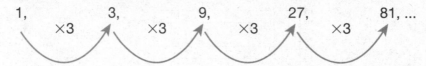

If you know any term in a geometric sequence, you can multiply it by the common ratio to find the next term. The following is a recursive definition of a geometric sequence:

$$a_n = a_{n-1} \cdot r$$

Suppose you wanted to find the 100th term in this sequence. As with arithmetic sequences, using the recursive definition would require a lot of steps. Fortunately, you can derive an explicit equation to find any term in a geometric sequence, as long as you know the first term. Examine the formulas for the first few terms.

$$a_1 = a_1$$
$$a_2 = a_1 \cdot r$$
$$a_3 = a_2 \cdot r = a_1 \cdot r \cdot r = a_1 \cdot r^2$$
$$a_4 = a_3 \cdot r = a_1 \cdot r^2 \cdot r = a_1 \cdot r^3$$
$$a_5 = a_4 \cdot r = a_1 \cdot r^3 \cdot r = a_1 \cdot r^4$$

Notice the pattern. To find a desired term, multiply the first term, a_1, by a power of the common ratio, r. The exponent of r is 1 less than the number of the desired term. Written mathematically, this is:

$$a_n = a_1 \cdot r^{n-1}$$

⊏ Connect

Below are the first four terms in a geometric sequence.

1, 2, 4, 8

Use a recursive process to find the next 3 terms in the sequence. Plot the first seven terms on a coordinate plane.

1

Find the common ratio.

Solve the recursive equation for r.

$$a_n = a_{n-1} \cdot r$$

$$r = \frac{a_n}{a_{n-1}}$$

Find the quotient of successive terms.

$$r = \frac{2}{1} = 2$$

$$r = \frac{4}{2} = 2$$

$$r = \frac{8}{4} = 2$$

So, the recursive formula for a_n is

$$a_n = a_{n-1} \cdot 2.$$

2

Find the next three terms.

$$a_5 = a_4 \cdot 2 = 8 \cdot 2 = 16$$

$$a_6 = a_5 \cdot 2 = 16 \cdot 2 = 32$$

$$a_7 = a_6 \cdot 2 = 32 \cdot 2 = 64$$

▶ The next three terms are 16, 32, and 64.

3

Plot a point to represent each term in the sequence.

Plot each point (n, a_n) for the first seven terms.

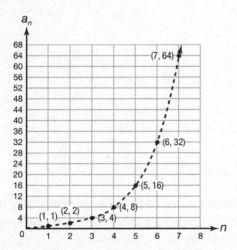

DISCUSS

Based on the graph, what type of relationship exists between the n-values and the a_n-values? Use what you know about functions to help you explain the relationship.

EXAMPLE A geometric sequence has an initial value of 1,024, and each term in the sequence is half of the previous term. Write an explicit formula to find any term in the sequence. Then use that formula to find the 9th term in the sequence.

1

Identify the values of a_1 and r.

You are told that the first term, a_1, is 1,024.

The next term is found by halving the previous term, or multiplying by $\frac{1}{2}$, so the common ratio, r, is $\frac{1}{2}$.

2

Write an explicit formula to find a_n.

Substitute the values of a_1 and r into the formula.

$a_n = a_1 \cdot r^{n-1}$,

$a_n = 1{,}024 \cdot \left(\frac{1}{2}\right)^{n-1}$

This can be simplified by using the laws of exponents.

$a_n = 1{,}024 \cdot \left(\frac{1}{2}\right)^{n} \cdot \left(\frac{1}{2}\right)^{-1}$

$a_n = 1{,}024 \cdot \left(\frac{1}{2}\right)^{n} \cdot 2$

$a_n = 2{,}048 \cdot \left(\frac{1}{2}\right)^{n}$

3

Find the 9th term in the sequence.

$f(9) = 2{,}048 \cdot \left(\frac{1}{2}\right)^{9} = 2{,}048 \cdot \left(\frac{1}{512}\right) = 4$

▶ The 9th term in the sequence is 4.

CHECK

Use a recursive process to find the 9th term. Compare this result to the answer above to check your work.

Problem Solving

READ

Jenny started a chain letter by e-mail. She sent it to five of her friends and asked them to each send it to five of their friends. Assume that no one breaks the chain and that no person receives the e-mail twice. How many e-mails will be sent during the 6th generation? (Treat Jenny's e-mails as the 1st generation of the letter.)

PLAN

Each person who receives the e-mail sends it to five friends.

Each of those people also sends it to five friends. So, the total number of e-mails sent in each generation is _____ times the number of e-mails sent in the previous generation.

So, a recursive process can be used to find the answer.

SOLVE

In the 1st generation, 5 e-mails were sent. So, $a_1 = 5$.

In the 2nd generation, 5 times as many e-mails will be sent, and so on.

2nd generation: $a_2 = 5 \cdot 5 =$ _____

3rd generation: $a_3 =$ _____ $\cdot 5 =$ _____

4th generation: $a_4 =$ _____ $\cdot 5 =$ _____

5th generation: $a_5 =$ _____ $\cdot 5 =$ _____

6th generation: $a_6 =$ _____ $\cdot 5 =$ _____

CHECK

The numbers of e-mails sent in each generation are the terms of a geometric sequence. So, check the answer by writing an explicit formula.

We know that $a_1 =$ _____ and the common ratio, r, is 5.

$a_n = a_1 \cdot r^{n-1}$

$a_n =$ _____ $\cdot ($_____$)^{n-1}$

Use the formula to find a_6.

$a_6 =$ _____ $\cdot ($_____$)^{6-1} =$ _____

Did you get the same value for a_6? _____

> If the chain is not broken, then exactly _____ e-mails will be sent in the sixth generation.

Practice

Determine if each sequence is a geometric sequence. If it is, identify the common ratio.

1. 5, 10, 15, 20, 25, ...

2. 7, −14, 28, −56, 112, ...

3. 16, 24, 36, 54, 81, ...

_____ _____ _____

> **REMEMBER** A common ratio can be positive or negative.

Write a recursive process for each geometric sequence. Then use it to find the specified term.

4. 1, 6, 36, 216, ...

$a_1 =$ _____

$a_n =$ _____

$a_6 =$ _____

5. $\frac{1}{4}, \frac{1}{16}, \frac{1}{64}, \frac{1}{256}, \cdots$

$a_1 =$ _____

$a_n =$ _____

$a_6 =$ _____

6. 0.05, 0.5, 5, 50, ...

$a_1 =$ _____

$a_n =$ _____

$a_7 =$ _____

 HINT What number is multiplied by each term to get the next term?

Write an explicit formula for the _n_th term and use it to find the specified term.

7. $3, 2, \frac{4}{3}, \frac{8}{9}, \ldots$

$a_n =$ _____

$a_6 =$ _____

8. 3, −9, 27, −81, ...

$a_n =$ _____

$a_8 =$ _____

9. 12, 24, 48, 96, ...

$a_n =$ _____

$a_{10} =$ _____

Use the given information to find the specified term in each geometric sequence.

10. $a_1 = 3, r = 20$

$a_4 =$ _____

11. $a_1 = 5{,}000; r = 0.2$

$a_6 =$ _____

12. $a_1 = 2, r = -4$

$a_7 =$ _____

Choose the best answer.

13. The formula $a_n = -10 \cdot (3)^{n-1}$ describes a geometric sequence. Which recursive formula also describes this sequence?

   A. $a_1 = 1; a_n = a_{n-1} \cdot -30$

   B. $a_1 = 3; a_n = a_{n-1} \cdot -10$

   C. $a_1 = -10; a_n = a_{n-1} \cdot 3$

   D. $a_1 = -1; a_n = a_{n-1} \cdot 30$

14. Which formula can be used to find the _n_th term in the sequence below?

   128, 96, 72, 54, ...

   A. $a_n = 128 \cdot \left(\frac{3}{4}\right)^{n-1}$

   B. $a_n = 128 \cdot \left(\frac{4}{3}\right)^{n-1}$

   C. $a_n = 128 \cdot \left(\frac{3}{4}\right)^{n}$

   D. $a_n = 128 \cdot \left(\frac{4}{3}\right)^{n}$

Use the geometric sequence below for questions 15–17.

    80, 40, 20, 10, …

15. Write an explicit formula in terms of n to show how to find the nth term in this sequence.

_____

16. Plot points (n, a_n) on the grid on the right to represent the first six terms in the sequence.

Find the average rate of change between each adjacent pair of points.

_____

_____

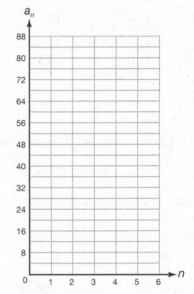

17. Think of this sequence as a function. What type of function is it? What are its domain and its range? Explain your thinking.

_____

_____

_____

18. **SHOW** A petri dish contains 4 viruses. Each hour, the number of viruses increases, as shown in the table. The population change can be modeled by a geometric sequence. Write a recursive formula and an explicit formula that can model this sequence. Use the formulas to predict how many viruses will be in the dish by the 7th hour.

Hour (n)	Population (a_n)
1	4
2	12
3	36
4	108
5	324

recursive formula: _____

explicit formula: _____

$a_7 = $ _____

UNIT 3 Review

Determine whether each relation represented is a function or not.

1.

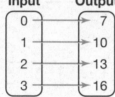

_____

2.

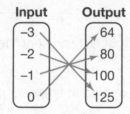

_____

3.

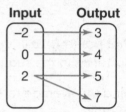

_____

Use the sequence below for questions 4–6.

18, 14, 10, 6, …

4. Write an explicit formula for the *n*th term.

_____

5. What is the tenth term in this sequence?

_____

6. Think of this sequence as a function. What type of function is it? What are its domain and its range?

_____

Graph each equation. Then identify the *x*- and *y*-intercepts of each graph.

7. $6x + 3y = 18$

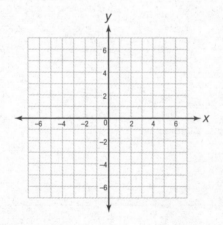

x-intercept: _____

y-intercept: _____

8. $f(x) = 2\left(\frac{1}{2}\right)^x$

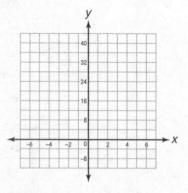

x-intercept: _____

y-intercept: _____

Fill in the blanks by writing an operation sign and a number to show how the y-values are changing over each interval. Then classify each function as linear or exponential.

9.

	+1	+1	+1	+1	+1
x	–3	–2	–1	0	1	2
y	125	25	5	1	$\frac{1}{5}$	$\frac{1}{25}$

_____

10.

	+1	+1	+1	+1	+1
x	–3	–2	–1	0	1	2
y	37	25	13	1	–11	–23

_____

Use the information below for questions 11 and 12. The graph below represents an exponential function f. The table lists several ordered pairs for a linear function g.

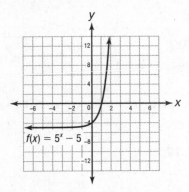

g(x) = 5x − 5	
x	**g(x)**
−1	−10
0	−5
1	0
2	5
3	10

11. Compare the positive intervals and negative intervals of the two functions.

_____

_____

12. Compare and contrast the end behavior of the functions.

_____

_____

Graph g. Then, write an explicit equation for g(x) in terms of x.

13. $g(x) = f(x + 2)$

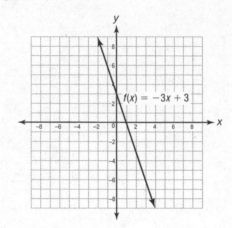

$f(x) = -3x + 3$

$g(x) = $ _____

14. $g(x) = -f(x)$

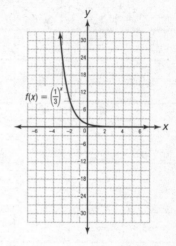

$f(x) = \left(\dfrac{1}{3}\right)^x$

$g(x) = $ _____

Choose the best answer.

15. Based on the graph on the right, which statement is **not** true?

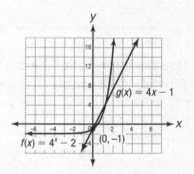

$g(x) = 4x - 1$

$f(x) = 4^x - 2$ $(0, -1)$

    A. Functions f and g have the same x-intercept.

    B. The ordered pair $(1, 2)$ is a solution for $f(x)$.

    C. The ordered pair $(2, 7)$ is a solution for $g(x)$.

    D. The value of $f(x)$ begins to exceed $g(x)$ during the interval between $x = 1$ and $x = 2$.

Identify how the graph of f was stretched or shrunk, horizontally or vertically, and by what factor, to create the graph of g.

16.

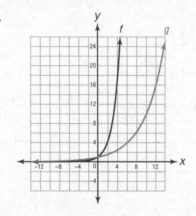

_____

17.

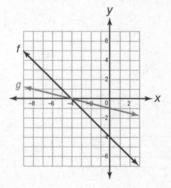

_____

Rewrite each side of the equation as a function. Then graph the functions to solve for *x*.

18. $2x + 6 = -\frac{1}{2}x - 4$

$f(x) =$ _____ $g(x) =$ _____

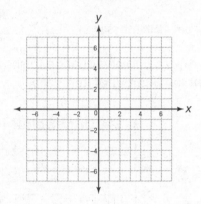

$x =$ _____

19. $3^x - 3 = 6$

$f(x) =$ _____ $g(x) =$ _____

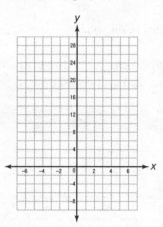

$x =$ _____

Solve.

20. **CREATE** The cost of using the Internet at an Internet café is a set fee plus a certain rate per minute. Four minutes of Internet use costs $3, and eight minutes of Internet use costs $4. On the grid, make a graph to represent this situation and write an equation to model the situation. Find the slope of the graph and interpret its meaning in this situation.

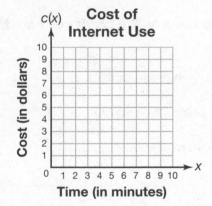

_____

_____

21. **EXPLAIN** An 8-inch candle is lit and begins to burn. Its height, *h*, after *t* hours can be modeled by the function $h(t) = 8 - 2t$. Graph this function and label its intercepts. Identify the domain for the graph and explain why you chose it.

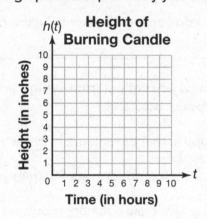

_____

_____

_____

TAKING CARE OF Business

Working in pairs or individually, pretend you are starting your own business.

1. The item I will sell is _____. The name of my new business is _____.

2. Set a price per item that you will charge. Create a table, a graph, and an equation to show *f*, the amount you will collect if you sell up to 10 items. Represent the number of items as *x*.

x	f(x) = _____
1	
2	
3	
4	
5	
6	
7	
8	
9	
10	

3. Explain how you determined the equation for *f*.

_____

4. Did you connect the points on the graph with a solid line? a dashed line? no line? Explain why.

_____

The amount you collect from selling your product is not the same as the profit you earn from selling your product.

5. Suppose that the amount of profit you earn is equal to $\frac{3}{5}$ of what you collect.

So, if each product costs \$5, then your profit for selling 1 product is: $\$5 \cdot \frac{3}{5} =$ _____.

Using algebraic notation, represent this as a transformation: $p(x) =$ _____ $f(x)$.

What type of transformation of *f* does it represent? _____

6. Write an equation for *p*. Then graph it on the coordinate plane above, using a different colored pen or pencil than you used to draw the graph of *f*. Does this show the transformation you expected?

_____

Profits are important to you, but your customers are only concerned with how much your product will cost them. They want to pay as little as possible.

The graph below shows how much one of your competitors, Company G, charges for the same product, including shipping.

7. Based on the graph, how much does Company G charge per product? Explain how you know.

    _____

8. Copy your original graph of function *f* from the previous page onto the graph above. Use a different color and label it *f*. After checking with your local shipper, you find that you will need to pay 15 dollars to ship any items. Transform the graph of *f* using this equation:

    $h(x) = f(x) + 15$

    Identify the transformation: _____

    Then write an explicit equation for *h*: $h(x) =$ _____

9. Based on your graph, when would it be cheaper for Mr. Smith to order from Company G? When would it be cheaper to order from you?

    _____

    _____

Coordinate Algebra

Expressions and Equations

Understand the connections between proportional relationships, lines, and linear equations.

Functions

Use functions to model relationships between quantities.

Statistics and Probability

Investigate patterns of association in bivariate data.

Statistics and Probability

Interpreting Categorical and Quantitative Data

Summarize, represent, and interpret data on a single count or measurement variable.

Summarize, represent, and interpret data on two categorical and quantitative variables.

Interpret linear models.

Functions

Interpreting Functions

Interpret functions that arise in applications in terms of the context.

Statistics and Probability

Interpreting Categorical and Quantitative Data

Summarize, represent, and interpret data on two categorical and quantitative variables.

Conditional Probability and the Rules of Probability

Understand independence and conditional probability and use them to interpret data.

Unit 4
Describing Data

Displaying and Analyzing Data

Collecting and Displaying Data

UNDERSTAND Often, one of the first steps to answering a question is collecting data. For example, suppose you wanted to know how tall bean plants grow in sunny conditions. To answer this question, you could find some bean plants on a farm or growing in the wild or anywhere that gets plenty of sunlight and record their heights. This is an example of an **observational study**.

However, another option is to grow bean plants of your own. You could grow some bean plants on your windowsill and some others in a dark closet. After a time, record their heights. This is an example of an **experimental study**. In this study, you directly controlled the conditions that affect the plants, such as temperature, water, and soil, so that the results depended only on the amount of light that the plants received.

UNDERSTAND No matter what type of study you choose, it helps to organize your data in a data display. If the data are numerical and you have relatively few data points, a **dot plot** may be a good way to display them. The base of a dot plot is a number line that lists the possible values of the data. Each data point is represented by a dot placed over its value on the number line. A sample dot plot is shown below.

Heights of Plants (in cm)

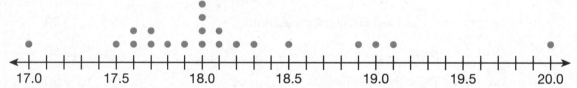

A **histogram**, another kind of data display, groups data points into ranges and shows how many of the data points fall in each range. All ranges or intervals in a histogram are of equal size, and they do not overlap. The sample histogram below shows the same data as in the dot plot above.

Heights of Plants

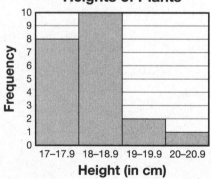

↞ Connect

The chairman of a company asked his chief financial officer to track the closing price of the company's stock over 20 trading days. The stock prices, in dollars, are listed below.

26.70, 26.50, 26.90, 26.70, 26.60, 25.50, 25.10, 25.30, 25.10, 26.50,

27.40, 26.60, 26.80, 26.70, 26.70, 27.60, 27.40, 27.80, 27.60, 27.90

Create a histogram for the stock price data.

1

Choose a title and intervals for the histogram.

Title the histogram "Stock Prices."

Given the spread of prices, intervals of 50 cents will work well for the data.

2

Group the data into intervals and count the frequencies.

Price Intervals	Data Points	Frequency
25.00–25.49	25.10, 25.30, 25.10	3
25.50–25.99	25.50	1
26.00–26.49		0
26.50–26.99	26.70, 26.50, 26.90, 26.70, 26.60, 26.50, 26.60, 26.80, 26.70, 26.70	10
27.00–27.49	27.40, 27.40	2
27.50–27.99	27.60, 27.80, 27.60, 27.90	4

3

Create the histogram.

Use the frequencies to make a bar for each interval.

▶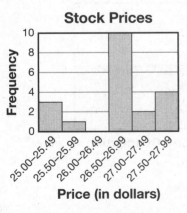

DISCUSS

What are some advantages of using a dot plot instead of a histogram?

Data Distributions

UNDERSTAND You can use the distribution of a data set, or its shape, to interpret it and to compare it to other data sets. Four kinds of distributions are described below.

- **Normal distribution**: The data set has one clear peak in the center with other data points spread equally on both sides of the peak. Because of its appearance, this kind of distribution is sometimes referred to as a bell curve. A normal distribution can also be called a symmetric distribution.

- **Skewed distribution**: The data set has one clear peak. But instead of being spread equally on either side of the peak, most or all of the data are concentrated on one side of the peak. This kind of distribution is said to have a "tail." Depending on the direction of the tail, the data can be described as skewed right or skewed left. The skewed distribution shown below is skewed to the left.

- **Bimodal distribution**: The data set has two clear peaks.

- **Uniform distribution**: The data items are equally spread across the range of the data set, and there are no clear peaks.

Examples of each of these kinds of distribution are graphed below.

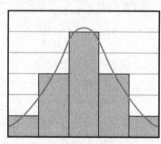

Normal Distribution

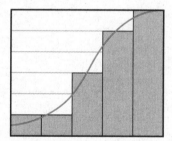

Skewed Distribution

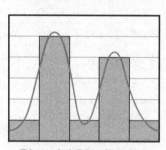

Bimodal Distribution

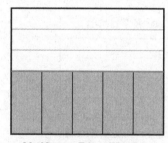

Uniform Distribution

⊏ Connect

The weights, in pounds, of a group of cats entered in a cat show are given below.

$1\frac{1}{2}$, 2, 2, 3, 3, 4, 4, 4, $4\frac{1}{2}$, 5, 5, 5, $5\frac{1}{2}$, $5\frac{3}{4}$,

6, 6, 6, 6, $6\frac{1}{4}$, $6\frac{1}{2}$, 7, 7, 7, 7, $7\frac{1}{2}$, $7\frac{3}{4}$, 8,

8, $8\frac{1}{2}$, $8\frac{1}{2}$, 9, 9, $9\frac{1}{4}$, $9\frac{3}{4}$, 10, 10, $10\frac{1}{2}$, 11, 13

Use the data to construct a histogram. Then describe the distribution of the data.

1 Choose intervals for your histogram.

The weights range from $1\frac{1}{2}$ to 13 pounds. Intervals of 2 pounds would be a good choice.

2 Divide the data into intervals and count frequencies.

Weight (w) Intervals	Data Points (in lb)	Frequency
$0 \le w < 2$	$1\frac{1}{2}$	1
$2 \le w < 4$	2, 2, 3, 3	4
$4 \le w < 6$	4, 4, 4, $4\frac{1}{2}$, 5, 5, 5, $5\frac{1}{2}$, $5\frac{3}{4}$	9
$6 \le w < 8$	6, 6, 6, 6, $6\frac{1}{4}$, $6\frac{1}{2}$, 7, 7, 7, 7, $7\frac{1}{2}$, $7\frac{3}{4}$	12
$8 \le w < 10$	8, 8, $8\frac{1}{2}$, $8\frac{1}{2}$, 9, 9, $9\frac{1}{4}$, $9\frac{3}{4}$	8
$10 \le w < 12$	10, 10, $10\frac{1}{2}$, 11	4
$12 \le w < 14$	13	1

3 Construct the histogram. Then describe the distribution.

▶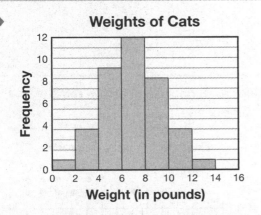

The histogram has one clear peak, and the rest of the data are spread relatively equally on both sides of the peak. The data show a normal distribution.

Notice that each interval includes its lower boundary value, but not the upper boundary. So, on the histogram, the bar located between 2 and 4 will include data points of 2 lb, but not 4 lb.

DISCUSS

How would the data have to change to show a skewed distribution? A bimodal distribution?

EXAMPLE A The list below shows how many points Corinna scored in each of 16 basketball games:

8, 3, 3, 9, 4, 7, 10, 4, 5, 9, 5, 7, 6, 8, 10, 6

Make a dot plot of Corinna's points.

1

Choose a range and title for the dot plot.

Title the plot "Corinna's Points Scored."

The least value is 3, and the greatest value is 10.

A number line from 0 to 14 will include all the data.

2

Plot each data point above a number line.

For each element in the data set, place a dot above its value on the number line. If multiple points have the same value, stack the dots on top of one another.

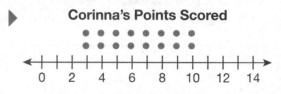

Leanne is on Corinna's team. The list below shows how many points Leanne scored in the same 16 basketball games:

13, 14, 9, 12, 13, 13, 14, 10, 9, 12, 6, 5, 7, 11, 10, 8

Make a dot plot of Leanne's points.

1

Choose a range and title for the dot plot.

Title the plot "Leanne's Points Scored."

The least value is 5, and the greatest value is 14.

Use the same range that you used for Corinna's dot plot.

2

Plot each data point above the number line.

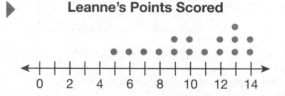

DISCUSS

Compare the shapes of the dot plots. What do their shapes tell you about the distributions of Corinna's and Leanne's scores?

EXAMPLE B The two histograms below show the ages of wait staff at two restaurants.

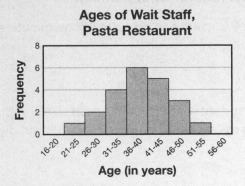

Ages of Wait Staff, Pasta Restaurant

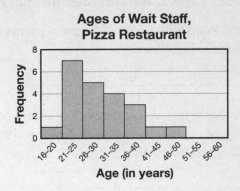

Ages of Wait Staff, Pizza Restaurant

Identify the kind of distribution shown by each histogram. Use the shapes of the data sets to compare them.

1

Describe the shape of the histogram for the pasta restaurant.

The histogram is nearly symmetrical and has a central peak at ages 36–40.

Its shape most closely matches a bell curve.

The ages of the wait staff at the pasta restaurant show a normal distribution.

2

Describe the shape of the histogram for the pizza restaurant.

The histogram has one peak. The majority of the data are in a "tail" that extends to the right of the peak.

The ages of the wait staff at the pizza restaurant show a distribution skewed the right.

3

Use the shapes of the histograms to interpret each data set.

The normal distribution of the data from the pasta restaurant shows that the ages of its wait staff are relatively evenly distributed around the 36–40 age range.

The data from the pizza restaurant is skewed to the right, and most of the data fall below the 36–40 age range. So, in general, the wait staff of the pizza restaurant is younger than that of the pasta restaurant.

TRY

The ages of the wait staff at a seafood restaurant are listed below.

18, 21, 23, 26, 26, 27, 28, 29, 30, 31, 35, 39, 42, 46, 48, 49, 49, 50, 51, 53, 54, 57

On a separate sheet of paper, create a histogram for the data. Compare its shape to the two histograms on this page.

Practice

For questions 1 and 2, tell whether the study is observational or experimental.

1. You measure how many pull-ups students in your P.E. class can perform in one minute each week for several weeks.

   _____

2. You provide half of a class of elementary school students with 20 minutes of spelling practice instead of recess. The other half of the class goes to recess. You record students' grades on a spelling test taken after recess.

   _____

For questions 3–5, use the given information. Create a histogram for each data set. Describe the distribution of each data set.

Students in the 1st and 2nd period biology classes took the same test. Their test scores are listed below.

3. 1st period test scores:

   100, 91, 86, 73, 81, 100, 93, 94, 86,
   86, 99, 93, 98, 84, 80, 97, 93,
   87, 70, 97, 94, 88, 85, 96, 90

4. 2nd period test scores:

   81, 87, 95, 85, 83, 82, 76, 68, 86,
   83, 93, 87, 76, 87, 71, 100, 76,
   91, 73, 80, 80, 84, 87, 88, 73

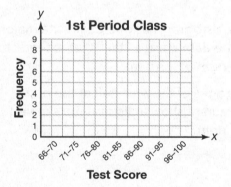

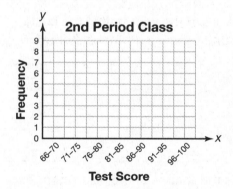

Distribution: _____

Distribution: _____

5. Compare and contrast the histograms for the biology classes in questions 4 and 5.

   _____

   _____

Create a dot plot for the given data. Describe the shape of the data.

6. Nathaniel opened 20 peanut shells and recorded the number of peanuts he found in each shell.

3, 2, 0, 1, 5, 2, 1, 2, 3, 1, 2, 2, 1, 2, 2, 3, 2, 3, 1, 2

 _____

Fill in each blank with an appropriate word or phrase.

7. A _____ shows data points as dots above a number line.

8. A _____ shows how frequently data occur within certain ranges or intervals.

9. _____ used in a histogram must be equal.

10. A _____ distribution is symmetric and resembles a bell curve.

11. A _____ distribution has two distinct peaks.

12. A _____ distribution has a "tail" that extends more to one side of the graph than the other.

13. **COMPARE** Antoine surveyed 200 high school students to find out how many hours they slept this past Saturday night and how many hours they slept this past Monday night. The histograms show the data he collected.

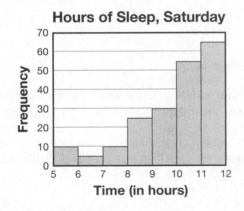
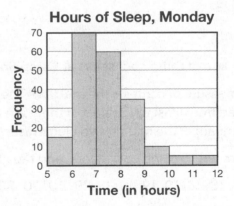

Compare the distributions of data on the two graphs. How do they differ? For what reason could they be so different? Explain.

_____

_____

_____

LESSON 25 Investigating Measures of Center

UNDERSTAND One way to describe a data set is by using a **measure of center**. A measure of center, such as the mean, represents the average of a set of data and can be used to describe the set.

The dot plot below shows the ages of all Camp Sparrow counselors. By eyeballing the dot plot, you can see that the data are centered around the value 19. If someone asked you how old the camp counselors are, you would probably say around 19.

Ages of Camp Counselors

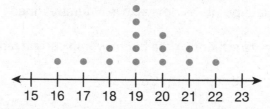

Each dot in the dot plot represents an element in the data set. All 15 elements from the data set are listed below.

16, 17, 18, 18, 19, 19, 19, 19, 19, 20, 20, 20, 21, 21, 22

A data set can have several kinds of measures of center. One measure of center is the **mean**, which is the average of the values in a data set. To calculate the mean, divide the sum of the elements by the total number of elements.

$$\text{mean} = \frac{16 + 17 + 18 + 18 + 19 + 19 + 19 + 19 + 19 + 20 + 20 + 20 + 21 + 21 + 22}{15}$$

$$= \frac{288}{15}$$

$$= 19.2$$

The mean age of camp counselors at Camp Sparrow is 19.2.

Another measure of center is the **median**. The median is the middle value when the elements are ordered from least to greatest. If there are an even number of elements, the median is the average (mean) of the middle two elements.

Since there are 15 camp counselors, and thus 15 ages, the middle number is the 8th value.

16, 17, 18, 18, 19, 19, 19, <u>19</u>, 19, 20, 20, 20, 21, 21, 22

The median age of the camp counselors is 19.

Some data sets contain **outliers**. An outlier is a data point that is either much greater or far less than the rest of the data points. It lies far outside the group that contains the rest of the data. For example, a camp counselor who was 41 would be an outlier. An outlier can affect which measure of center best describes the data set. In general, when a data set contains an outlier, the median is a better measure of center than the mean.

⊏ Connect

Below are the scores that Justin earned on his last 8 homework assignments.

80, 95, 0, 90, 95, 80, 85, 90

What are his mean homework score and median homework score?

1

Find the mean score.

$$\text{mean} = \frac{80 + 95 + 0 + 90 + 95 + 80 + 85 + 90}{8}$$

$$\text{mean} = \frac{615}{8}$$

▶ mean = 76.875

2

To find the median score, first list the scores from least to greatest.

0, 80, 80, 85, 90, 90, 95, 95

3

Because there is an even number of terms in the set, find the mean of the two middle numbers.

The two middle numbers are 85 and 90.

0, 80, 80, <u>85</u>, <u>90</u>, 90, 95, 95

▶ $\text{median} = \frac{85 + 90}{2} = \frac{175}{2} = 87.5$

DISCUSS

Compare the mean and median of Justin's homework grades. Which measure better describes the center of the data? Explain.

EXAMPLE A The histograms shown relate the heights of the members of the girls' basketball teams this year and last year. Compare the median heights for the two teams.

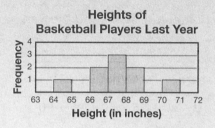

1

Determine the number of members on each team.

Count the number of players in each bin and add these frequencies together.

The total number of players this year is
$1 + 2 + 2 + 1 + 2 + 1 = 9$.

The total number of players last year was
$1 + 2 + 3 + 2 + 1 = 9$.

2

Identify the player with the median height for each year.

Both teams have 9 members, so the player with the median height will be the fifth player when the players are arranged in order of height.

3

Identify the locations of the median-height players on the histograms.

Each box in the histograms represents a single player. Number the boxes in the histograms and locate the fifth box in each histogram.

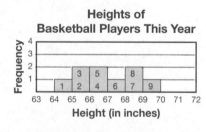

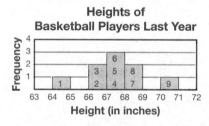

4

Compare the medians.

▶ Since the median this year falls between 66 and 67 inches, and the median height last year fell between 67 and 68 inches, the median height was greater last year.

 Why is it not possible to use these histograms to find an exact median and mean?

EXAMPLE B Two classes held contests to see which could memorize the greatest number of digits of the number π. Eight students from each class competed. The dot plots show the total number of digits recalled by each of the competitors. Compare the number of digits recalled by competitors in each class.

Digits Recalled, Class A

Digits Recalled, Class B

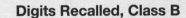

1

Select a measure of center.

In Class A, most students recalled 10 to 15 digits, while one student recalled 30 digits.

In Class B, all students recalled 11 to 15 digits.

Because the data set for Class A contains one outlier, the median is best for comparing the competitors from the two classes.

2

Find the median for Class A.

A dot plot shows data ordered from least to greatest, so the data are:

10, 12, 12, <u>14</u>, <u>14</u>, 14, 15, 30.

The median is: $\frac{14 + 14}{2} = \frac{28}{2} = 14$.

3

Find the median for Class B.

The data are: 11, 12, 12, <u>13</u>, <u>13</u>, 14, 14, 15.

The median is: $\frac{13 + 13}{2} = \frac{26}{2} = 13$.

4

Compare the medians.

Class A had a median of 14 digits, while Class B had a median of 13 digits.

▶ On average, Class A remembered more digits of π than Class B.

TRY

Calculate the mean number of digits recalled by the competitors in each class.

Practice

Locate the specific interval that contains the median for each data set that is displayed. When possible, determine the exact median.

1.

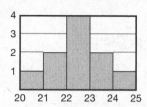

_____

2.

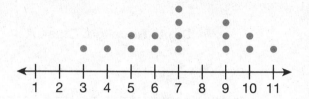

_____

HINT Where does the center of the data appear to lie?

Find the mean and median for each data set.

3. 5, 25, 10, 15, 20

median: _____

mean: _____

4. 1, 7, 3, 2, 6

median: _____

mean: _____

5. 10, 90, 10, 60, 40, 30

median: _____

mean: _____

REMEMBER Before finding the median, order the data from least to greatest.

Write _true_ or _false_ for each statement. If false, rewrite the statement to make it true.

6. The mean of a data set is equal to the sum of the elements in the set multiplied by the number of elements in the set.

_____

7. If a data set contains an odd number of elements, the median is equal to the mean of the two middle elements when the elements are ordered from least to greatest.

_____

8. An outlier is a value that is very different from the other values in a data set.

_____

9. If a data set includes an outlier, the median will probably be a better measure of center than the mean.

_____

Find the median for each data set or determine the interval in which the median must fall. Then compare the medians.

10. The dot plots show Kyla's Spanish quiz scores during the 1st and 2nd semesters.

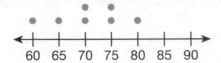

1st Semester Quiz Scores

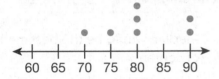

2nd Semester Quiz Scores

median score, 1st semester: _____

median score, 2nd semester: _____

Comparison: _____

11. The histograms show the daily high temperatures in two cities.

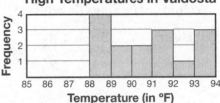

High Temperatures in Valdosta

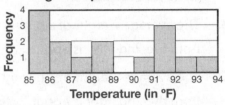

High Temperatures in Atlanta

median high temperature, Valdosta: _____

median high temperature, Atlanta: _____

Comparison: _____

Find the mean for each data set. Then compare the means.

12. The tables show the number of ads that were sold by the actors and stage-crew members working on a school play.

Actor	Rajiv	Amy	Penny	Leonard	Adriel
Ads Sold	4	4	5	6	7

Crew Member	Tina	Ben	Ronny	Irene	Cris
Ads Sold	6	7	8	9	9

mean number sold, actors: _____

mean number sold, crew members: _____

Comparison: _____

13. The dot plots show the number of hours of television watched yesterday by students in two homerooms.

Hours of Television Watched, Room 101

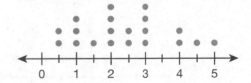

Hours of Television Watched, Room 102

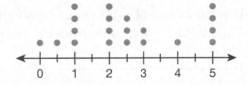

mean number of hours, Room 101: _____

mean number of hours, Room 102: _____

Comparison: _____

Choose the best answer.

14. Which statement accurately compares the average weight of a puppy from the 2nd litter to the average weight of a puppy from the 1st litter?

Weights of Puppies (in ounces)

1st Litter	$3\frac{1}{2}$, 4, 4, $4\frac{1}{2}$
2nd Litter	$4\frac{1}{2}$, 5, 7, $7\frac{1}{2}$

A. The average weight is about the same for both litters.

B. The average weight of a puppy from the 2nd litter is about $\frac{1}{2}$ as great.

C. The average weight of a puppy from the 2nd litter is about $1\frac{1}{2}$ times as great.

D. The average weight of a puppy from the 2nd litter is about $2\frac{1}{2}$ times as great.

15. To compare two shipments, five packages from each shipment were chosen at random and weighed. Which measure or measures of center would be best to use if you wanted to compare the weight of a typical package from each shipment?

Weights of Packages (in pounds)

1st Shipment	2, 4, 6, 8, 10
2nd Shipment	3, 3, 5, 8, 50

A. Median would be the best measure of center.

B. Mean would be the best measure of center.

C. Median and mean would both be equally good measures of center.

D. Neither the mean nor the median would be a good measure of center.

Solve.

16. Students in two biology classes began growing mung bean plants on the same day. The dot plots show the heights of the plants one week after being planted.

Plant Heights (in cm), Class A

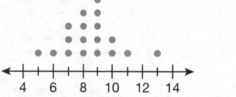

Plant Heights (in cm), Class B

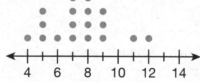

Use a measure of center to compare the heights of plants in Class A to the heights of plants in Class B. Show and/or explain the work you did to determine your answer.

_____

_____

_____

17. The dot plots show the hourly wages of supermarket cashiers at two stores.

Hourly Wages (in dollars), Thrifty Shop

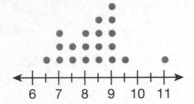

Hourly Wages (in dollars), Wayne Foods

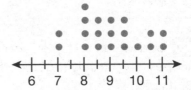

Use a measure of center to compare the wages of cashiers at Thrifty Shop and at Wayne Foods. Explain the work you did to make your comparison.

_____

_____

_____

18. **COMPARE** The histograms show the number of health bars sold by 9th-grade and 10th-grade students.

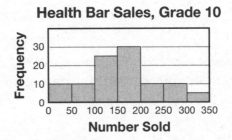

Locate the specific interval that contains the median for each data set, and use those medians to compare the number of health bars sold by 9th-grade students to the number sold by 10th-grade students. Could you use these data to do a detailed comparison of the two grades' sales? Explain your answer.

_____

_____

_____

19. **CHOOSE** The table on the right lists the scores for students in two P.E. classes who went bowling on Friday.

Which measure of center—mean or median—is best for comparing the data sets? Explain why. Use that measure to compare Classes 1 and 2.

Bowling Scores

Class 1	Class 2
78, 80, 82, 95, 98, 102, 105, 110, 120, 290	75, 80, 88, 90, 103, 105, 110, 112, 115, 120

_____

_____

_____

UNDERSTAND In addition to center, another characteristic of a data set is its **spread**. The spread describes how closely together the data points are grouped. Compare the data shown in the dot plots below.

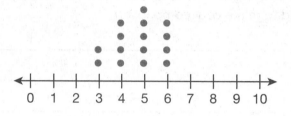

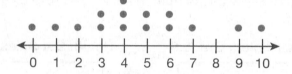

The first dot plot shows data that are clustered closely together. The second dot plot shows data that are more spread apart. The data in the second dot plot are said to be much more variable than those in the first plot.

UNDERSTAND When data are in a visual display, such as a dot plot or histogram, you can see the spread in the display. When the data are a list of values, you can use measures of variability, such as **mean absolute deviation (MAD)**, to examine the spread. The MAD is the average distance between the elements in a data set and the center of the data set.

The MAD measures variability by showing how much the data points in a set vary from the mean, $\bar{x}$. To calculate the MAD for a data set, follow these steps:

1. Find the mean of the data, $\bar{x}$.

2. For each element in the data set:

   a. Subtract the mean from the data point, x. This difference, $(x - \bar{x})$, is the deviation from the mean.

   b. Take the absolute value of each difference to find the absolute deviation from the mean: $|x - \bar{x}|$.

3. Last, calculate the MAD by finding the mean of the absolute deviations: add the absolute deviations together and divide the sum by the number of absolute deviations (which is the same as the number of elements in the data set).

← Connect

The number of ads sold by each of the 10 students on the yearbook staff is listed below.

1, 3, 3, 4, 6, 8, 8, 8, 9, 10

The histogram on the right displays the same information.

Calculate the mean absolute deviation (MAD) for this data set.

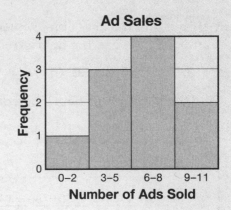

Ad Sales

1

Calculate the mean.

To find the mean, add all of the values and divide by the number of elements.

$$\bar{x} = \frac{1 + 3 + 3 + 4 + 6 + 8 + 8 + 8 + 9 + 10}{10}$$

$$= \frac{60}{10}$$

$$= 6$$

2

Calculate the absolute deviations from the mean.

Data Point (x)	Deviation from Mean (x − x̄)	Absolute Deviation from Mean (|x − x̄|)
1	1 − 6 = −5	|−5| = 5
3	3 − 6 = −3	|−3| = 3
3	3 − 6 = −3	|−3| = 3
4	4 − 6 = −2	|−2| = 2
6	6 − 6 = 0	|0| = 0
8	8 − 6 = 2	|2| = 2
8	8 − 6 = 2	|2| = 2
8	8 − 6 = 2	|2| = 2
9	9 − 6 = 3	|3| = 3
10	10 − 6 = 4	|4| = 4

3

Calculate the MAD.

Find the mean of the absolute deviations.

$$MAD = \frac{5 + 3 + 3 + 2 + 0 + 2 + 2 + 2 + 3 + 4}{10}$$

$$= \frac{26}{10}$$

$$= 2.6$$

▶ The mean absolute deviation is 2.6.

Whether a data point is above or below the mean does not matter. We are only interested in its distance from the mean, which is always a positive value.

What does the MAD of 2.6 tell you about the spread of the data?

Does the histogram support your response?

EXAMPLE A The local library asked a random sample of patrons how many books each had borrowed last year. The data are shown below.

0, 3, 15, 22, 30, 50, 61, 75

Find the MAD for the data. Then describe the spread of the data.

1

Find the mean.

$$\bar{x} = \frac{0 + 3 + 15 + 22 + 30 + 50 + 61 + 75}{8}$$

$$= \frac{256}{8}$$

$$= 32$$

2

Find the absolute deviations from the mean.

Data Point (x)	Deviation from Mean (x − x̄)	Absolute Deviation from Mean (|x − x̄|)
0	0 − 32 = −32	|−32| = 32
3	3 − 32 = −29	|−29| = 29
15	15 − 32 = −17	|−17| = 17
22	22 − 32 = −10	|−10| = 10
30	30 − 32 = −2	|−2| = 2
50	50 − 32 = 18	|18| = 18
61	61 − 32 = 29	|29| = 29
75	75 − 32 = 43	|43| = 43

3

Find the MAD. Then describe the spread.

$$\text{MAD} = \frac{32 + 29 + 17 + 10 + 2 + 18 + 29 + 43}{8}$$

$$= \frac{180}{8}$$

$$= 22.5$$

Since the data range from 0 to 75, a MAD of 22.5 shows that many data points are spread far from the mean.

▶ The mean absolute deviation is 22.5. Because the MAD is large compared to the mean, this MAD shows that the data are quite variable.

DISCUSS

Why is it important to find the absolute values of the deviations from the mean before calculating the mean deviation? What would happen if you found the mean of the deviations (x − x̄)?

EXAMPLE B Julie recorded the following as her grades for her first six French assignments.

89, 90, 94, 94, 97, 100

The mean for these data is 94 and the MAD is 3.

But Julie forgot that, because she turned in the first assignment three days late, her grade was marked down from 89 to 59. Calculate the mean and MAD for her actual grades. Compare and interpret the mean absolute deviations of the two sets.

1

Calculate the mean of the new data set.

The new data set replaces 89 with 59:

59, 90, 94, 94, 97, 100

This lower grade will pull down the mean.

$$\bar{x} = \frac{59 + 90 + 94 + 94 + 97 + 100}{6} = \frac{534}{6} = 89$$

2

Calculate the MAD.

Data Point (x)	Deviation from Mean ($x - \bar{x}$)	Absolute Deviation from Mean ($|x - \bar{x}|$)
59	$59 - 89 = -30$	$|-30| = 30$
90	$90 - 89 = 1$	$|1| = 1$
94	$94 - 89 = 5$	$|5| = 5$
94	$94 - 89 = 5$	$|5| = 5$
97	$97 - 89 = 8$	$|8| = 8$
100	$100 - 89 = 11$	$|11| = 11$

$$MAD = \frac{30 + 1 + 5 + 5 + 8 + 11}{6} = \frac{60}{6} = 10$$

3

Compare and interpret the mean absolute deviations.

The outlier, 59, affects both the mean and the MAD of the data set. While the means are relatively close to each other, the MAD of Julie's actual grades, 10, is more than 3 times that of her recorded grades, 3.

▶ The introduction of an outlier makes Julie's actual grades much more variable than her recorded grades. This is reflected in the change in the MAD from 3 to 10.

DISCUSS

Suppose two data sets, *A* and *B*, have the same mean, 12. The MAD for set *A* is 4, and the MAD for set *B* is 1.5. Based only on that information, which data set do you think has more variability? Explain.

Practice

For questions 1 and 2, compare the variability of the data sets shown by each pair of graphs.

1.

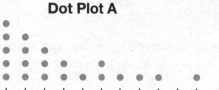

Dot Plot A

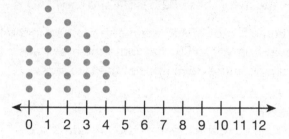

Dot Plot B

_____

2.

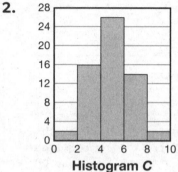

Histogram *C*   Histogram *D*

_____

Find the mean absolute deviation for each data set, using the given mean.

3. 5, 9, 12, 18
$\bar{x} = 11$

4. 39, 42, 45, 47, 52
$\bar{x} = 45$

5. −15, 5, 20, 50
$\bar{x} = 15$

_____   _____   _____

Write *true* or *false* for each statement. If false, rewrite the statement so it is true.

6. The mean absolute deviation is a measure of center.

_____

7. To find the absolute deviation from the mean, subtract each data point, *x*, from the mean, $\bar{x}$.

_____

_____

8. The larger the mean absolute deviation is for a data set, the more variable the data in the set are.

_____

_____

Solve.

9. Below are the cholesterol levels of a sample of people participating in a health study.

   75, 103, 130, 175, 190, 202, 220, 241

   Calculate the MAD. Explain what the MAD indicates about the spread of the data.

   _____

   _____

   _____

10. Below are the weights, in kilograms, of a group of packages to be shipped.

    0.9, 1.2, 1.3, 1.5, 3.5, 9.6

    Given that $\bar{x} = 3$, find the MAD. Do the mean and the MAD give a good idea of the center and spread of the data as a whole? Explain.

    _____

    _____

    _____

Use the information below for questions 11 and 12.

Keitaro competes in the long jump. The distances, in meters, that he jumped during his most recent meet are shown below.

   4.8, 4.8, 4.9, 5.0, 5.1, 5.4

11. **SHOW** Keitaro wants to know, on average, how variable his jumps were during the recent meet. Calculate the mean and MAD for the distances shown above. Then, describe the spread of the data.

    _____

    _____

    _____

12. **COMPARE** Keitaro's last jump of 5.4 meters is declared to be a foul at the last minute. The length is not recorded, and he does not get another attempt. Keitaro records this distance as 0.0 meters. Calculate the mean and MAD for the new set. Compare the variability of both data sets.

    _____

    _____

    _____

    _____

Constructing and Analyzing Box Plots

UNDERSTAND One way to examine the spread, or variability, of a data set is to measure its **range**. The range of a data set is the difference of the greatest value and the least value of the data set. The greatest value is called the **upper extreme**. The least value is called the **lower extreme**. The range shows the spread of all the data in the set.

An outlier can greatly affect the range. Even when most of the data are grouped closely together, an outlier value makes the range large. For such a data set, the range would give a misleading indication of the spread of the data.

A better measure of the spread of a data set such as this is the **interquartile range (IQR)**. The interquartile range measures the spread of the middle 50% of the data. The middle 50% of the data in a set is bounded by the **first quartile (Q_1)** and the **third quartile (Q_3)**. Recall that the median, M, divides a set of data into two halves. The first quartile is the median of the lower half of the data set. The third quartile is the median of the upper half of the data set.

The diagram below shows the extremes, quartiles, and median of a data set, as well as the range and interquartile range. It also helps illustrate how the median and quartiles divide a data set into four discrete sets of data.

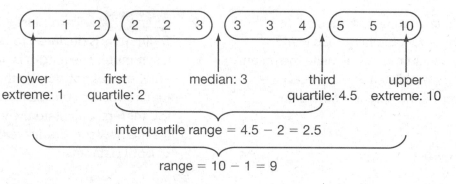

A **box plot** (sometimes called a box-and-whisker plot) is an excellent way to display the extremes, quartiles, and median of a data set.

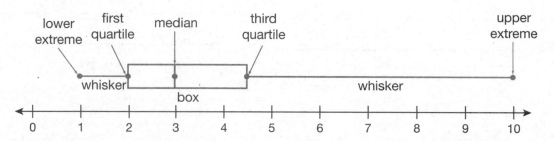

The box contains the middle 50% of the data, bounded by the first and third quartiles. The whiskers are on either end of the box. The left whisker contains the lower 25% of the data, and the right whisker contains the upper 25% of the data.

⊷ Connect

Calculate the range and the interquartile range for the data listed below.

12, 10, 16, 19, 12, 17, 14, 20, 15, 18

Does it look like this data set contains an outlier? Explain.

1

Order the data from least to greatest. Does it look like there is an outlier?

10, 12, 12, 14, 15, 16, 17, 18, 19, 20

No data point is much greater than or much less than the rest of the data.

▶ The set does not seem to contain an outlier.

2

Calculate the range.

range = upper extreme − lower extreme

range = 20 − 10

▶ range = 10

3

Identify the median, the first quartile, and the third quartile.

The data set contains ten data values, so the median is the average of the fifth and sixth values.

10, 12, 12, 14, <u>15</u>, <u>16</u>, 17, 18, 19, 20

$M = \dfrac{15 + 16}{2} = \dfrac{31}{2} = 15.5$

The lower half of the data set is 10, 12, 12, 14, 15.

This half contains five data values, so the first quartile is the third value. $Q_1 = 12$.

The upper half of the data is 16, 17, 18, 19, 20.

This half contains five data values, so the third quartile is the third value of this half, or the eighth value in the entire set. $Q_3 = 18$.

4

Calculate the interquartile range.

The interquartile range is the difference of the third and first quartiles.

$IQR = Q_3 - Q_1$

$IQR = 18 - 12$

▶ $IQR = 6$

Create an outlier by changing the value of the upper extreme in the data set. Calculate the range and IQR of the new set. Does the outlier affect the IQR? the range?

EXAMPLE A The data below show the number of miles that members of a running club ran last week.

4, 6, 8, 9, 10, 12, 16, 16, 30

Create a box plot to display the data. Then find the interquartile range of the data.

1

Identify the median.

The data are already in order. Find the middle data value.

4, 6, 8, 9, <u>10</u>, 12, 16, 16, 30

$M = 10$

2

Identify the first and third quartiles.

The lower half of the data set is 4, 6, 8, 9.

$Q_1 = \frac{6 + 8}{2} = \frac{14}{2} = 7$

The upper half of the data set is 12, 16, 16, 30.

$Q_3 = \frac{16 + 16}{2} = \frac{32}{2} = 16$

3

Create a box plot.

Draw a number line from 0 to 30. Plot points above 7 and 16 to represent the first and third quartiles. Draw a box connecting them. Plot a point for the median above 10. Draw a vertical line segment through it. Plot points above 4 and 30 to show the extremes. Draw a whisker from each extreme to the nearest edge of the box.

Miles Run by Running Club Members

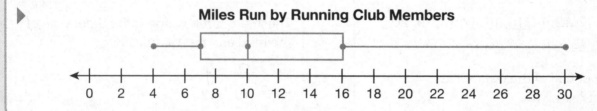

4

Calculate the IQR.

▶ $IQR = Q_3 - Q_1 = 16 - 7 = 9$

Notice that the IQR is the length of the box in the box plot.

DISCUSS

Calculate the range of the data set and compare it to the IQR. Which is a better measure of the spread of this data set? Why?

EXAMPLE B The box plots below represent the numbers of cookbooks sold by 20 male athletes and 20 female athletes as part of a fund-raiser for school sports. Compare the medians and interquartile ranges for the two samples.

Number of Cookbooks Sold

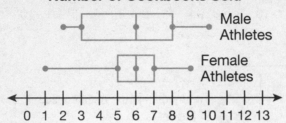

1

Identify and compare the medians.

On a box plot, the median is the point within the box.

The median for male athletes is 6.

The median for female athletes is also 6.

▶ On average, male and female athletes sold the same number of cookbooks, 6.

2

Identify and compare the interquartile ranges.

On a box plot, the IQR is the length of the box, which is the difference of the third and first quartiles.

For male athletes, $Q_3 = 8$ and $Q_1 = 3$, so the IQR $= 8 - 3 = 5$.

For female athletes, $Q_3 = 7$ and $Q_1 = 5$, so the IQR $= 7 - 5 = 2$.

▶ The IQR for female athletes is small, compared to the median, which means that many of the female athletes sold about the same number of cookbooks. The IQR for male athletes is much larger, which means that there was greater variability in these data. In other words, some of the male athletes sold many cookbooks and others sold few.

DISCUSS

Which of the data sets graphed in the box plot is more likely to contain an outlier? Explain.

Practice

Use the box plot for questions 1–5.

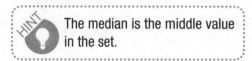

1. What is the median? _____

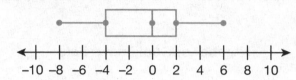
The median is the middle value in the set.

2. What is the lower extreme? _____

3. What is the upper extreme? _____

4. What is the first quartile? _____

5. What is the third quartile? _____

Find the median M, the first quartile Q_1, and the third quartile Q_3 of the data.

6. 1, 2, 3, 5, 7, 9, 10

$M = $ _____

$Q_1 = $ _____

$Q_3 = $ _____

7. 10, 12, 12, 15, 17, 19, 21, 25

$M = $ _____

$Q_1 = $ _____

$Q_3 = $ _____

> REMEMBER The median divides the data set into two halves.

8. $-2, -1, 2, 3, 4, 6, 7, 7, 9$

$M = $ _____

$Q_1 = $ _____

$Q_3 = $ _____

9. 25, 35, 40, 45, 45, 50, 60, 65, 75, 95

$M = $ _____

$Q_1 = $ _____

$Q_3 = $ _____

10. 15, 12, 18, 25, 36, 48, 28, 15

$M = $ _____

$Q_1 = $ _____

$Q_3 = $ _____

11. 1.5, 2.5, 4.5, 8.5, 3.5, 0.5, 0.75, 2.25, 3.25

$M = $ _____

$Q_1 = $ _____

$Q_3 = $ _____

Write *true* or *false* for each statement. If false, rewrite each statement so it is true.

12. A box plot uses a box and whiskers to show the spread of a set of data.

_____

13. In a box plot, the box represents the upper 25% of the data.

_____

14. The quartiles and the median divide a data set into four smaller sets of data.

_____

15. The interquartile range is the difference between the upper extreme and the lower extreme.

_____

Calculate the range and the interquartile range of the data.

16.

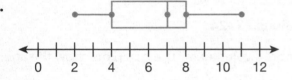

range = _____

IQR = _____

17.

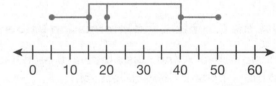

range = _____

IQR = _____

18.

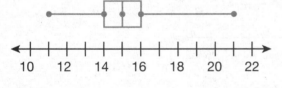

range = _____

IQR = _____

19.

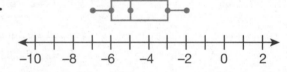

range = _____

IQR = _____

Choose the best answer.

20. The box plot shows the test scores earned by students in a biology class. Which statement about the test scores is **not** true?

Biology Test Scores

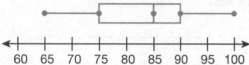

A. The scores ranged from 65 to 100.

B. The median score earned was an 85.

C. 25% of students scored less than 75 points on the test.

D. 50% of students had scores that ranged from 75 to 85 points.

21. The box plot shows the prices of 20 skirts for sale at a boutique. Which statement about the prices is true?

Skirt Prices (in dollars)

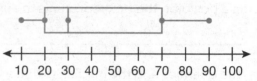

A. The highest-priced skirt costs $100.

B. The median price of a skirt is $70.

C. Half the skirts have prices that range from $20 to $70.

D. The prices of the skirts are close to the median and not very variable.

Use the box plots and information below for questions 22–24.

Music festival *A* and music festival *B* each had one hundred volunteers. The box plots show the ages of the volunteers at each festival.

Ages of Music Festival Volunteers

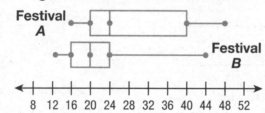

22. Compare the median ages of volunteers at each festival.

_____

23. Which festival has more variability in the ages of its volunteers? Explain your answer.

_____

_____

24. Suppose a woman who is 60 years old signs up today to volunteer at festival *B*. Which measure(s) of variability will be affected: the range or the interquartile range? by how much? Explain your answers.

_____

_____

Use the box plots for questions 25–28.

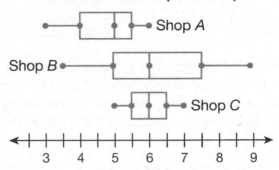

Sandwich Prices (in dollars)

25. Identify the median price of a sandwich at each shop.

    Shop A: M = _____

    Shop B: M = _____

    Shop C: M = _____

26. Calculate the IQR of sandwich prices at each shop.

    Shop A: IQR = _____

    Shop B: IQR = _____

    Shop C: IQR = _____

27. If you wanted to buy a sandwich but not spend much money, which shop would you try first? Why?

    _____

    _____

28. Compare the variability of the sandwich prices at the three shops.

    _____

    _____

    _____

Use the information below for questions 29 and 30.

Mrs. Heath visited her aunt in Nome, Alaska, for the first ten days of January 2012. She recorded the daily low temperature, in degrees Fahrenheit (°F), each day:

$-27, -27, -31, -33, -34, -33, -34, -25, -29, -26$

29. **ORGANIZE** Organize these data by displaying them in a box plot. Use the number line provided below.

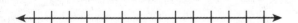

30. **JUSTIFY** Mrs. Heath said, "The weather was very, very cold and did not vary much during the trip." Is her statement accurate? Use one or more measures of variability to justify your answer.

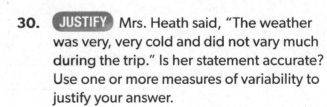

Constructing and Analyzing Two-Way Frequency Tables

UNDERSTAND Data can be classified as being either quantitative data or categorical data. **Quantitative data** involve numbers that usually result from measurement. Temperature, height, cost, and population are examples of quantitative data. **Categorical data** take on values that are names or labels. Gender, profession, and nationality are examples of categorical data.

When researchers collect data, they often ask more than one question. Comparing the results of those questions can reveal relationships among the data. To compare two categorical variables, you can enter the frequencies for each category into a **two-way frequency table**.

The two-way frequency table below displays the results of a survey that examined the relationship between gender and video game play. The table shows **joint frequencies** and **marginal frequencies**.

	Play Daily	Play Occasionally	Total
Boys	16	8	24
Girls	4	12	16
Total	20	20	40

Joint frequencies are in the body of the table.

Marginal frequencies are in the "Total" row and "Total" column.

Sometimes you are less interested in the actual frequency count than in the percentage of data values that fall into each category. These percentages are the **relative frequencies**. When displayed in a table, they form a **two-way relative frequency table**. The percentages in the middle of a relative frequency table are called **conditional frequencies**.

	Play Daily	Play Occasionally	Total
Boys	40%	20%	60%
Girls	10%	30%	40%
Total	50%	50%	100%

Conditional frequencies are in the body of the table.

Marginal frequencies are in the "Total" row and "Total" column.

Two-way tables help us see associations between two variables. For example, the above table shows that 40% of the students surveyed are boys who play video games daily and that 10% of the students surveyed are girls who play video games daily, so 50%, or half, of the students surveyed play video games daily. Based on this survey, it seems that boys are more likely to play video games daily than girls.

⟜ Connect

Kyra asked students and parents of students at her high school whether they are in favor of or against a proposal to remove the juice machine from the school cafeteria. The two-way frequency table on the right displays the results of the survey.

	For	Against	Total
Students	5	37	42
Parents	20	18	38
Total	25	55	80

Identify and interpret the marginal and joint frequencies in the table.

1 Identify and interpret the marginal frequencies.

Marginal frequencies are in the "Total" column and in the "Total" row.

The marginal frequencies in the "Total" column show that 42 students and 38 parents were surveyed. Roughly equal numbers of parents and students were surveyed.

The marginal frequencies in the "Total" row show that 25 people surveyed supported the proposal and 55 were against it. More than twice as many people surveyed were against the proposal as were in favor of it.

Both sets of marginal frequencies show that Kyra surveyed a total of 80 people.

2 Identify and interpret the joint frequencies by row.

Joint frequencies are in the body of the table, not the "Total" column or row.

The first row shows that 5 students support the proposal, while 37 oppose it.

A large majority of students do not support removing the juice machine.

The second row shows that 20 parents support the proposal, while 18 oppose it.

Parents are about evenly split on the proposal.

3 Identify and interpret the joint frequencies by column.

The first column shows that 5 students and 20 parents are for the proposal.

Many more parents than students support removing the juice machine.

The second column shows that 37 students and 18 parents are against the proposal.

Many more students than parents are against the proposal.

DISCUSS

Would your understanding of the situation be different if you only had the marginal frequencies? What do you learn from the joint frequencies that is not shown in the marginal frequencies?

EXAMPLE A The P.E. teachers at a high school are organizing an intramural league. They asked ninth-grade students which sport they would most like to play. The results are shown in the frequency table below.

	Basketball	Kickball	Volleyball	Total
Boys	50	30	12	92
Girls	18	32	58	108
Total	68	62	70	200

Create a two-way relative frequency table for the entire table. Based on the data, should the P.E. teachers create a basketball league? Explain.

1

Calculate each relative frequency.

Find the relative frequencies for the entire table. Each relative frequency will be the quotient of the corresponding frequency divided by the total frequencies

	Basketball	Kickball	Volleyball	Total
Boys	$\frac{50}{200} = 0.25$	$\frac{30}{200} = 0.15$	$\frac{12}{200} = 0.06$	$\frac{92}{200} = 0.46$
Girls	$\frac{18}{200} = 0.09$	$\frac{32}{200} = 0.16$	$\frac{58}{200} = 0.29$	$\frac{108}{200} = 0.54$
Total	$\frac{68}{200} = 0.34$	$\frac{62}{200} = 0.31$	$\frac{70}{200} = 0.35$	$\frac{200}{200} = 1.00$

2

Determine whether basketball is the most popular choice.

The two-way relative frequency table shows 34% of students surveyed prefer basketball. That is not significantly more than the percent who prefer kickball and is less than the percent who prefer volleyball.

▶ The data show that there is some support, but not overwhelming support, for a basketball league.

DISCUSS

Based on the data, is there an obvious choice for which sport the teachers should select? Explain your thinking.

EXAMPLE B Carter surveyed 20 ninth-grade students and 30 twelfth-grade students at random. He asked the students whether they were involved in school clubs. After creating a two-way frequency table of his results, he calculated the relative frequencies for each row of his table. The relative frequencies are shown on the right.

	One or More Clubs	No Clubs	Total
9th Grade	30%	70%	100%
12th Grade	80%	20%	100%
Total	60%	40%	100%

Create a frequency table for Carter's data. Then create a two-way relative frequency table for the columns in the frequency table.

1

Use the relative frequencies and the given information to create a frequency table.

You know that Carter surveyed 20 ninth-graders and 30 twelfth-graders. Use those numbers to fill in the Total column. Then use the relative frequencies to calculate the frequencies.

▶

	One or More Clubs	No Clubs	Total
9th Grade	$0.3 \cdot 20 = 6$	$0.7 \cdot 20 = 14$	20
12th Grade	$0.8 \cdot 30 = 24$	$0.2 \cdot 30 = 6$	30
Total	$0.6 \cdot 50 = 30$	$0.4 \cdot 50 = 20$	50

2

Use the frequencies in the table you created to find the relative frequencies by column.

To create a two-way relative frequency table based on columns, divide each value in a column by the total frequency for that column.

▶

	One or More Clubs	No Clubs	Total
9th Grade	$\frac{6}{30} = 20\%$	$\frac{14}{20} = 70\%$	$\frac{20}{50} = 40\%$
12th Grade	$\frac{24}{30} = 80\%$	$\frac{6}{20} = 30\%$	$\frac{30}{50} = 60\%$
Total	$\frac{30}{30} = 100\%$	$\frac{20}{20} = 100\%$	$\frac{50}{50} = 100\%$

DISCUSS

What associations do you find in the data in the relative frequency table? Do you see different associations in the data when you look at the relative frequency table by rows compared to the relative frequency table by columns?

Practice

Circle and label marginal frequencies and either joint frequencies or conditional frequencies.

1.

	Smart Phone	No Smart Phone	Total
Boys	15	10	25
Girls	19	6	25
Total	34	16	50

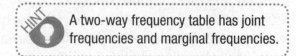

HINT: A two-way frequency table has joint frequencies and marginal frequencies.

2.

	Smart Phone	No Smart Phone	Total
Boys	30%	20%	50%
Girls	38%	12%	50%
Total	68%	32%	100%

Fill in each blank with an appropriate word or phrase.

3. A two-way frequency table allows you to organize _____ data.

4. _____ frequencies are entries in the "Total" row and "Total" column of a frequency table.

5. _____ frequencies are entries in the body of a two-way relative frequency table.

6. Given a two-way frequency table, you can find relative frequencies for each _____, for each

_____, or for the entire table.

Use the information and the two-way frequency table for questions 7 and 8.

A group of U.S. history teachers asked students where they would most like to go for an overnight field trip. The table shows the results.

	Washington, D.C.	Williamsburg, VA	Total
Boys	77	28	105
Girls	20	75	95
Total	97	103	200

7. Interpret the marginal frequencies.

_____

_____

8. Interpret the joint frequencies.

_____

_____

Use the information and the two-way relative frequency table for questions 9 and 10.

Byron asked fellow high school students and their parents if they support a proposal to replace the current school food vendor with a new food vendor.

	New Vendor	Current Vendor	Total
Parents	0.36	0.14	0.50
Students	0.24	0.26	0.50
Total	0.60	0.40	1.00

9. Interpret the marginal frequencies.

_____

_____

10. Interpret the conditional frequencies.

_____

_____

Use this information for question 11.

Twenty students were asked which type of music they like best. Three boys said hip-hop, four boys said jazz, and two boys said rock. Six girls said hip-hop, one girl said jazz, and four girls said rock.

11. Use the grid below to create a two-way frequency table for the data.

Use the information below for questions 12–15.

Erika asked ten high school seniors if they owned a car and if they had an after-school job. Her results are shown in the table.

Car	yes	yes	no	no	yes	no	no	yes	no	yes
Job	yes	no	yes	yes	yes	no	no	yes	no	yes

12. Use Erika's results to complete the two-way frequency table below.

	Car	No Car	Total
Job			
No Job			
Total			

13. Complete the table below to show relative frequencies for each column in the table you created for question 12. Express the frequencies as percentages.

	Car	No Car	Total
Job			
No Job			
Total			

14. Does the two-way relative frequency table show a possible association between owning a car and having an after-school job? Explain.

_____

_____

_____

15. Does the two-way relative frequency table show a possible association between **not** owning a car and having an after-school job? Explain.

_____

_____

_____

Use the information and table for questions 16–20.

The two-way frequency table shows the results of a survey in which ninth-grade students were asked which world language elective they most wanted to take next semester.

	Spanish	French	German	Total
Boys	80	30	10	120
Girls	30	20	30	80
Total	110	50	40	200

Use the grids below to create three different two-way relative frequency tables for the data. Express frequencies as decimals. Round to the nearest thousandth.

16. Show relative frequencies for the entire table.

	Spanish	French	German	Total
Boys				
Girls				
Total				

17. Show relative frequencies for each row.

	Spanish	French	German	Total
Boys				
Girls				
Total				

18. Show relative frequencies for each column.

	Spanish	French	German	Total
Boys				
Girls				
Total				

19. **EXAMINE** Examine the two-way relative frequency tables you created above. Describe two or more associations you see in the data.

_____

_____

_____

20. **CONCLUDE** The school will offer a total of 8 sections of world language classes for ninth-grade students next semester. How many sections should be Spanish? French? German? Explain your answers.

_____

_____

_____

Constructing and Analyzing Scatter Plots

UNDERSTAND When you study the relationship between two variables—such as the heights and shoe sizes of a group of students—you are working with **bivariate data**. Bivariate data can be written as a set of (x, y) ordered pairs and graphed on a coordinate plane. This kind of graph is called a **scatter plot.** A scatter plot can help you interpret bivariate data. The scatter plot below shows a set of ordered pairs in which the x-values represent heights and the y-values represent shoe sizes.

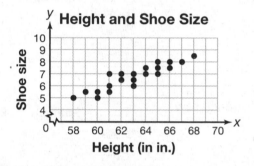

Look at the shape formed by the plotted points. The shape resembles a straight line. This suggests a linear relationship between the variables. You can draw a line to fit, or model, the data. The line you draw represents a linear function. If the line is a good fit, you can use the graph and the equation of the line to interpret and make predictions about the data.

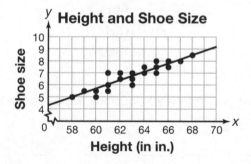

The line appears to be a good fit. The data points slant up from left to right, indicating a positive linear relationship. The line has a positive slope and is close to most data points.

You could also show that the line is a good fit for the data by calculating **residuals**. For each point (x, y) on the scatter plot, there is a corresponding point $(x, \hat{y})$ on the line of fit. A residual is equal to the difference $y - \hat{y}$. Residuals measure the difference of each actual y-value and the expected y-value ($\hat{y}$), which is based on the equation of the line of fit.

Residuals help you determine how accurately the linear function could predict actual points on the scatter plot. That is, if the values of the residuals are relatively small, the linear function is a good fit for the data. So, for any value of x, you could use the equation of the line to make a good prediction about what the value of y would be, and vice versa.

⊏ Connect

Draw a line of fit for each of the scatter plots. Determine how well each fits the data.

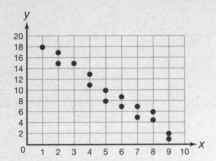
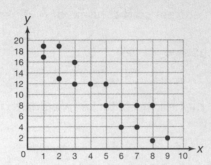

1

Draw a line to model the data for each scatter plot.

For each plot, draw a line that has about as many points above it as below it.

▶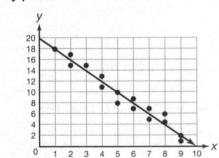

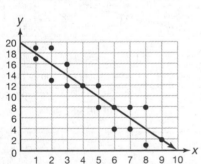

2

Use residuals to determine how well the lines fit the data in the first plot.

Pick several data points, such as (1, 18), (4, 11), (6, 7), and (8, 6). Find the corresponding points, $(x, \hat{y})$, on the line for those x-values: (1, 18), (4, 12), (6, 8), and (8, 4). Calculate the residuals.

(1, 18): $y - \hat{y} = 18 - 18 = 0$

(4, 11): $y - \hat{y} = 11 - 12 = -1$

(6, 7): $y - \hat{y} = 7 - 8 = -1$

(8, 6): $y - \hat{y} = 6 - 4 = 2$

▶ None of the residuals have large values. The line fits the first data set well.

3

Use residuals to determine how well the line fits the data in the second plot.

Pick several data points: (1, 19), (4, 12), (6, 4), and (8, 8). Find the corresponding points on the line: (1, 18), (4, 12), (6, 8), and (8, 4). Calculate the residuals.

(1, 19): $y - \hat{y} = 19 - 18 = 1$

(4, 12): $y - \hat{y} = 12 - 12 = 0$

(6, 4): $y - \hat{y} = 4 - 8 = -4$

(8, 8): $y - \hat{y} = 8 - 4 = 4$

▶ Some of the residuals have large values. The line does not fit the second data set well.

DISCUSS

Are the lines drawn the only possible lines of fit that could have been drawn for these scatter plots? Why or why not?

EXAMPLE For a health project, Dylan recorded the number of grams of fat and the number of calories in lunch entrees sold at his favorite diner.

Fat (in grams)	4	6	8	8	10	12	14	16	18	18	20
Calories	300	250	300	400	450	400	350	500	400	500	500

Create a scatter plot for the data. Draw a line to fit the data. Find the equation of the line.

1

Use the ordered pairs of data items to create a scatter plot.

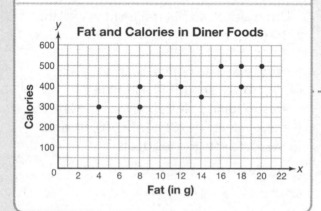

2

Draw a line to fit the data.

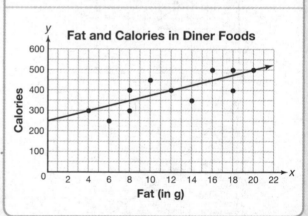

3

Write an equation for the line of fit.

The points (4, 300) and (12, 400) are on the line. Use those points to find the slope.

$$m = \frac{400 - 300}{12 - 4} = \frac{100}{8} = 12.5$$

The y-intercept is at (0, 250), so $b = 250$.

▶ The equation of the line is
$y = 12.5x + 250$.

DISCUSS

Explain what the slope of the line tells you in this context. Do the data show a positive linear relationship or a negative linear relationship?

Problem Solving

READ

The scatter plot shows the ages of various Model Z smartphones, in months, and the prices for which they sold. Predict how much Trent will pay if he buys a Model Z smartphone that is 5 years old.

Prices of Smartphones over Time

PLAN

Draw a _____ to fit the data. Write the equation

of the _____, and use it to predict the price

for a phone that is 5 years, or _____ months, old.

SOLVE

On the scatter plot, draw a line that fits the data.

Choose two points on the line, (_____, _____) and (_____, _____).

Use the points to find the slope of the line. $m =$ _____

In this context, the slope represents _____.

Find the y-intercept of the line. Extend the line to the y-axis if necessary. $b =$ _____

The equation for the line is $y =$ _____.

In this context, the y-intercept represents _____.

To predict the cost of a 5-year-old smartphone, substitute 60 for x in the equation. $ _____

CHECK

Pick three data points from the scatter plot: (_____, _____), (_____, _____), (_____, _____).

Find the points with corresponding x-values on the line of fit:

(_____, _____), (_____, _____), (_____, _____).

Calculate the residual for each point. Each residual is relatively _____.

Does the line fit the data well? _____ Is your answer a reasonable prediction? _____

▶ A good prediction is that Trent will pay about _____ for a Model Z smartphone that is 5 years old.

Practice

Describe the relationship shown in each scatter plot as either *positive* or *negative*.

1.

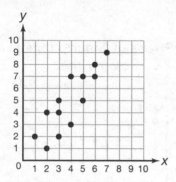

_____

2.

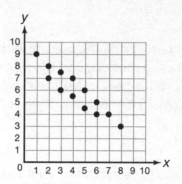

_____

 HINT A line that slants from lower left to upper right has a positive slope.

Use the information and table below for questions 3 and 4.

The table below shows T-shirt sales data for a store one weekend.

Price, x (in dollars)	4	8	8	12	12	16	20	20	24	24
Number Sold, y	32	26	30	22	26	20	12	20	14	10

3. Create a scatter plot for the data. Then draw a line of fit for the data.

4. Find the slope of the line of fit. What does it represent in the context of this problem?

_____

_____

Assess the fit of the lines to the data.

5. The lines of fit in the scatter plots below are identical.

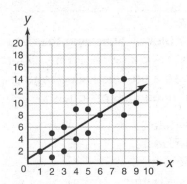 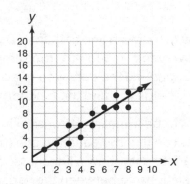

Which line better fits the data in its scatter plot? How did you determine your answer?

_____

_____

Use the information and scatter plot below for questions 6 and 7.

The scatter plot shows the number of hours of sleep that students got the night before a test and their scores on the test.

6. **INTERPRET** Draw a line of fit for the scatter plot. Identify the slope and *y*-intercept of the line. What does each represent in the context of this problem?

_____

_____

_____

7. **PREDICT** Write the equation of the line. Then use the equation to predict a student's test score if she gets only 2 hours of sleep before the next test.

_____

_____

_____

LESSON 30 · Best Fit and Correlation

UNDERSTAND You can draw a line of fit for a scatter plot by analyzing the data visually. Someone else, however, could look at the same data and draw a slightly different line. To find the line that best fits the data, you need to use a process called regression analysis. Regression analysis helps you find the function that minimizes residuals.

When there seems to be a linear relationship in the data, regression analysis can find the equation of a **line of best fit**. But not all bivariate data show a linear association. In some cases, the relationship between the variables is better modeled by a curve, as in the scatter plot shown. For data that do not have a linear association, you will need to find a **curve of best fit**. To find the equation of either a line of best fit or a curve of best fit, you can use a graphing calculator to perform a regression analysis.

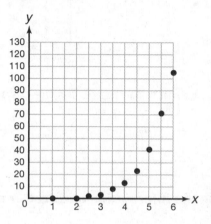

UNDERSTAND Once you have determined the line of best fit for bivariate data, you can use the **correlation coefficient**, r, to describe the strength and direction of the relationship between the two variables.

These statements will help you interpret a correlation coefficient.

- The value of r is always in the range $-1 \leq r \leq 1$.

- If r is close to 1, the data show a strong positive correlation

- If r is close to -1, the data show a strong negative correlation.

- If $r = 0$, the data do not show a linear correlation.

When bivariate data have a strong correlation, the predictions you make by using the line of best fit are likely to be very accurate. When there is a weak correlation, these predictions will tend to be less accurate. A positive correlation means that as one variable increases, the other variable tends to increase also. A negative correlation means that as one variable increases, the other tends to decrease.

The correlation coefficient, r, is calculated using a rather complex formula involving residuals. Fortunately, you can use a calculator to do that work for you!

Keep in mind that there is a crucial difference between correlation and causation. A strong correlation does not tell you that x is the cause of y. For example, buying lemonade and going to the beach might be strongly correlated, but one does not cause the other.

⊏ Connect

On a graphing calculator, create a scatter plot and draw a curve of best fit for the data in the table below.

Time, x (in minutes)	0	2	4	6	8	10
Number of Bacteria, y	5	11	25	57	130	290

1

Enter the data into your calculator.

Press STAT. Then select **1: Edit**.

Use L1 for time and L2 for number of bacteria. Enter each ordered pair in the table, as shown below.

L1	L2	L3 2
0	5	------
2	11	
4	25	
6	57	
8	130	
10	290	
------	------	
L2(1)=5		

2

Perform an exponential regression.

Press STAT.

Move the cursor to the **CALC** menu. Then select **0:ExpReg**. Press ENTER.

```
ExpReg
  y=a*b∧x
  a=4.934294253
  b=1.503276798
  r²=.999954037
  r=.9999770182
```

▶ Rounding *a* and *b*, the equation for the curve of best fit is $y = 4.93(1.5)^x$.

3

Create a scatter plot.

To show scatter plots on your calculator, turn the STAT PLOT on. Press 2nd Y=.

Select **1: Plot 1**. Press ENTER.

If **Off** is highlighted, move the cursor to highlight **On**. Press ENTER.

Then, press ZOOM. Choose **9: ZoomStat**.

4

Graph the curve of best fit.

Press Y= and for Y₁ enter 4.93(1.5)∧X. Then press GRAPH.

▶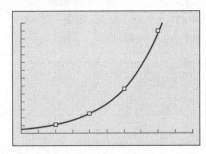

CHECK

On your graphing calculator, press 2nd GRAPH. This brings up a table for $y = 4.93(1.5)^x$. Compare your calculator table to the table above. Does it show that the curve is a good fit for the data? Is the fit perfect?

EXAMPLE The table on the right shows the daily high temperatures on six days and the number of cups of hot soup and of cold soup that were sold at a soup stand on each day.

Find a line of best fit to model the relationship between high temperatures and hot soup sales. Find another line of best fit to model the relationship between high temperatures and cold soup sales. Compare the lines.

Daily High Temperature	Cups of Hot Soup Sold	Cups of Cold Soup Sold
30	85	1
40	70	16
50	45	35
60	22	52
70	12	60
80	2	86

1

Enter the data in your calculator.

Press STAT. Then select **1: Edit**. Enter daily high temperatures in L1, hot soup sales in L2, and cold soup sales in L3.

2

Perform a linear regression for high temperatures (L1) and hot soup sales (L2).

Press STAT. Move the cursor to the **CALC** menu. Select **4:LinReg(ax+b)**. Press ENTER.

```
LinReg
  y=ax+b
  a=-1.748571429
  b=135.5047619
  r²=.972959429
  r=-.9863870908
```

▶ The equation modeling high temperatures vs. hot soup sales is $y = -1.75x + 135.5$.

3

Perform a linear regression for high temperatures (L1) and cold soup sales (L3).

Press STAT. Move the cursor to the **CALC** menu. Then select **4:LinReg(ax+b)**. Press ENTER. Now press 2nd STAT. Select **1:L1**. Press **,**. Then press 2nd STAT again. Select **3:L3**. Press ENTER.

```
LinReg
  y=ax+b
  a=1.64
  b=-48.53333333
  r²=.9877168439
  r=-.9938394457
```

▶ The equation modeling high temperatures vs. cold soup sales is $y = 1.64x - 48.5$.

4

Compare the lines.

The line for hot soup sales shows a negative correlation. The line for cold soup sales shows a positive correlation.

The correlation coefficients are close to -1 and 1, respectively. The lines are good fits for the data.

MODEL

Create a scatter plot for both sets of data. Then graph the lines of best fit. Compare how well the lines fit the data.

Problem Solving

READ

The table shows data for a cup of hot water that is cooling.

Find an equation for an exponential function that models the data. Then predict how many degrees Fahrenheit above room temperature the water will be if left to cool for 20 minutes.

Time (in minutes)	Degrees Fahrenheit above Room Temperature
0	134
2	113
4	95
6	80
8	67
10	56

PLAN

Use a graphing calculator to perform a(n)

_____ regression.

Then use a calculator table to solve the problem.

SOLVE

Enter the data in your calculator as L1 and L2.

Perform the exponential regression but with a few extra steps.

Press STAT .

Move the cursor to the **CALC** menu. Then select **0:ExpReg**.

Now press VARS . Move the cursor to **Y-VARS.** Select **1:Function**. Then select **1:Y$_1$**.
Press ENTER twice.

The screen shows that the equation is _____.

Press Y= . Because of those extra steps, the equation is already entered as Y$_1$.

Press 2nd GRAPH to bring up the table of values.

Scroll down. The table shows that when $x = 20$, $y \approx$ _____.

CHECK

Substitute 20 for x in the equation for the curve of best fit and solve.

$y =$ _____

Do you get the same answer? Why or why not? _____

_____

▶ After 20 minutes, the hot water will probably be about _____ °F above room temperature.

Practice

Use *line* or *curve* to tell which kind of model best fits each data set.

1.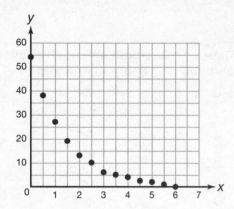

_____

2.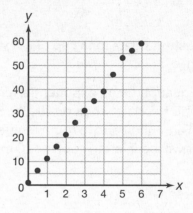

_____

Use *strong*, *weak*, *positive*, *negative*, or *no linear correlation* to describe what each correlation coefficient, *r*, tells you about a bivariate data set.

3. $r = 0$

_____

4. $r = 0.250$

_____

5. $r = -0.895$

_____

> **REMEMBER** The closer *r* is to 1 or −1, the stronger the correlation.

Write *true* or *false* for each statement. If false, rewrite the statement so it is true.

6. A line of best fit will help you predict values for variables with complete accuracy.

_____

_____

7. Not all bivariate data show a linear correlation, so sometimes data are better modeled by a curve than a line.

_____

_____

8. If regression analysis shows that there is a strong correlation between two variables, *x* and *y*, then *x* must cause *y*.

_____

_____

Choose the best answer.

Use a calculator for questions 9 and 10.

9. Which equation is the best model for the table of values shown below?

x	y
1	3
2	6.5
3	10
4	14
5	17

    A. $y = -0.55x + 3.55$

    B. $y = 0.55x + 3.55$

    C. $y = 3.55x - 0.55$

    D. $y = -3.55x - 0.55$

10. Which equation is the best model for the table of values shown below?

x	y
1	12
2	48
3	190
4	770
5	3,070

    A. $y = 4(2.99^{-x})$

    B. $y = 4(2.99^{x})$

    C. $y = 2.99(4^{-x})$

    D. $y = 2.99(4^{x})$

Use the information and table for questions 11—13.

The table to the right shows the daily high temperatures on six days and the number of air conditioners and space heaters a store sold on those days.

Daily High Temperature (in °F)	Air Conditioners Sold	Space Heaters Sold
30	0	20
40	4	14
50	8	12
60	11	6
70	16	2
80	23	1

11. Find the equation of the line of best fit that models the relationship between high temperatures and air conditioner sales. Then, find the correlation coefficient.

_____

12. Find the equation of the line of best fit that models the relationship between high temperatures and space heater sales. Then, find the correlation coefficient.

_____

13. Compare and contrast the two lines of best fit and the correlation coefficients. How do the two lines differ? Which is a better fit for its data set? Explain your answers.

_____

_____

_____

Use the information, table, and scatter plot below for question 14.

Mrs. Chen started a business 20 years ago. The table and scatter plot show the number of employees her growing business has had over a period of 20 years.

Years in Business	Number of Employees
0	3
5	7
10	19
15	46
20	115

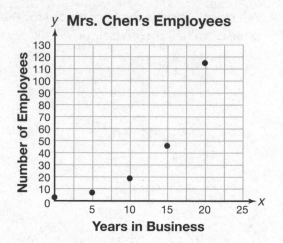

14. Use your calculator to perform an exponential regression for the data. What is the equation of the curve of best fit? Graph that curve on the scatter plot above.

_____

Use the information, table, and scatter plot below for questions 15 and 16.

The table and scatter plot both show the heights and weights of a randomly selected sample of football players from an all-star team.

Height (in inches)	Weight (in pounds)
67	150
68	180
69	175
70	180
71	190
72	185
72	200
73	210
74	200
75	220

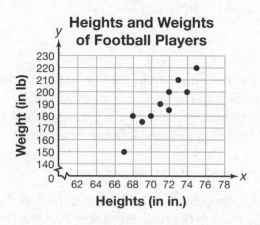

15. Use your calculator to perform a linear regression of the data. What is the equation of the line of best fit? What is the correlation coefficient?

_____

16. Graph that line on the scatter plot above. How good a fit is the line?

_____

Choose the best answer.

17. What does the screenshot on the right show about the data being considered?

    A. A line with a positive slope is a good fit for the data.

    B. A line with a negative slope is a good fit for the data.

    C. A linear function is not a good model for the data.

    D. An exponential function is the only good model for the data.

```
LinReg
 y=ax+b
 a=−26.18521429
 b=58.89810714
 r²=.5700873883
 r=−.7550413156
```

Solve.

18. **PREDICT** A scientist is studying how the population of ducks in a pond has been changing over a 40-year period. The table on the right shows her data.

    Use an exponential model to predict the population of ducks in 2020. Show or explain your work.

    _____

    _____

Year	Population
1970 (Enter: 0)	900
1980 (10)	450
1990 (20)	225
2000 (30)	150
2010 (40)	100

19. **CONCLUDE** The scatter plot below shows data for the number of ice cream cones sold and the number of bee stings treated at a lake resort. Based on the data, can you conclude that eating ice cream causes bee stings? If not, what can you conclude?

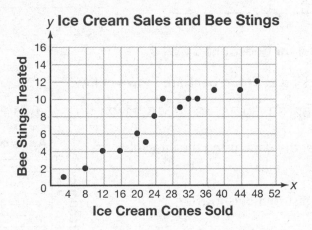

_____

_____

4 Review

Calculate the specified measure of center for each pair of data sets. Then write a statement comparing those measures in the context of the question.

1. The dot plots show the scores for the members of two different quiz bowl teams.

Quiz Bowl Scores, Team A

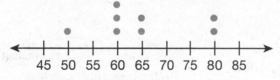

Quiz Bowl Scores, Team B

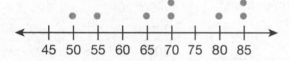

mean score, Team A: _____

mean score, Team B: _____

Comparison: _____

_____

2. The dot plots show the ages of members of two glee clubs.

Ages of School Glee Club Members

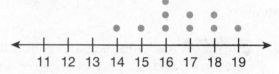

Ages of All-County Glee Club Members

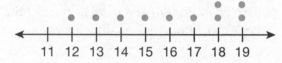

median age, School Glee Club: _____

median age, All-County Glee Club: _____

Comparison: _____

_____

Use the information below for questions 3 and 4.

The ages of volunteers working at a food bank are shown below.

12, 70, 25, 27, 13, 31, 20, 62, 33, 20, 15, 48, 35, 16, 21, 24, 19, 39, 45, 19, 53, 19

3. Create a histogram for the data, using the intervals shown on the graph.

4. Describe the type of distribution shown.

_____

Ages of Food Bank Volunteers

8	
7	
6	
5	
Frequency 4	
3	
2	
1	
0	

10–19 20–29 30–39 40–49 50–59 60–69 70–79

Ages (in Years)

Calculate the mean absolute deviation for each data set, using the given mean.

5. 4, 10, 15, 19
$\bar{x} = 12$

_____

6. 20, 25, 35, 65, 75
$\bar{x} = 44$

_____

7. 2, 4, 5, 5, 6
$\bar{x} = 4.4$

_____

Use the information below and the two-way frequency table on the right for questions 8–10.

At Sam's high school, students are required to take social studies for three years. Sam asked fellow high school students and their parents if they supported a proposal to require students to take social studies every year of high school.

	Every Year	Not Every Year	Total
Parents	70	34	104
Students	28	68	96
Total	98	102	200

8. Use the table to create a two-way relative frequency table based on the total number of people surveyed.

	Every Year	Not Every Year	Total
Parents			
Students			
Total			

9. Identify and interpret the marginal frequencies for the table you created.

_____

_____

10. Identify and interpret the conditional frequencies for the table you created.

_____

_____

For questions 11–13, according to the given correlation coefficient describe the linear association of two variables as *positive* or *negative* and as *strong* or *weak*.

11. $r = -0.992$

12. $r = 0.289$

13. $r = 0.865$

_____   _____   _____

Use the information and graphs below for question 14.

Sarah and Gabe each conducted the same psychology experiment involving memory. They recorded their data in these scatter plots. Their lines of fit are identical.

a.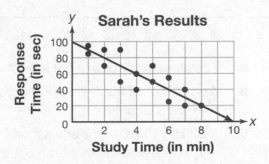

b.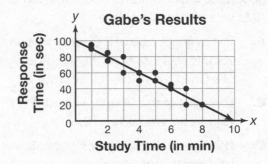

14. Which line is a better fit for the data it models? How did you determine your answer?

_____

Choose the best answer.

15. The scatter plot compares the number of bags of popcorn sold and the number of beverages sold at a movie theater each day over two weeks. Which conclusion can be drawn from the scatter plot?

A. There is a negative correlation between popcorn sales and beverage sales.

B. There is a positive correlation between popcorn sales and beverage sales.

C. There is no correlation between popcorn sales and beverage sales.

D. Buying popcorn causes people to buy beverages.

16. Which measure or measures of center would be best to use if you wanted to compare the average amount of time that Johanna and Latifah exercise in a typical week?

Daily Exercise over One Week (in minutes)

Johanna	20, 20, 30, 35, 40
Latifah	20, 20, 25, 25, 100

A. Median would be the best measure of center.

B. Mean would be the best measure of center.

C. Median and mean would both be equally good measures of center.

D. Neither the mean nor the median would be a good measure of center.

17. The mean age of all volunteers at Children's Hospital is 25, and the MAD for the ages is 4. The mean age of all volunteers at County Hospital is also 25, but the MAD is 6. If there are about the same number of volunteers at both hospitals, which statement comparing the data sets is most likely true?

A. The average age of a County Hospital volunteer is less than the average age of a Children's Hospital volunteer.

B. The ages of the County Hospital volunteers are less variable.

C. The ages of the County Hospital volunteers are more variable.

D. The ages of volunteers at both hospitals are equally variable.

18. The box plot below shows the prices of the hats for sale. Which statement about the prices is **not** true?

Hat Prices (in dollars)

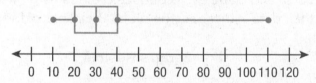

A. The average price of a hat is $40.

B. About 25% of the hats have prices that are $20 or less.

C. It is likely that there is at least one very expensive hat that is an outlier.

D. The prices of most hats are close to the median and not very variable.

Use the information and table below for questions 19 and 20.

The owner of several bookstores wanted to know what happened to book sales several weeks after an anticipated book's release date. She collected data from her stores. Her data are shown below.

Weeks Since Release	1	2	2	2	3	3	4	4	5
Copies Sold	56	60	52	48	52	40	48	40	40

19. Use the grid on the right to create a scatter plot for the data. Eyeball the scatter plot and draw a line to fit the data. Describe the relationship shown by the scatter plot.

_____

Book Sales and Release Dates

20. Identify the slope and the *y*-intercept of the line you drew. What do they represent in this situation?

_____

_____

Solve.

21. PREDICT A hotel added several large banquet halls 6 years ago. The table shows the number of events hosted at the hotel since the banquet halls opened.

Years Since Opening	Number of Events
1	10
2	19
3	32
4	52
5	80
6	130

Use your calculator to perform an exponential regression for these data. Use your model to predict the number of events that will be held in 2 years (8 years since the halls opened).

_____

22. COMPARE Students in Mr. Jackson's 3rd and 4th period world history classes took the same test. The double box plot represents their scores.

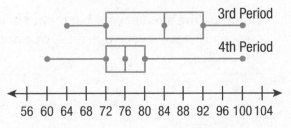

World History Test Scores

Compare the median test scores of students in both classes. Then compare the variability of the test scores in both classes. Use measures of center and variability to explain how you made your comparisons.

_____

_____

_____

_____

Make It BIG

Materials: graphing calculator

Working in small groups or individually, pretend that you and some friends have started up a band and are trying to make it big. However, making money while making music is harder than you might think.

1. What is the name of your band? What style of music does your band play?

   _____

2. One of your bandmates says she got a very good deal on a new guitar. She spent $199. Below are the prices of new guitars at a local store. Identify the first quartile, median, and third quartile of the data. Then create a box plot of these data.

   $200, $220, $150, $300, $250, $280, $350, $180, $200, $300

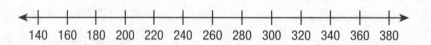

3. Compare the amount your bandmate paid for the guitar to the box plot above. Did she get a very good deal, an average deal, or a not very good deal? Explain.

   _____

   _____

Another way to earn money is by selling CDs at your shows, but how much should you charge for a CD? You decide to experiment and vary the price at each show. You then record how many CDs are sold at each show.

Price, in dollars (x)	5	8	10	12	15	20
CDs Sold (y)	20	16	15	11	5	1

4. What type of correlation do you think these data show and why?

   _____

5. Create a scatter plot of the data in the table.

CD Prices and Sales

6. Use a calculator to find the equation of a line of best fit to model the data. Then graph the line of best fit on the scatter plot above. How good a fit is the line?

_____

_____

7. Based on your equation and your line of best fit, how many CDs do you predict you would sell if you set the price at $14? Explain or show your work.

_____

_____

_____

8. Do you think a higher price causes fewer people to buy CDs? What other factors might affect how many CDs you sell?

_____

_____

Grade 8	Coordinate Algebra	Analytic Geometry
Geometry Understand congruence and similarity using physical models, transparencies, or geometry software.	**Geometry** **Congruence** Experiment with transformations in the plane.	**Geometry** **Congruence** Understand congruence in terms of rigid motions. **Similarity, Right Triangles, and Trigonometry** Understand similarity in terms of similarity transformations.

Unit 5
Transformations in the Coordinate Plane

Transformations

Translations, Reflections, and Rotations

UNDERSTAND When a geometric figure is drawn on a coordinate plane, every point in the figure is assigned an ordered pair. Each **vertex** corresponds to a point on the plane. The side between two vertices corresponds to the **line segment** that has those points as endpoints. The length of that side is equal to the distance between the two endpoints. Whenever two line segments share a common endpoint, they form an **angle**. An angle tells how the points on one line segment relate to the points on another line segment.

Moving all the points in a figure according to the same rule is called a **transformation**. When a figure is transformed, the figure that is produced is called the **image**. The original figure is called the **preimage**.

A translation is a slide of a figure to a new location. The diagram shows a triangle translated horizontally 6 units.	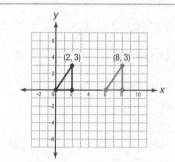
A reflection is a flip of a figure across a line. The diagram shows a triangle reflected across the *y*-axis.	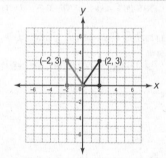
A rotation is a turn of a figure around a point. The diagram shows a triangle rotated by a $\frac{1}{2}$ turn (180°).	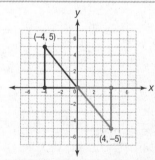

Notice that in each of these transformations, the image is exactly the same size and shape as the preimage. These transformations preserve the lengths of line segments and preserve the measures of angles.

Connect

Figure *ABCDEF* was put through a series of transformations. Identify each transformation.

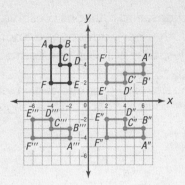

1

Identify the transformation from *ABCDEF* to *A'B'C'D'E'F'*.

The figure has been turned on its side.

Vertex *A* is in the upper left corner of *ABCDEF*, but *A'* is in the upper right corner of *A'B'C'D'E'F'*. However, the vertex names are in the same order when read clockwise.

The figure appears to have been rotated.

Notice that each point on *A'B'C'D'E'F'* is the same distance from the origin as its corresponding point on *ABCDEF*. Figure *ABCDEF* was rotated around the origin.

2

Identify the transformation from *A'B'C'D'E'F'* to *A"B"C"D"E"F"*.

Figure *A"B"C"D"E"F"* is a mirror image of figure *A'B'C'D'E'F'*.

Vertex *A'* is in the upper right corner of *A'B'C'D'E'F'*, but *A"* is in the lower right corner of *A"B"C"D"E"F"*. The vertex names are in a different order when read clockwise.

The figure appears to have been reflected.

Each point on *A"B"C"D"E"F"* is the same distance from the *x*-axis as its corresponding point on *A'B'C'D'E'F'*. Figure *A'B'C'D'E'F'* was reflected across the *x*-axis.

3

Identify the transformation from *A"B"C"D"E"F"* to *A'''B'''C'''D'''E'''F'''*.

Figure *A'''B'''C'''D'''E'''F'''* is oriented the same way as figure *A"B"C"D"E"F"*, but it was shifted to a different location on the graph.

Vertex *A"* is in the lower right corner of *A"B"C"D"E"F"*, and *A'''* is in the lower right corner of *A'''B'''C'''D'''E'''F'''*.

Since the orientation did not change, figure *A'''B'''C'''D'''E'''F'''* is the result of a translation.

DISCUSS

Compare the figures. Did the size or shape of the figure change as it was transformed? How could you confirm this?

Dilations, Stretches, and Shrinks

UNDERSTAND Translations, reflections, and rotations preserve distances and angle measures in transformed figures. Other transformations do not always preserve these properties. The table below reviews some of those transformations.

A dilation enlarges or reduces the size of a figure by a certain scale factor. The graphs show two different dilations of the same square. Notice that the lengths of the sides change, but the angle measures are preserved.

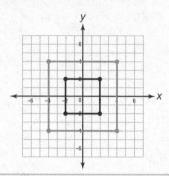

A vertical stretch pulls the points of a figure in a vertical direction: up and down, away from the x-axis.	A vertical shrink pushes the points of a figure in a vertical direction: down and up, toward the x-axis.
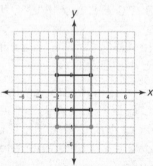	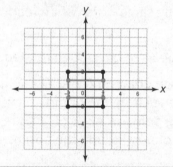
A horizontal stretch pulls the points of a figure in a horizontal direction: left and right, away from the y-axis.	A horizontal shrink pushes the points of a figure in a horizontal direction: right and left, toward the y-axis.
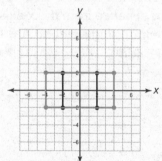	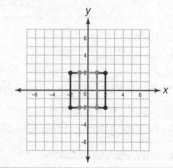

A dilation pulls a figure in both a horizontal and a vertical direction, while an individual stretch or shrink pulls a figure only horizontally or vertically. Because of this, a dilation changes the size, but not the shape, of figure, whereas a stretch or a shrink changes both the size and shape of a figure.

⊂ Connect

Identify the type of transformation that was applied to triangle *ABC* to produce triangle *A'B'C'*. How does this transformation change the size and/or shape of the triangle?

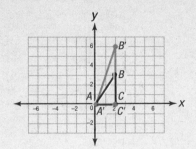

1

Determine if the figure was transformed horizontally.

Since a transformation is applied equally to every point on a figure, you can look at some of the points to identify the transformation.

To find out if the figure has been stretched or shrunk horizontally, look at the *x*-coordinates of the points.

The *x*-coordinates of *A*, *B*, and *C* are the same as the *x*-coordinates of the *A'*, *B'*, and *C'*, so the figure was not transformed horizontally.

2

Determine if the figure was transformed vertically.

To find out if the figure has been stretched or shrunk vertically, look at the *y*-coordinates of the points.

The *y*-coordinates of *A* and *C* did not change, but the *y*-coordinate of *B* doubled from 3 to 6.

▶ Triangle *ABC* was stretched vertically.

3

Examine the size and shape of the preimage and image.

Triangle *A'B'C'* has the same width as triangle *ABC*, but it has a greater height. So, the size of the figure has changed.

$\overline{A'B'}$ rises at a steeper angle than $\overline{AB}$, so the shape of the triangle has also changed.

▶ Neither distance nor angle measure were preserved in this transformation.

TRY

Does the transformation shown change the size and/or shape of the triangle?

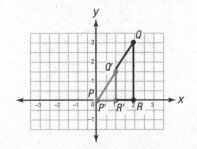

EXAMPLE A Describe the transformation that was applied to △DEF to form △D'E'F'.

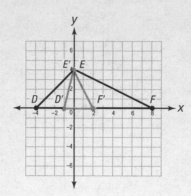

1

Compare the size and shape of the image and preimage.

The preimage is the same height as the image, but it is wider.

$\overline{D'E'}$ and $\overline{F'E'}$ are steeper than $\overline{DE}$ and $\overline{FE}$, so the figures have different shapes.

These differences indicate that a horizontal shrink has been applied.

2

Determine by what factor the preimage was shrunk.

In order to determine by what factor the preimage was shrunk, compare the width of the image to the width of the preimage. You can find the width of each triangle by simply counting along the x-axis.

Triangle $\overline{DEF}$ extends from −4 to 8, so it is 12 units wide.

Triangle $\overline{D'E'F'}$ extends from −1 to 2, so it is 3 units wide.

To find the factor of the horizontal shrink, divide the width of the image by the width of the preimage.

$$\frac{3}{12} = \frac{1}{4}$$

▶ Triangle DEF was horizontally shrunk by a factor of $\frac{1}{4}$ to form triangle D'E'F'.

TRY

By what factor was △DEF dilated to form △D'E'F' on the grid below?

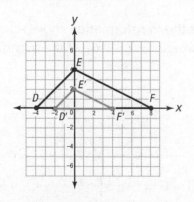

EXAMPLE B Identify transformations that could be applied to figure *A* to form figure *B*.

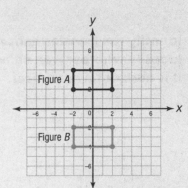

1

Compare the size and shape of the image and the preimage.

Figures *A* and *B* have the same height and width, so they have the same size and shape. No dilation, stretch, or shrink was applied to figure *A* to produce figure *B*.

2

Determine if figure *A* can form figure *B* through a translation.

The two figures have the same orientation, but figure *B* is lower than figure *A*.

The upper left corner of figure *B* is 6 units below the upper left corner of figure *A*. In fact, this is true about every point on the two figures.

▶ A translation of 6 units down will transform figure *A* into figure *B*.

3

Determine if figure *A* can form figure *B* through a reflection.

Figure *B* is a mirror image of figure *A* and the *x*-axis is halfway between them.

▶ A reflection across the *x*-axis will transform figure *A* into figure *B*.

4

Determine if figure *A* can form figure *B* through a rotation.

If you were to turn this coordinate grid upside down, it would look the same. Turning the grid upside down is a way of rotating it.

▶ A half-turn rotation, or a rotation of 180°, around the origin will transform figure *A* into figure *B*.

Could the same transformations be applied to *MNOP* to form *M′N′O′P′*?

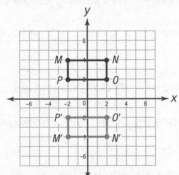

Practice

Identify the transformation of △ABC as a dilation, a stretch, or a shrink. If it is a dilation, identify whether it an enlargement or a reduction. If it is a stretch or a shrink, identify whether it is horizontal or vertical.

1.

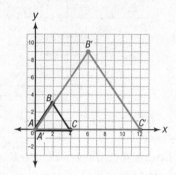

_____

2.

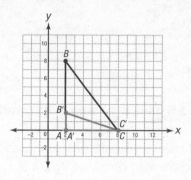

_____

> **REMEMBER** A dilation changes the size, but not the shape, of a figure.

Identify a transformation that could be applied to △ABC to form △A′B′C′.

3.

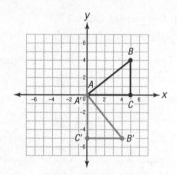

_____

4.

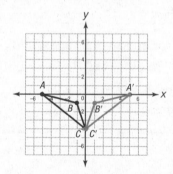

_____

Write an appropriate word or phrase in each blank.

5. A(n) _____ is the part of a line that falls between two points, called endpoints.

6. In a geometric figure, a(n) _____ is formed by two line segments that have a common endpoint.

7. A(n) _____ is a slide of a figure to a new location on a coordinate plane.

8. A(n) _____ is an enlargement or a reduction of a figure in both a horizontal and vertical direction by the same scale factor.

9. A(n) _____ stretch pulls the points of a figure away from the y-axis.

Choose the best answer.

10. Across which of the following was trapezoid *MNPQ* reflected to form trapezoid *M′N′P′Q′*?

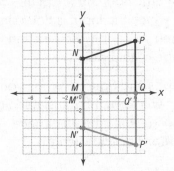

    A. the origin

    B. the *x*-axis

    C. the *y*-axis

    D. the center of the trapezoid

11. Around which point was △*DEF* rotated to produce △*D′E′F′*?

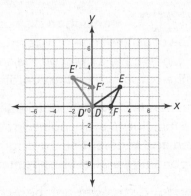

    A. point *D*

    B. point *E*

    C. point *F*

    D. the center of the triangle

Solve.

12. **COMPARE** Mei-lin uses a computer drawing program to draw a polygon on a grid. She then uses the program to rotate the drawing 90° and enlarge it by 200%. How will her original drawing compare to the final image? Will the lengths of the line segments be the same in both drawings? Will the angle measures be the same in both drawings? Explain how you know.

_____

_____

_____

32 Translations

UNDERSTAND A **translation** is an operation that slides a geometric figure in the plane. You can think of a translation of a geometric figure as a function in which the input is not a single value, x, but rather a point on the coordinate plane, (x, y). When you apply the function to a point, the output will be the coordinates of the translated image of that point.

You can translate not only individual points but also entire graphs and figures. When you apply a function to every point on a figure, the resulting points will form the translated figure. For each **line segment** on the original figure, the translated image will contain either a corresponding **parallel line segment** or a **collinear line segment** of equal length.

In a **horizontal translation,** the x-coordinate changes, but the y-coordinate stays the same. A horizontal translation of a units can be represented by the function $T(x, y) = (x + a, y)$. If $a > 0$, the figure slides to the right. If $a < 0$, the figure slides to the left.

The transformation shown on the right is the result of applying the function $T(x, y) = (x + 7, y)$ to $\triangle JKL$. In this example, a is a positive number, 7, so the figure slides to the right.

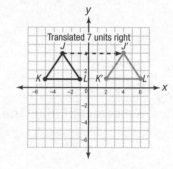

In a **vertical translation**, the y-coordinate changes, but the x-coordinate stays the same. A vertical translation of b units can be represented by the function $T(x, y) = (x, y + b)$. If $b > 0$, the figure slides up. If $b < 0$, the figure slides down.

The transformation shown on the right is the result of applying the function $T(x, y) = (x, y + 5)$ to $\triangle DFG$. In this example, b is a positive number, 5, so the figure slides up.

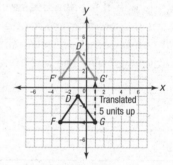

In a slant translation, both the x- and y-coordinates change. Slant translations can be described by the function $T(x, y) = (x + a, y + b)$.

The transformation shown on the right is the result of applying the function $T(x, y) = (x - 8, y - 6)$ to $\triangle ABC$. In this example, a and b are both negative, so the figure slides to the left and down.

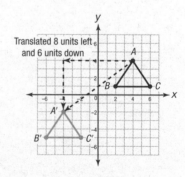

⊂ Connect

Translate trapezoid *WXYZ* 4 units to the left and 2 units up to form trapezoid *W'X'Y'Z'*. Identify the coordinates of the vertices of the translated image.

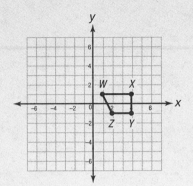

1

Starting at point *W*, count 4 units to the left and 2 units up.

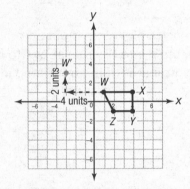

Plot point *W'* there. Notice that its coordinates are (−3, 3).

2

Translate every other point in the same way—by sliding it 4 units to the left and 2 units up. Then connect the points to form trapezoid *W'X'Y'Z'*.

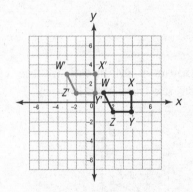

▶ The coordinates of the vertices of the translated image, *W'X'Y'Z'*, are *W'*(−3, 3), *X'*(0, 3), *Y'*(0, 1), and *Z'*(−2, 1).

DISCUSS

What function represents the translation that you performed? How do you know?

$T(x, y) = $ _____

EXAMPLE A Translate △PQR according to the rule below:

$T(x, y) = (x + 6, y - 1)$

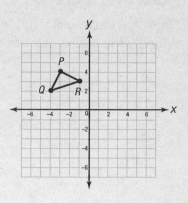

1 Identify the coordinates of the vertices of △PQR.

The vertices are $P(-3, 4)$, $Q(-4, 2)$, and $R(-1, 3)$.

2 Treat each point as an input and substitute it into the rule above to find the coordinates of the translated image.

$T(-3, 4) = (-3 + 6, 4 - 1) = (3, 3)$

$T(-4, 2) = (-4 + 6, 2 - 1) = (2, 1)$

$T(-1, 3) = (-1 + 6, 3 - 1) = (5, 2)$

3 Plot points P', Q', and R'. Connect them to form the translated image.

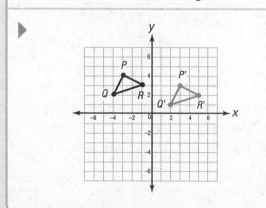

DISCUSS

On the diagram in Step 3, trace the path of each vertex of △PQR to its translated image on △P'Q'R'. Compare how each point moves from the preimage (or original figure) to the image. Explain what this means about the relationship between the sides of the preimage and the sides of the image.

EXAMPLE B Use a function to describe how parallelogram *ABCD* could be translated so it covers parallelogram *WXYZ* exactly.

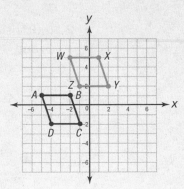

1

Describe the slide needed to move vertex *C* of parallelogram *ABCD* onto point *Y*, the corresponding point on parallelogram *WXYZ*.

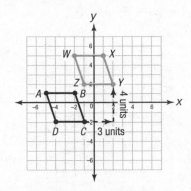

The diagram shows that point *C* must slide 3 units to the right and 4 units up to move onto point *Y*. Every other point in *ABCD* must slide in the same way.

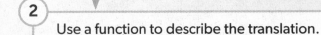

2

Use a function to describe the translation.

A horizontal translation of 3 units to the right is in the positive direction. It can be represented by the expression *x* + 3.

A vertical translation of 4 units up is also in the positive direction. It can be represented by the expression *y* + 4.

▶ The rule for the translation is:
$T(x, y) = (x + 3, y + 4)$.

CHECK

Substitute the coordinates of the vertices of parallelogram *ABCD* into the rule $T(x, y) = (x + 3, y + 4)$. Check that the resulting coordinates match those of the vertices of parallelogram *WXYZ*.

Practice

Draw the image for each translation of the given preimage. Use prime (') symbols to name points on each image.

1. Translate $\overleftrightarrow{AB}$ 3 units to the right.

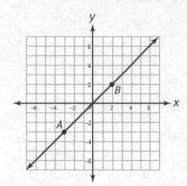

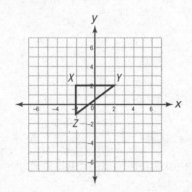

2. Translate trapezoid *PQRS* 7 units to the left and 4 units down.

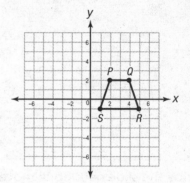

> HINT
> A translation to the right affects the *x*-coordinate.

3. $T(x, y) = (x, y - 4)$

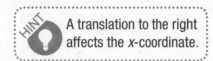

4. $T(x, y) = (x - 8, y + 3)$

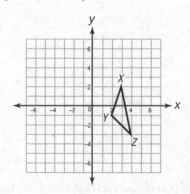

> REMEMBER The preimage and the image should be the same size and same shape.

Write a function to describe how the quadrilateral *ABCD* was translated to form *A'B'C'D'* in each graph.

5.

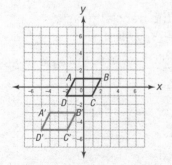

$T(x, y) = $ _____

6.

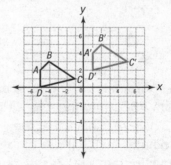

$T(x, y) = $ _____

Use the graph on the right for questions 7–9.

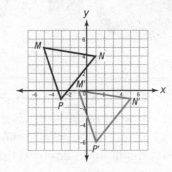

7. Name the line segment that is parallel to $\overline{MN}$. _____

8. Name a line segment that is parallel to $\overline{MP}$. _____

9. How does $\overline{NP}$ compare to $\overline{N'P'}$?

_____

Solve.

10. A triangle with vertices $A(1, -3)$, $B(-7, 12)$, and $C(5, 0)$ is translated according to the rule $T(x, y) = (x - 3, y + 9)$. What are the coordinates of the vertices of the translated image?

_____

_____

_____

11. Point P at $(-4, 3)$ is translated to form its image, point P', at $(6, 1)$. Write a function to represent the translation. If point $R(-5, -6)$ and point $S(1, 2)$ are also translated using that rule, what will be the coordinates of their images?

_____

_____

_____

12. **DESCRIBE** A librarian wants to move the bookcase shown in the diagram from its current location to the "New" location. Describe a series of translations that could be used to move the bookcase to its new location, keeping in mind that it cannot be moved through a wall.

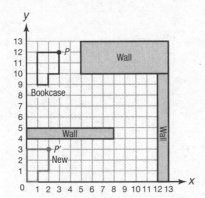

_____

_____

13. **EXPLAIN** Use a function to describe the translation that moves pentagon *ABCDF* so it covers pentagon *KLMNP* exactly. Then write the function that moves pentagon *KLMNP* so it covers pentagon *ABCDF* exactly. Compare the two functions and explain any differences between them.

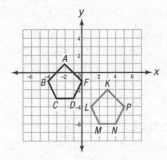

_____

_____

_____

LESSON 33 Reflections

UNDERSTAND A **reflection** is a transformation that flips a figure across a line called a **line of reflection**. Each reflected point is the same distance from the line of reflection as its corresponding point on the preimage, but it is on the opposite side of the line. The resulting image and the preimage are mirror images of one another. The line of reflection can be the *x*-axis, the *y*-axis, or any other line in the coordinate plane.

You can think of a reflection of a figure as a function, in which the input is not a single value, *x*, but rather a point on the coordinate plane, (*x*, *y*). When you apply the function to a point on a figure, the output will be the coordinates of the reflected image of that point.

When a point is reflected across the *y*-axis, the sign of its *x*-coordinate changes. The function for a reflection across the *y*-axis is:

$$R_{y\text{-axis}}(x, y) = (-x, y)$$

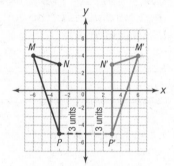

When a point is reflected across the *x*-axis, the sign of its *y*-coordinate changes. The function for a reflection across the *x*-axis is:

$$R_{x\text{-axis}}(x, y) = (x, -y)$$

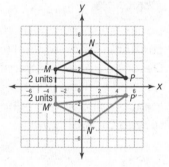

Another common line of reflection is the diagonal line *y* = *x*. To reflect over this line, swap the *x*- and *y*-coordinates. The function for a reflection across line *y* = *x* is:

$$R_{y = x}(x, y) = (y, x)$$

The path that a point takes across the line of reflection is always **perpendicular** to the line of reflection. Perpendicular lines form right angles when they cross one another. As shown in the diagram on the right, the path from point *P* to point *P'* forms right angles with the line of reflection, *y* = *x*.

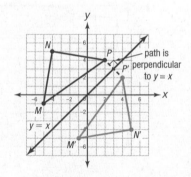

⟐ Connect

Reflect △ABC across the x-axis. Then reflect △ABC across the y-axis.

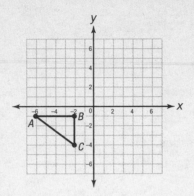

1

Identify the coordinates of the vertices of △ABC.

The vertices of the triangle are A(−6, −1), B(−2, −1), and C(−2, −4).

2

To reflect the vertices of △ABC across the x-axis, change the signs of the y-coordinates. Then draw the image.

$A(−6, −1) \rightarrow A'(−6, 1)$

$B(−2, −1) \rightarrow B'(−2, 1)$

$C(−2, −4) \rightarrow C'(−2, 4)$

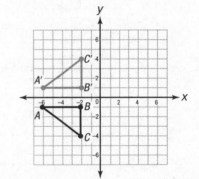

3

To reflect the vertices of △ABC across the y-axis, change the signs of the x-coordinates. Then draw the image.

$A(−6, −1) \rightarrow A''(6, −1)$

$B(−2, −1) \rightarrow B''(2, −1)$

$C(−2, −4) \rightarrow C''(2, −4)$

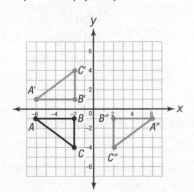

TRY

Use function notation to describe how △ABC is transformed to △A′B′C′ and how △ABC is transformed to △A″B″C″.

EXAMPLE A Graph the image of quadrilateral *JKLM* after the reflection described below.

$$F(x, y) = (y, x).$$

Then describe the reflection in words.

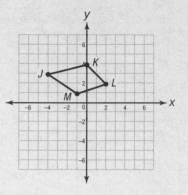

1

Identify the coordinates of the vertices of quadrilateral *JKLM*.

The quadrilateral has vertices $J(-4, 3)$, $K(0, 4)$, $L(2, 2)$, and $M(-1, 1)$.

2

Apply the function to the vertices.

$F(-4, 3) = (3, -4)$

$F(0, 4) = (4, 0)$

$F(2, 2) = (2, 2)$

$F(-1, 1) = (1, -1)$

3

Graph the image.

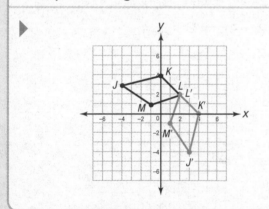

4

Describe the reflection in words.

Find the line that lies halfway between corresponding points of the figure.

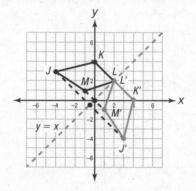

Each of these halfway marks lies on the line $y = x$.

▶ The function performs a reflection across the line $y = x$.

TRY

Apply the same function, $F(x, y) = (y, x)$, to $J'K'L'M'$. What image results?

Figures can be reflected over horizontal or vertical lines that are not the x- or y-axis as well.

EXAMPLE B Trapezoid *STUV* is graphed on the right. Reflect this trapezoid over the line x = 4.

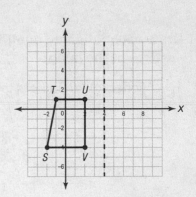

1

Reflect vertices *U* and *V*.

Point *U*, at (2, 1), is 2 units to the left of x = 4. So, its reflection will be 2 units to the right of x = 4. So, plot a point at (6, 1) and name it *U′*.

Use the same strategy to plot point *V′*.

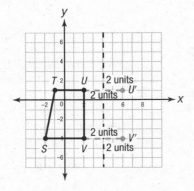

2

Find and plot the other two points of the image.

Point *T* at (−1, 1) is 5 units to the left of x = 4. So, plot point *T′* 5 units to the right of x = 4 at (9, 1).

Point *S* is 6 units to the left of x = 4. So, plot point *S′* at (10, −4), which is 6 units to the right of x = 4.

 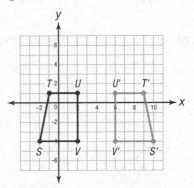

DISCUSS

How could you describe the reflection of trapezoid *STUV* over the line x = 4 using function notation?

Practice

Draw each reflected image as described and name its vertices. Identify the coordinates of the vertices of the image.

1. Reflect △ABC across the x-axis.

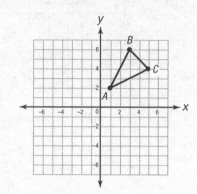

A'(___, ___) B'(___, ___) C'(___, ___)

> **REMEMBER** When a point is reflected across the x-axis, the sign of its y-coordinate changes.

2. Reflect pentagon GHJKL across the line y = 3.

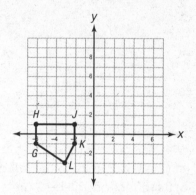

G'(___, ___) H'(___, ___) J'(___, ___)

K'(___, ___) L'(___, ___)

Fill in each blank with an appropriate word or phrase.

3. A reflection results in two figures that look like _____.

4. Lines that meet and form right angles are called _____ lines.

5. A point and its reflection are each the same distance from _____.

6. The path that a point takes across the line of reflection is _____ to the line of reflection.

Use the given function to transform △DEF. Then describe the transformation in words.

7. R(x, y) = (−x, y)

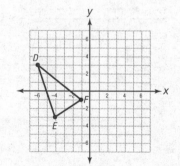

_____

8. R(x, y) = (y, x)

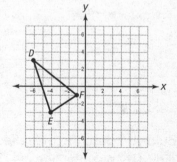

_____

Identify the coordinates of the image for each reflection as described.

9. Reflect $M(3, 4)$ across the x-axis.

$M'(\underline{\hspace{1cm}}, \underline{\hspace{1cm}})$

10. Reflect $N(-2, -8)$ across the y-axis.

$N'(\underline{\hspace{1cm}}, \underline{\hspace{1cm}})$

11. Reflect $P(-2, 0)$ across the line $y = x$.

$P'(\underline{\hspace{1cm}}, \underline{\hspace{1cm}})$

12. Reflect $Q(5, 10)$ across the line $y = x$.

$Q'(\underline{\hspace{1cm}}, \underline{\hspace{1cm}})$

Describe how quadrilateral $ABCD$ was reflected to form quadrilateral $A'B'C'D'$, using both words and function notation.

13.

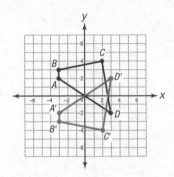

Words: _____

Function: _____

14.

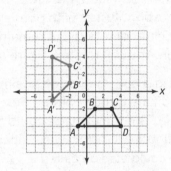

Words: _____

Function: _____

Solve.

15. **JUSTIFY** Camille drew the square below on a coordinate plane. She says that if she reflects the square over the x-axis it will look exactly the same as if she reflects it over the y-axis. Is she correct or incorrect? Use words, numbers and/or drawings to justify your answer.

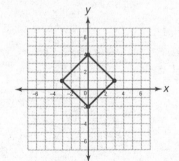

_____

_____

16. **DRAW** Patrick reflected a figure in two steps. The result was that each point (x, y) was transformed to the point $(-y, x)$. Draw a triangle (any triangle) on the grid below and transform it as described. Then describe what two reflections Patrick performed.

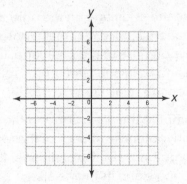

_____

_____

Lesson 34 Rotations

UNDERSTAND A **circle** is the set of all points that are the same distance from a point called the center. Visualize turning the circle shown on the right so that point A moves onto point B. If you did that, the points would remain the same distance from the center, but they would be in a different location.

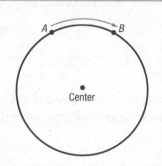

A **rotation** is a transformation that turns a figure around a point, called the **center of rotation**. Just as with points on a circle, when you rotate a point around a center of rotation, it remains the same distance from the center of rotation. You can rotate a figure any number of degrees.

Counterclockwise is considered the positive direction, so the rotation shown on the right would be described as −45° rotation around the origin. The same image could be obtained, however, by rotating the figure 315° clockwise, since 360 − 45 = 315. So, this rotation could also be called a 315° rotation around the origin.

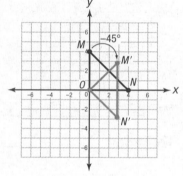

You can represent a rotation as a function for which the input is a coordinate pair. The output of that function is the image produced by the rotation.

A 90° rotation is equivalent to a −270° rotation and has the function:

$$R_{90°}(x, y) = (-y, x)$$

A 180° rotation is equivalent to a −180° rotation and has the function:

$$R_{180°}(x, y) = (-x, -y).$$

A 270° rotation is equivalent to a −90° rotation and has the function:

$$R_{270°}(x, y) = (y, -x)$$

Compare the preimage on the right and its image after a 180° rotation. Notice that the hypotenuse of the image is parallel to the hypotenuse of the preimage. Corresponding sides of the triangle and its image after a 180° rotation always lie on parallel lines or on the same line.

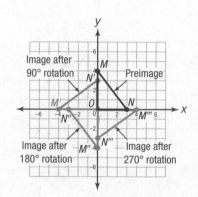

Now compare the preimage and the other images. Notice that the hypotenuse of each of these images is perpendicular to the hypotenuse of the preimage. Corresponding sides of the triangle and its image after a 90° or 270° rotation lie on perpendicular lines.

⇥ Connect

Triangle *GHJ* is graphed on the coordinate plane. Draw the image of this triangle after counterclockwise rotations of 90°, 180°, and 270° about the origin.

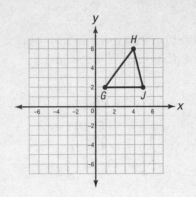

1

Apply the functions for the given counterclockwise rotations to the vertices of the triangle.

The vertices of $\triangle GHJ$ are $G(1, 2)$, $H(4, 6)$, and $J(5, 2)$.

The function that represents a 90° rotation around the origin is $R_{90°}(x, y) = (-y, x)$.

$R_{90°}(1, 2) = (-2, 1)$

$R_{90°}(4, 6) = (-6, 4)$

$R_{90°}(5, 2) = (-2, 5)$

The function that represents a 180° rotation around the origin is $R_{180°}(x, y) = (-x, -y)$.

$R_{180°}(1, 2) = (-1, -2)$

$R_{180°}(4, 6) = (-4, -6)$

$R_{180°}(5, 2) = (-5, -2)$

The function that represents a 270° rotation around the origin is $R_{270°}(x, y) = (y, -x)$.

$R_{270°}(1, 2) = (2, -1)$

$R_{270°}(4, 6) = (6, -4)$

$R_{270°}(5, 2) = (2, -5)$

2

Graph and label each image.

Plot the vertices of each image, label them, and connect them.

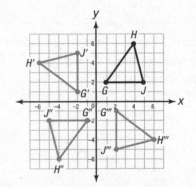

 TRY

Identify the coordinates of the vertices of the images if the rotations had been in a clockwise direction.

EXAMPLE A Quadrilateral *STUV* is graphed on the coordinate plane. Transform quadrilateral *STUV* using this function:

$$R_\theta(x, y) = (-y, x)$$

Identify the degree measure of the rotation that the function performs. (Note: The Greek letter theta (θ) is often used to represent unknown angle measures.)

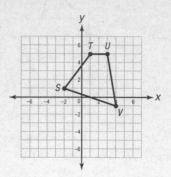

1

Identify the coordinates of the vertices of quadrilateral *STUV*.

The figure has vertices $S(-2, 1)$, $T(1, 5)$, $U(3, 5)$, and $V(4, -1)$.

2

Identify the coordinates of the rotated image and the degree measure of the rotation.

$R_\theta(x, y) = (-y, x)$, so:

$S(-2, 1) \rightarrow S'(-1, -2)$

$T(1, 5) \rightarrow T'(-5, 1)$

$U(3, 5) \rightarrow U'(-5, 3)$

$V(4, -1) \rightarrow V'(1, 4)$

When the opposite value of *y* is taken and the values of *x* and −*y* are switched, this indicates a 90° rotation.

3

Graph the rotated image and identify the transformation. Check your answer visually.

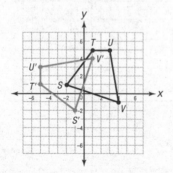

Eyeballing the graph confirms that this is a 90° rotation.

▶ The function notation and a visual comparison of $\overline{TU}$ and $\overline{T'U'}$ indicate that $S'T'U'V'$ is the result of a 90° rotation.

What is the relationship between the corresponding sides of the preimage and its image?

EXAMPLE B Triangle *BCD* was rotated to form its image, triangle *B'C'D'*. Identify the transformation and write a function to describe it.

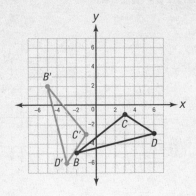

1

Identify the coordinates of the vertices of both triangles.

The vertices of the preimage, △*BCD*, are *B*(−2, −5), *C*(3, −1), and *D*(6, −3).

The vertices of the image, △*B'C'D'*, are *B'*(−5, 2), *C'*(−1, −3), and *D'*(−3, −6).

2

Compare the triangles visually to identify the transformation.

From eyeballing the figures, it looks like △*BCD* was turned about $\frac{1}{4}$ clockwise around the origin to form △*B'C'D'*. That is a −90° rotation, which is the same as a 270° rotation.

3

Use the function for a 270° rotation to confirm your guess.

The function for a 270° rotation is $R_{270°}(x, y) = (y, -x)$. Apply this function to the vertices of △*BCD*.

$R_{270°}(-2, -5) = (-5, 2)$ This is *B'*.

$R_{270°}(3, -1) = (-1, -3)$ This is *C'*.

$R_{270°}(6, -3) = (-3, -6)$ This is *D'*.

Since each point (x, y) on △*BCD* has a corresponding point (y, −x) on its image, △*B'C'D'* is the result of a 270° rotation.

▶ The transformation is a 270° rotation, which can be represented by the function $R_{270°}(x, y) = (y, -x)$.

TRY

Identify and write a function to describe the rotation needed to move △*B'C'D'* back onto △*BCD*. How does this notation compare to the notation for the 270° rotation?

Practice

Identify the number of degrees (45°, 90°, 180°, or 270°) by which each quadrilateral *ABCD* has been rotated about the origin to form its image.

1.

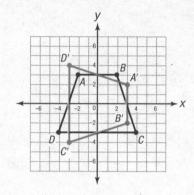

_____

2.

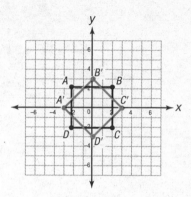

_____

> **REMEMBER** A −90° rotation is equal to a 270° rotation.

Describe how △*DEF* was rotated to form △*D′E′F′* both in words and in function notation.

3.

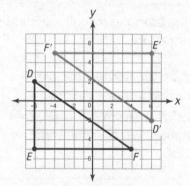

Words: _____

Function: _____

4.

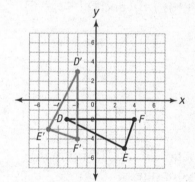

Words: _____

Function: _____

Write *true* or *false* for each statement. If false, rewrite the statement to make it true.

5.   A circle is the set of all points that are equidistant from a point called the center.

_____

6.   A quarter-turn in the counterclockwise direction is equivalent to a −90° rotation.

_____

7.   Corresponding sides of a preimage and an image after a 270° rotation are parallel.

_____

Use the given function to rotate △KLM to form △K′L′M′. Identify the coordinates of the vertices of the image. Then identify the degree measure of the rotation.

8. $R_\theta(x, y) = (-x, -y)$

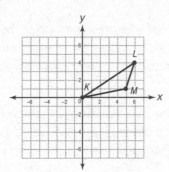

K′(___, ___) L′(___, ___) M′(___, ___)

_____

9. $R_\theta(x, y) = (-y, x)$

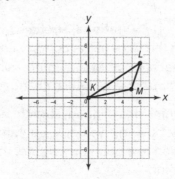

K′(___, ___) L′(___, ___) M′(___, ___)

_____

Solve.

10. **EXPLAIN** Sal drew a rectangle on a coordinate plane. He then rotated it 90° as shown below. Is there another way he could have rotated the rectangle that would have yielded the same image? Explain your reasoning.

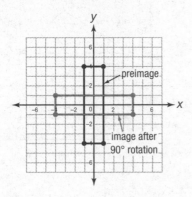

_____
_____
_____

11. **DRAW** An artist drew a blue and white trapezoid on a computer. She wants to copy and rotate this image three times about the origin to create a figure that looks like a pinwheel. Describe three rotations she could use. Draw the pinwheel that would result from those three rotations.

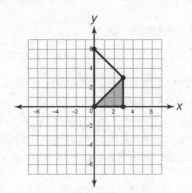

_____
_____

Dilations, Stretches, and Shrinks

UNDERSTAND **Dilations**, stretches, and shrinks change the size of a figure. They do so by changing the sizes of the component parts of a figure, such as the lengths of line segments or arcs that are part of the figure. In stretches and shrinks, the measures of angles can also increase or decrease, which changes the shape of the figure.

You can think of a dilation, stretch, or shrink of a geometric figure as a function, in which the input is not a single value, x, but rather a point on the coordinate plane, (x, y). When you apply the function to a point on a figure, the output will be the coordinates of the transformed image of that point.

A **horizontal stretch** pulls the points of a figure away from the y-axis, while a **horizontal shrink** pushes the points of a figure toward the y-axis.

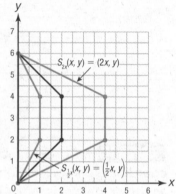

The functions that perform horizontal stretches and shrinks multiply the x-coordinate of each point on the preimage by some constant.

Horizontal stretch: $S_{ax}(x, y) = (ax, y), |a| > 1$

Horizontal shrink: $S_{ax}(x, y) = (ax, y), 0 < |a| < 1$

A **vertical stretch** pulls the points of a figure away from the x-axis, while a **vertical shrink** pushes the points of a figure toward the x-axis.

The functions that perform vertical stretches and shrinks multiply the y-coordinate of each point on the preimage by some constant.

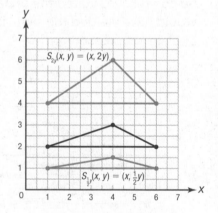

Vertical stretch: $S_{by}(x, y) = (x, by), |b| > 1$

Vertical shrink: $S_{by}(x, y) = (x, by), 0 < |b| < 1$

Notice that the slopes of some of the lines changed after the transformations. This is a sign that the measures of the angles were not preserved in these transformations. You can use a protractor to measure corresponding angles in the figures and confirm that they have different measures.

A dilation pulls the points of a figure away from or pushes them toward a point, called the **center of dilation**. The x-coordinate and y-coordinate of each point change by the same factor.

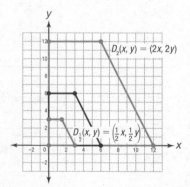

If the center of dilation is the origin, then: $D_k(x, y) = (kx, ky)$

If $|k| > 1$, the figure is enlarged.

If $0 < |k| < 1$, the figure is reduced.

⌁Connect

Triangle *XYZ* is shown. Graph its image after the transformation described below.

$$S_{3y}(x, y) = (x, 3y)$$

Is this an example of a stretch or a shrink? in what direction and by what factor?

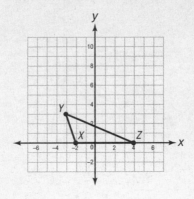

1

Identify the coordinates of the vertices of △*XYZ*.

The vertices of the triangle are $X(-2, 0)$, $Y(-3, 3)$, and $Z(4, 0)$.

2

Apply the function to the vertices and graph the output points.

$S_{3y}(-2, 0) = (-2, 3(0)) = (-2, 0)$

$S_{3y}(-3, 3) = (-3, 3(3)) = (-3, 9)$

$S_{3y}(4, 0) = (4, 3(0)) = (4, 0)$

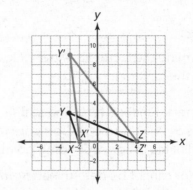

3

Describe the transformation.

Points *X* and *Z* do not change, but point *Y* stretches vertically upward.

$Y(-3, 3) \longrightarrow Y'(-3, 9)$

So, this is an example of a vertical stretch.

$S_{3y}(x, y) = (x, 3y)$ shows that we can find the coordinates of the image by keeping the *x*-coordinate the same and multiplying the *y*-coordinate by 3. This means the factor is 3.

▶ The function represents a vertical stretch by a factor of 3.

DISCUSS

Which component parts of the figure change? Which stay the same?

EXAMPLE A Triangle *PQR* was transformed to produce △*P′Q′R′* as shown on the graph. Identify the transformation and use function notation to describe it.

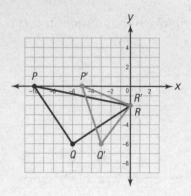

1

Identify the coordinates of the vertices of the triangles.

Triangle *PQR* has vertices $P(-10, 0)$, $Q(-6, -6)$, and $R(0, -2)$.

Triangle *P′Q′R′* has vertices $P'(-5, 0)$, $Q'(-3, -6)$, and $R'(0, -2)$.

2

Identify the type of transformation.

The image, △*P′Q′R′*, is not the same shape as its preimage, △*PQR*. Its line segments have different lengths, and its angles have different measures.

So, the transformation must be some kind of stretch or shrink.

The *y*-coordinates of the points have not changed.

The *x*-coordinates have changed. The points moved closer to the *y*-axis.

The transformation is a horizontal shrink.

3

Determine the factor for the shrink. Then write the function.

The general function for a horizontal shrink is $S_{ax}(x, y) = (ax, y)$. Compare the *x*-coordinates of corresponding points.

The factor cannot be determined from *R* and *R′*, since their *x*-coordinates are both 0.

$P \longrightarrow P': \dfrac{-5}{-10} = \dfrac{1}{2} \qquad Q \longrightarrow Q': \dfrac{-3}{-6} = \dfrac{1}{2}$

The *x*-coordinate was multiplied by a factor of $\frac{1}{2}$.

▶ The transformation can be represented by the function $S_{\frac{1}{2}x}(x, y) = \left(\frac{1}{2}x, y\right)$.

If this were a vertical shrink instead of a horizontal shrink, how would the function notation differ? Assume that the scale factor is the same and write the new function notation.

EXAMPLE B Quadrilateral *ABCZ* is shown. Draw quadrilateral *A'B'C'Z'*, which is the result of a dilation from the origin by a scale factor of $\frac{3}{2}$. Then write a function to describe the dilation.

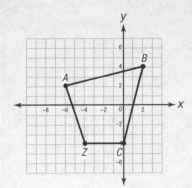

1

Identify the coordinates of the vertices of quadrilateral *ABCZ*.

The quadrilateral has vertices $A(-6, 2)$, $B(2, 4)$, $C(0, -4)$, and $Z(-4, -4)$.

2

Find the coordinates of the vertices of the image. Then use them to graph the image.

This is a dilation from the origin, so multiply both the *x*- and *y*-coordinates by the scale factor, $\frac{3}{2}$.

$A(-6, 2) \rightarrow \left(\frac{3}{2}(-6), \frac{3}{2}(2)\right) \rightarrow A'(-9, 3)$

$B(2, 4) \rightarrow \left(\frac{3}{2}(2), \frac{3}{2}(4)\right) \rightarrow B'(3, 6)$

$C(0, -4) \rightarrow \left(\frac{3}{2}(0), \frac{3}{2}(-4)\right) \rightarrow C'(0, -6)$

$Z(-4, -4) \rightarrow \left(\frac{3}{2}(-4), \frac{3}{2}(-4)\right) \rightarrow Z'(-6, -6)$

▶

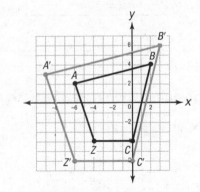

3

Use function notation to describe the dilation.

The function notation must show that each *x*-coordinate and each *y*-coordinate is multiplied by $\frac{3}{2}$.

▶ The function $D_{\frac{3}{2}}(x, y) = \left(\frac{3}{2}x, \frac{3}{2}y\right)$ represents the transformation.

TRY

Write a function to describe how the image, quadrilateral *A'B'C'Z'*, can be transformed back into quadrilateral *ABCZ*.

Practice

Draw the image after each described transformation and identify its vertices.

1. Stretch △ABC vertically by a factor of 3.

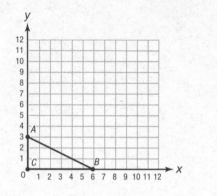

A'(___, ___), B'(___, ___), C'(___, ___)

2. Shrink △FGH horizontally by a factor of $\frac{2}{3}$.

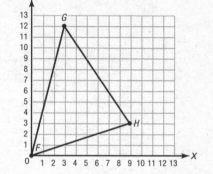

F'(___, ___), G'(___, ___), H'(___, ___)

> **REMEMBER** A horizontal transformation affects the *x*-coordinates. A vertical transformation affects the *y*-coordinates.

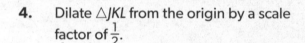

3. Dilate △JKL from the origin by a scale factor of 2.

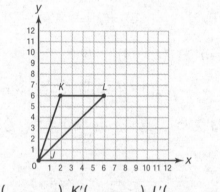

J'(___, ___), K'(___, ___), L'(___, ___)

4. Dilate △JKL from the origin by a scale factor of $\frac{1}{2}$.

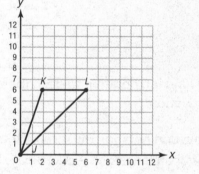

J'(___, ___), K'(___, ___), L'(___, ___)

Use the given function notation to transform quadrilateral *FGHJ*.

5. $D_{\frac{1}{4}}(x, y) = \left(\frac{1}{4}x, \frac{1}{4}y\right)$

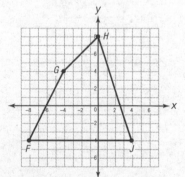

6. $S_{\frac{3}{2}y}(x, y) = \left(x, \frac{3}{2}y\right)$

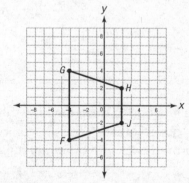

Describe how △KLM was transformed to its image, △K'L'M', both in words and in function notation.

7.

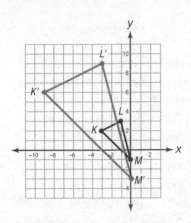

Words: _____

Function notation: _____

8.

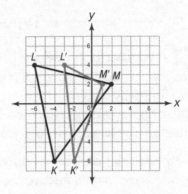

Words: _____

Function notation: _____

Use the graph of △MNP and its images below for questions 9 and 10.

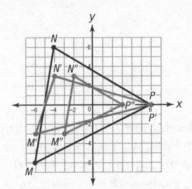

9. **COMPARE** Triangle *MNP* was transformed to △*M'N'P'* in one step. That image was then transformed to △*M"N"P"* in another step. Use function notation to describe each of those transformations. Then compare and contrast the two transformations.

transformation of △*MNP* to △*M'N'P'*: _____

transformation of △*M'N'P'* to △*M"N"P"*: _____

_____

_____

10. **EXPLAIN** Use function notation to describe how △*MNP* could have been transformed to △*M"N"P"* in one step. Explain your reasoning.

_____

_____

Lesson 36 Symmetry and Sequences of Transformations

Types of Symmetry

UNDERSTAND A **regular polygon** is a polygon with all sides equal in length and all angles equal in measure. If a regular polygon has *n* sides, then it also has *n* **lines of symmetry**. If you reflect a figure over a line of symmetry, the image looks exactly like and is in the same location as the original preimage. When this happens, we say that the reflection maps the figure onto itself. This type of symmetry is called **line symmetry** or **reflectional symmetry**.

For example, the regular pentagon shown below has 5 lines of symmetry. One of them is the *y*-axis. If this pentagon is reflected across the *y*-axis, point *B* is carried onto point *D* and vice versa, point *A* is carried onto point *E* and vice versa, and point *C* maps onto itself because it is on the line of reflection. The reflection maps the original figure back onto itself, so its image is identical to its preimage.

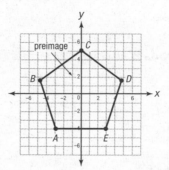
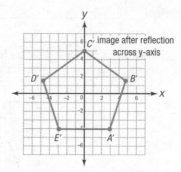

The pentagon also has **rotational symmetry**. Any figure will map onto itself after a 360° turn, but a figure that has rotational symmetry will map onto itself more than once during a 360° turn. Notice that if a circle is drawn through all five vertices, the circle is divided into five equal-length arcs. To find the measure of each arc, divide 360° by the number of sides.

$$360° \div 5 = 72°$$

Rotating the pentagon 72 degrees maps it onto itself.

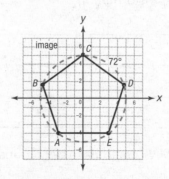
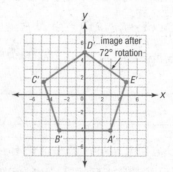

If you were to rotate the pentagon another 72°, which is a 144° rotation from the original preimage, you would produce the same figure again. You can do this 3 more times. In general, a regular polygon with *n* sides will map onto itself *n* times during a 360° turn.

ꓱ Connect

Describe two ways in which the rectangle graphed below could be mapped back onto itself.

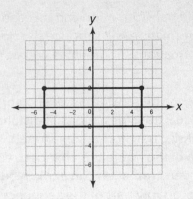

1
Look for rotational symmetry.

If you rotate the rectangle 180°, the upper left corner maps onto the lower right corner and vice versa. The resulting figure is identical to the original rectangle.

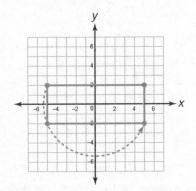

▶ A rotation of 180° will map the rectangle back onto itself.

2
Look for line symmetry.

If you reflect the rectangle over the x-axis, then the top half maps onto the bottom half and vice versa.

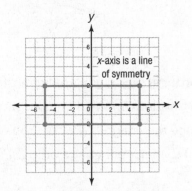

x-axis is a line of symmetry

▶ A reflection across the x-axis maps the rectangle back onto itself.

DISCUSS

Is there a third way to map the rectangle onto itself in one step? If so, describe it. If not, explain why not.

Transformations in Sequence

UNDERSTAND Sometimes, a single transformation can be used to produce a particular image. Other times, no one transformation will produce the desired image. In that case, you will need to use a series of transformations. Sometimes two or more different sequences can produce the same final image.

To determine the necessary sequence of transformations, compare the preimage to the image much as you have done for individual transformations. If distances and/or angle measures are not conserved, then some type of size transformation (stretch, shrink, dilation) is probably part of the sequence. If the orientation of the figure has changed, then a reflection or rotation has probably taken place. If no other transformation can explain part of the way in which a figure has been moved, a translation is probably part of the sequence.

Consider △*TVW* and its image △*T'V'W'* below. The image is vertically "shorter" than the preimage, but it is just as wide as the preimage, so a vertical shrink is part of the sequence. However, the image, △*T'V'W'*, is lower than it would be after a vertical shrink of △*TVW* from the x-axis.

You must vertically shrink the preimage by a factor of $\frac{1}{2}$ and then translate it 4 units down to produce △*T'V'W'*.

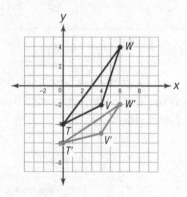
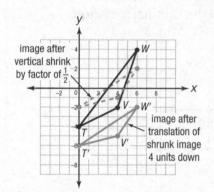

The order in which you apply transformations does not always matter, but in this case, it does. If you translate △*TVW* 4 units down and *then* vertically shrink it by a factor of $\frac{1}{2}$, you do not produce the image, △*T'V'W'*. You would still need to perform another translation (2 units down) to map your image onto △*T'V'W'*.

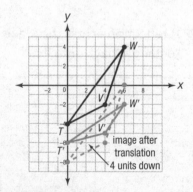
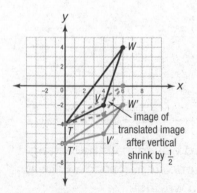

←← Connect

Describe a sequence of transformations that could be used to map trapezoid *ABCD* onto trapezoid *A'B'C'D'*.

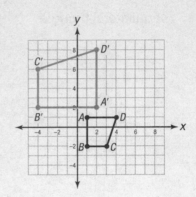

1

Compare the size and shape of the image and the preimage.

Since every line segment has doubled in length, a dilation (an enlargement) by a factor of 2 has taken place.

2

Compare the image after the dilation to the final image.

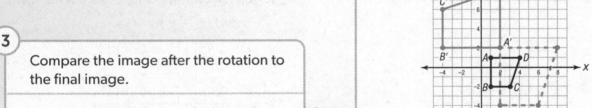

In trapezoid *A'B'C'D'*, side $\overline{C'D'}$ is at the top of the figure. Perform a 90° rotation as the second step.

3

Compare the image after the rotation to the final image.

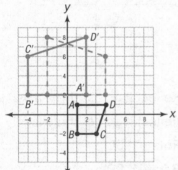

The final trapezoid is the mirror image of how the rotated image looks, so reflect it across the *y*-axis.

▶ The sequence used could have been a dilation by a scale factor of 2 followed by a 90° rotation followed by a reflection across the *y*-axis.

On the first coordinate plane shown above, show what happens if you perform the 90° rotation first, the dilation by a factor of 2 second, and the reflection across the *y*-axis last. Does switching the order of the first two transformations produce a different final image? Explain.

Practice

Determine if the given figure has rotational symmetry, line symmetry, both, or neither.

1. isosceles trapezoid

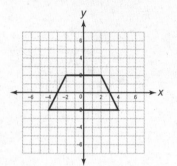

_____

2. equilateral triangle

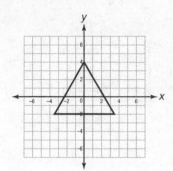

_____

3. parallelogram

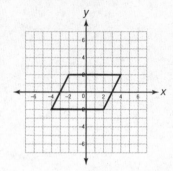

_____

> **HINT** A figure has rotational symmetry if some turn of less than 360° maps it back onto itself.

Choose the best answer.

4. Which sequence of transformations could be used to transform *ABCD* to *A′B′C′D′*?

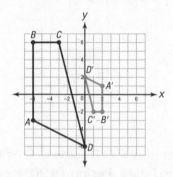

- **A.** dilation by a factor of $\frac{1}{3}$ followed by a reflection across the *y*-axis
- **B.** dilation by a factor of $\frac{1}{3}$ followed by a 180° rotation about the origin
- **C.** vertical shrink by a factor of $\frac{1}{3}$ followed by a translation 4 units to the right
- **D.** reflection across the *y*-axis followed by a 180° rotation about the origin

5. Which does **not** describe a way to map regular hexagon *PQRSTU* back onto itself?

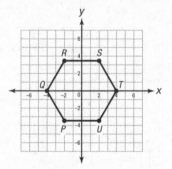

- **A.** Reflect it across the *x*-axis.
- **B.** Reflect it across the *y*-axis.
- **C.** Rotate it 60°.
- **D.** Rotate it 90°.

Write *true* or *false* for each statement. If false, rewrite the statement to make it true.

6. Any figure will map back onto itself after a 360° turn about its center.

_____

7. A figure that has line symmetry must also have rotational symmetry.

_____

Solve.

8. **SHOW** Describe a sequence of two transformations that could map △*FGH* onto △*F'G'H'*.

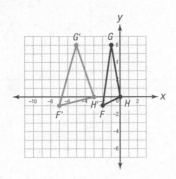

_____

_____

9. **EXPLAIN** Reverse the order of the transformations in your sequence from question 8 and draw the image on the grid below. Does this affect the final image produced? Explain.

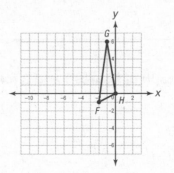

_____

_____

10. **DRAW** A certain quadrilateral can be mapped onto itself after 90°, 180°, and 270° rotations, and it can also be mapped onto itself by a reflection over the *x*-axis or a reflection over the *y*-axis. On the grid below, draw a quadrilateral that fits that description.

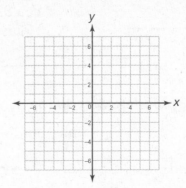

Describe a reflection or a rotation (of less than 360°) that can be used to map each figure back onto itself.

1. parallelogram

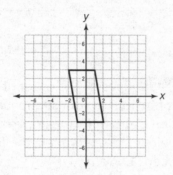

_____

2. kite

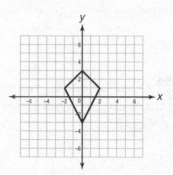

_____

Use the graph of figures 1 and 2 for questions 3 and 4.

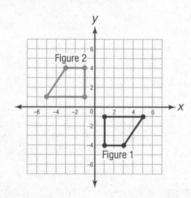

3. Describe how Figure 1 could be rotated to form Figure 2 in one step.

_____

4. Describe a sequence of transformations (that does not include a rotation) that could be used to map Figure 1 onto Figure 2.

_____

Match each transformation to an appropriate description by writing a letter in the blank.

5. _____ Dilations

6. _____ Reflections, rotations, and translations

7. _____ Stretches and shrinks

A. Preserve distances and angle measures

B. Preserve angle measures but not distances

C. Do not preserve all distances or all angle measures

Fill in each blank with an appropriate word or phrase.

8. A(n) _____ is the set of all points that are the same distance from a point called the center.

9. Two lines are _____ if they intersect to form right angles.

10. A(n) _____ is a figure that consists of the part of a line that falls between two points called endpoints.

11. A(n) _____ is a figure created by two distinct rays or line segments that meet at a common endpoint.

**Use the given function to transform the given figure and graph the image. Use prime (')
symbols to name the vertices. Describe each transformation in words.**

12. $T(x, y) = (x - 4, y + 2)$

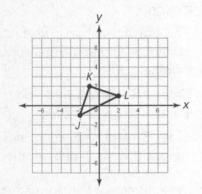

_____

13. $D_3(x, y) = (3x, 3y)$

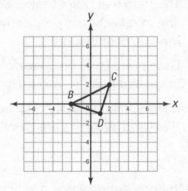

_____

14. $R(x, y) = (x, -y)$

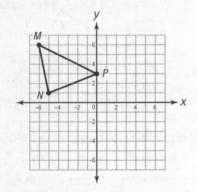

_____

15. $R_\theta(x, y) = (-y, x)$

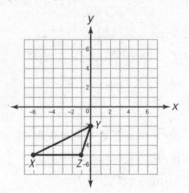

_____

Choose the best answer.

16. Quadrilateral *JKLM* and its reflected image are shown. Which statement is true of these two quadrilaterals?

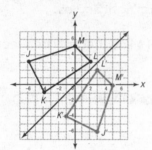

A. The image shows the result of a reflection across the *x*-axis.

B. The path that point *L* takes across the line of reflection is perpendicular to the line of reflection.

C. Each point (*x*, *y*) on quadrilateral *JKLM* maps to a point (−*y*, *x*) on its image.

D. Corresponding sides of quadrilateral *JKLM* and its image are parallel.

17. Triangle *ABC* is transformed to triangle *A′B′C′*. Which statement is **not** true of these two figures?

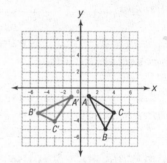

A. This transformation shows the image of △*ABC* after a 270° rotation about the origin.

B. This transformation preserved the distances and angle measures of the original figure.

C. Sides $\overline{AB}$ and $\overline{A'B'}$ lie on lines that are parallel to one another.

D. Sides $\overline{BC}$ and $\overline{B'C'}$ lie on lines that are perpendicular to one another.

18. Which does **not** describe a way to map this regular octagon back onto itself?

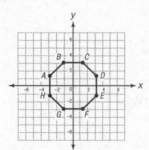

A. Reflect it across the *x*-axis.

B. Reflect it across the *y*-axis.

C. Rotate it 45°.

D. Rotate it 80°.

19. Which sequence of transformations can be used to map △*MNP* onto △*M′N′P′*?

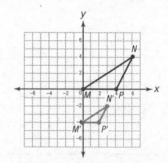

A. dilation by a factor of $\frac{1}{2}$ followed by a translation 4 units down

B. dilation by a factor of $\frac{1}{2}$ followed by a 270° rotation

C. vertical shrink by a factor of $\frac{1}{2}$ followed by a translation 4 units down

D. vertical shrink by a factor of $\frac{1}{2}$ followed by a 270° rotation

Describe how △DEF was transformed to its image, △D′E′F′, using both words and function notation.

20.

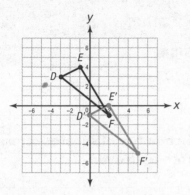

Words: _____

Function: _____

21.

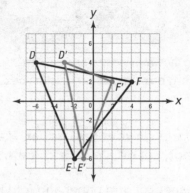

Words: _____

Function: _____

22.

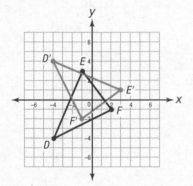

Words: _____

Function: _____

23.

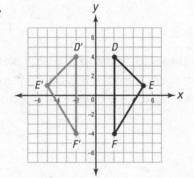

Words: _____

Function: _____

Solve.

24. **DESCRIBE** Alicia drew pentagon *HJKLM* by using a computer drawing program. She then transformed it to pentagon *H′J′K′L′M′* in two steps. Use words and/or drawings to describe a series of transformations she could have used. Did the transformations she used change the lengths of line segments or the measures of angles in her drawing?

_____

_____

_____

_____

_____

Cut It Out

Explore symmetry and transformations by cutting out shapes on grid paper.

MATERIALS
- 2–3 copies of Math Tool: Grid Paper
- scissors

Count the squares on your grid paper. Make sure to have an even number of squares across and down. If not, cut off a row or column so that those numbers are both even.

1. Take one sheet of grid paper and fold it in half. Then trace the path shown (or if your grid paper is smaller than what is shown, trace as much of the path as you can).

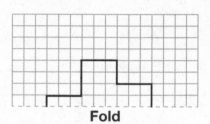

Fold

2. Keep the paper folded and use your scissors to cut along the path that you traced. Remove the figure from the paper, and unfold your paper. Sketch a picture to show how the graph paper looks.

3. Does the figure you cut out have line symmetry? Does it have rotational symmetry? Explain your answers.

_____

_____

4. Refold your paper. Decide how you could change the cutout so that when you unfold the paper, it will have both line symmetry and rotational symmetry. Draw additional lines or shade the diagram on the right to show how you will alter the cutout.

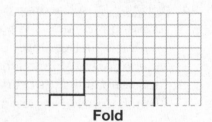

Fold

5. Trace your design at the fold, cut out the additional squares, and unfold your paper. Does the cutout image show rotational and line symmetry? If it doesn't, refold the paper and cutout more squares. When you believe it has both types of symmetry, have a partner check your work. Then sketch a picture to show how the unfolded paper looks.

6. How do you know that the figure you created has rotational symmetry? How many degrees do you need to rotate your image before it maps back onto itself?

_____

_____

Take a second sheet of grid paper and cut it so it has 16 squares across and 16 squares down.

7. Fold the paper in half. Then, fold the paper again to make a strip that is 4 squares across and 16 squares down. Trace a shape along the folded edge, cut out the shape, and put the cutout shape aside.

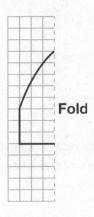

Fold

8. Unfold the paper and sketch a picture of the shape.

9. Are the shapes that were created reflections of one another? Explain.

_____

10. Could you map one shape onto the other using a single rotation? Why or why not?

_____

11. Could you map one shape onto another using a single translation? Why or why not?

_____

Grade 8

Coordinate Algebra

Analytic Geometry

Expressions and Equations

Work with radicals and integer exponents.

Understand the connections between proportional relationships, lines, and linear equations.

Geometry

Expressing Geometric Properties with Equations

Use coordinates to prove simple geometric theorems algebraically.

Geometry

Understand and apply the Pythagorean Theorem.

Geometry

Similarity, Right Triangles, and Trigonometry

Understand similarity in terms of similarity transformations.

Expressing Geometric Properties with Equations

Use coordinates to prove simple geometric theorems algebraically.

Unit 6
Connecting Algebra and Geometry through Coordinates

Parallel and Perpendicular Lines

UNDERSTAND **Parallel lines** lie in the same plane but never intersect. On a coordinate plane, lines that are parallel to each other have the same slope but different *y*-intercepts.

Consider two cars traveling in the same direction at the same constant speed. Both cars are traveling at a rate of 50 miles per hour, but Car A is 100 miles ahead of Car B. The following functions describe the distance of each car from Car B's starting point, in miles, after *t* hours.

Car A: $d_A(t) = 50t + 100$

Car B: $d_B(t) = 50t$

The graphs of these equations are shown on the right.

The equations have the same slope, 50, but different *y*-intercepts. The function for Car A has a *y*-intercept of 100, and the function for Car B has a *y*-intercept of 0. In real terms, at the time when Car B leaves, Car A is 100 miles away. Since the cars travel at the same rate, they will always be 100 miles apart and will never meet, just as the parallel lines in the graph will never intersect.

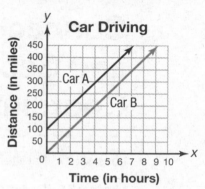

UNDERSTAND **Perpendicular lines** intersect to form right angles. On a coordinate plane, lines that are perpendicular have slopes that are opposite reciprocals of each other. This means that if one line has a slope of *m*, then a line perpendicular to it will have a slope of $-\frac{1}{m}$. The product of a number and its opposite reciprocal is always −1.

$$m \cdot -\frac{1}{m} = -1$$

The two lines shown on the right are perpendicular. Use the slope formula, $m = \frac{y_2 - y_1}{x_2 - x_1}$ to find the slope of each line.

One line passes through the points (2, 3) and (4, 2).

$$m = \frac{2 - 3}{4 - 2} = \frac{-1}{2} = -\frac{1}{2}$$

The other line passes through the points (1, 1) and (2, 3).

$$m = \frac{3 - 1}{2 - 1} = \frac{2}{1} = 2$$

The negative reciprocal of $-\frac{1}{2}$ is $\frac{2}{1}$, or 2, so the lines are perpendicular.

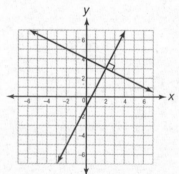

⊷ Connect

Are lines *a* and *b* parallel?

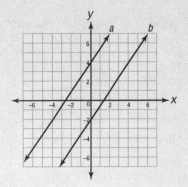

1

Observe the lines.

The lines do not intersect at any visible point, so they appear to be parallel. However, the lines may intersect at some point not on the grid, so observation alone is not enough to prove that they are parallel.

2

Find the slope of line *a*.

Find two points on the line, and use the slope formula to calculate its slope.

Line *a* passes through the points (0, 4) and (−2, 1).

$$m_a = \frac{1 - 4}{-2 - 0} = \frac{-3}{-2} = \frac{3}{2}$$

3

Find the slope of line *b*.

Line *b* passes through the points (0, −2) and (2, 1).

$$m_b = \frac{1 - (-2)}{2 - 0} = \frac{3}{2}$$

4

Compare the slopes of lines *a* and *b*.

Both lines have a slope of $\frac{3}{2}$. The y-intercept of line *a* is 4, and the y-intercept of line *b* is −2. The slopes are the same, and the y-intercepts are different.

▶ Lines *a* and *b* are parallel.

TRY

Find the equation of another line that is parallel to lines *a* and *b*. Then graph that line on the same coordinate plane.

EXAMPLE A The equations of two lines are shown below. Are lines r and s perpendicular?

Line r: $4y + 12 = x$

Line s: $8y + 2x = 16$

1

Find the slope of line r.

Rewrite the line in slope-intercept form. The coefficient of x will be the slope.

Solve for y.

$4y + 12 = x$

$4y = x - 12$

$y = \frac{1}{4}x - 3$

The slope is $\frac{1}{4}$.

2

Find the slope of line s.

Rewrite the line in slope-intercept form. The coefficient of x will be the slope.

Solve for y.

$8y + 2x = 16$

$8y = -2x + 16$

$y = -\frac{1}{4}x + 2$

The slope is $-\frac{1}{4}$.

3

Compare the slopes of lines r and s.

$\frac{1}{4} \cdot \left(-\frac{1}{4}\right) = -\frac{1}{16}$

The product of the slopes is not -1, so the slopes are not opposite reciprocals.

▶ Lines r and s are not perpendicular.

TRY

Determine whether the following lines are perpendicular.

$3y - 2x = 6$

$3x = 14 - 2y$

EXAMPLE B Line p represents the equation $2y + 2 = 6x$. Find the following:

- line n, a line that is parallel to line p and that passes through the point $(6, 2)$

- line q, a line that is perpendicular to line p and that passes through the point $(6, 2)$.

1

Rewrite the equation for line p in slope-intercept form. Find the slope.

Solve for y.

$2y + 2 = 6x$

$2y = 6x - 2$

$y = 3x - 1$

The slope of line p is 3.

2

Find the equation of line n.

A line parallel to line p has the same slope, 3. Use point-slope form to write the equation of a line with a slope of 3 that passes through $(6, 2)$. Then, convert the equation to slope-intercept form.

$y - y_1 = m(x - x_1)$

$y - 2 = 3(x - 6)$

$y - 2 = 3x - 18$

▶ $y = 3x - 16$

3

Find the equation of line q.

A line perpendicular to line p has a slope that is the negative reciprocal of 3. The negative reciprocal of 3 is $-\frac{1}{3}$ since $3 \cdot \left(-\frac{1}{3}\right) = -1$.

Use point-slope form to write the equation of a line with a slope of $-\frac{1}{3}$ that passes through $(6, 2)$. Then convert the equation to slope-intercept form.

$y - y_1 = m(x - x_1)$

$y - 2 = -\frac{1}{3}(x - 6)$

$y - 2 = -\frac{1}{3}x + 2$

▶ $y = -\frac{1}{3}x + 4$

CHECK

Graph lines p, n, and q on the same coordinate grid. Confirm that line p is parallel to line n and is perpendicular to line q.

Practice

Fill in the blank or write the answer to the question.

1. A line that is parallel to $y = \frac{3}{4}x - 9$ has slope $m =$ _____.

2. A line that is perpendicular to $3y = 11 - 8x$ has slope $m =$ _____.

> **REMEMBER** The slopes of perpendicular lines are opposite reciprocals.

3. A line that is parallel to $y = 12$ has slope $m =$ _____.

4. Are the lines $2y - x = 6$ and $6x - 3y - 33 = 0$ parallel, perpendicular, or neither?

_____

 HINT Write the equation of a line in slope-intercept form to find its slope.

Choose the best answer.

5. Which equation represents a line that is perpendicular to the line shown below?

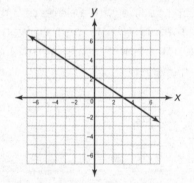

  A. $y = \frac{2}{3}x + 5$

  B. $y = \frac{3}{2}x - 4$

  C. $y = -\frac{2}{3}x - 6$

  D. $y = -\frac{3}{2}x + 1$

6. Which equation represents a line that is parallel to the line shown below?

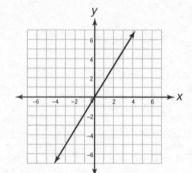

  A. $y = \frac{3}{5}x + 1$

  B. $y = -\frac{3}{5}x + 1$

  C. $y = \frac{5}{3}x - 1$

  D. $y = -\frac{5}{3}x - 1$

7. Which describes the lines $y = \frac{7}{8}x + 12$ and $y = -\frac{8}{7}x + 7$?

  A. parallel

  B. perpendicular

  C. neither parallel nor perpendicular

8. Which describes the lines $x - 2y = -6$ and $4y + 4 = 2x$?

  A. parallel

  B. perpendicular

  C. neither parallel nor perpendicular

Choose the best answer.

9. Which describes the lines shown below?

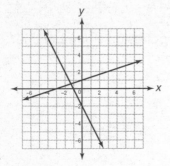

A. parallel

B. perpendicular

C. neither parallel nor perpendicular

10. Which describes the lines shown below?

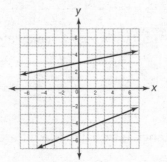

A. parallel

B. perpendicular

C. neither parallel nor perpendicular

Write the equation of the line that is described. Give your answer in slope-intercept form.

11.

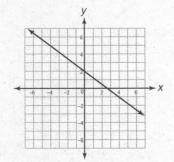

A line that is parallel to the one shown above and that passes through the point (8, −7).

_____

12.

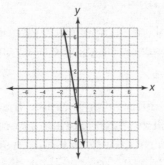

A line that is perpendicular to the one shown above and that passes through the point (12, 3).

_____

13. A line that is parallel to $3y = x + 12$ and that passes through the point (6, −8).

_____

14. A line that is perpendicular to $y − x = 7$ and that passes through the point (−2, −2).

_____

Solve.

15. **EXPLAIN** Lines *s*, *t*, and *u* all lie on the same plane. Line *s* is parallel to line *t*. Line *t* is perpendicular to line *u*. What is the relationship between lines *s* and *u*? How do you know?

_____

UNDERSTAND It's easy to calculate the distance between two points on a number line.

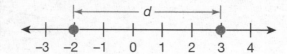

The distance is equal to the difference of the two numbers.

$$d = 3 - (-2) = 5$$

It's just as easy to calculate the length of a vertical or horizontal line segment on the coordinate plane.

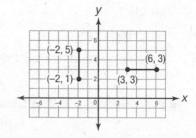

For a vertical line segment, the x-coordinates of the endpoints are the same. So, the length of the line segment is simply the difference of the y-coordinates.

$$d = 5 - 1 = 4$$

For a horizontal line segment, the y-coordinates of the endpoints are the same. So, the length of the line segment is simply the difference of the x-coordinates.

$$d = 6 - 3 = 3$$

Finding the length of a line segment that is not horizontal or vertical is trickier. Recall the **Pythagorean Theorem**, which states that, for any right triangle with legs of length a and b and hypotenuse of length c, $a^2 + b^2 = c^2$. You can think of a diagonal line on the coordinate grid as the hypotenuse of a triangle with one vertical leg and one horizontal leg.

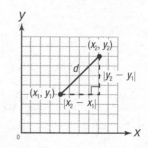

The horizontal leg has a length of $|x_2 - x_1|$. The vertical leg has a length of $|y_2 - y_1|$. You can substitute these expressions into the Pythagorean Theorem and solve for d, the length of the diagonal line.

$$(x_2 - x_1)^2 + (y_2 - y_1)^2 = d^2$$
$$\sqrt{(x_2 - x_1)^2 + (y_2 - y_1)^2} = d$$
$$d = \sqrt{(x_2 - x_1)^2 + (y_2 - y_1)^2}$$

This formula is called the distance formula. It can be used to find the length of any line segment on the coordinate plane, as long as its endpoints are known.

⤙Connect

The coordinate grid shows point *A*, point *B*, and the line segment connecting them.

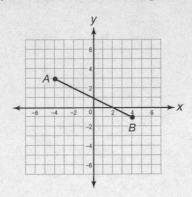

Use the distance formula to find *AB*, the length of the line segment.

1

Find the coordinates of the endpoints.

Point *A* is located at $(-4, 3)$.

Point *B* is located at $(4, -1)$.

Let $A(-4, 3) = (x_1, y_1)$ and
let $B(4, -1) = (x_2, y_2)$.

2

Apply the distance formula.

Substitute the coordinates into the formula and evaluate the radicand.

$$d = \sqrt{(x_2 - x_1)^2 + (y_2 - y_1)^2}$$
$$= \sqrt{(4 - (-4))^2 + (-1 - 3)^2}$$
$$= \sqrt{(8)^2 + (-4)^2}$$
$$= \sqrt{64 + 16}$$
$$= \sqrt{80}$$

3

Determine if the result can be simplified further.

The radicand, 80, is not a perfect square. However, it has factors that are perfect squares. Simplify by factoring out any perfect square factors.

$$d = \sqrt{80}$$
$$d = \sqrt{16 \cdot 5}$$
$$d = \sqrt{16} \cdot \sqrt{5}$$
▶ $$d = 4\sqrt{5}$$

TRY

Substitute the points in the reverse order: Let $B(4, -1) = (x_1, y_1)$ and let $A(-4, 3) = (x_2, y_2)$. Do you get the same result? Why do you think this is?

EXAMPLE A Parallelogram *DEFG* is shown on the coordinate grid.

What is the perimeter of parallelogram *DEFG*?

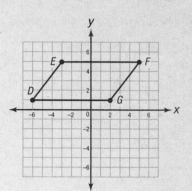

1

Determine what lengths to find.

Recall that opposite sides of a parallelogram are congruent. So, you only need to find the lengths of two adjacent sides. Find the lengths of $\overline{DE}$ and $\overline{EF}$.

2

Find the length of $\overline{EF}$.

The coordinates of the endpoints of $\overline{EF}$ are $E(-3, 5)$ and $F(5, 5)$. Since $\overline{EF}$ is horizontal, you do not need to use the distance formula. The *y*-coordinates are the same. To find the length, find the absolute value of the difference of the *x*-coordinates.

$$EF = |-3 - 5| = |-8| = 8$$

Opposite sides of a parallelogram are congruent, so $GD = EF$.

$$GD = EF = 8$$

3

Find the length of $\overline{DE}$.

The coordinates of the endpoints of $\overline{DE}$ are $D(-6, 1)$ and $E(-3, 5)$. Since $\overline{DE}$ is diagonal, use the distance formula. Let $D(-6, 1) = (x_1, y_1)$ and $E(-3, 5) = (x_2, y_2)$.

$$DE = \sqrt{(-3 - (-6))^2 + (5 - 1)^2}$$

$$DE = \sqrt{(3)^2 + (4)^2}$$

$$DE = \sqrt{9 + 16}$$

$$DE = \sqrt{25}$$

$$DE = 5$$

Opposite sides of a parallelogram are congruent, so $FG = DE$.

$$FG = DE = 5$$

4

Find the perimeter.

$$P = DE + EF + FG + GD$$

$$P = 5 + 8 + 5 + 8$$

$$P = 26$$

▶ The perimeter of parallelogram *DEFG* is 26 units.

DISCUSS

Imagine a regular octagon in a coordinate plane. How many side lengths would you need to find in order to calculate its perimeter?

EXAMPLE B Right triangle QRS is shown on the coordinate plane.

Find the area of △QRS.

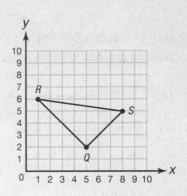

1

Determine what lengths to find.

△QRS is a right triangle with the right angle at ∠Q. In a right triangle, the legs form the base and the height. So, find QR and QS.

2

Find the length of $\overline{QR}$.

Let $Q(5, 2) = (x_1, y_1)$ and $R(1, 6) = (x_2, y_2)$.
$QR = \sqrt{(1 - 5)^2 + (6 - 2)^2}$
$QR = \sqrt{(-4)^2 + (4)^2}$
$QR = \sqrt{32}$
$QR = 4\sqrt{2}$

3

Find the length of $\overline{QS}$.

Let $Q(5, 2) = (x_1, y_1)$ and $S(8, 5) = (x_2, y_2)$.
$QS = \sqrt{(8 - 5)^2 + (5 - 2)^2}$
$QS = \sqrt{(3)^2 + (3)^2}$
$QS = \sqrt{18}$
$QS = 3\sqrt{2}$

4

Find the area of △QRS.

The area of a triangle is half of the base times the height. Let $\overline{QR}$ be the base and let $\overline{QS}$ be the height.

$A = \frac{1}{2}bh$

$A = \frac{1}{2}QR \cdot QS$

$A = \frac{1}{2}(4\sqrt{2})(3\sqrt{2})$

$A = 12$

▶ The area of △QRS is 12 square units.

TRY

Find the area of △XYZ with vertices X(−4, 2), Y(2, 2) and Z(−1, 5).

Practice

Use the coordinate grid below for questions 1–4. Find the distance in units between each given pair of points and write it in simplest form.

1. *D* and *E* _____

2. *A* and *C* _____

3. *B* and *D* _____

4. *A* and *E* _____

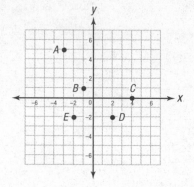

Use the information below for questions 5 and 6. Choose the best answer.

Figure *WXYZ* on the coordinate grid below is a square.

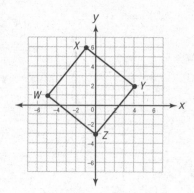

5. What is the perimeter of *WXYZ*?
   - **A.** $2\sqrt{41}$ units
   - **B.** 20 units
   - **C.** $4\sqrt{39}$ units
   - **D.** $4\sqrt{41}$ units

6. What is the area of *WXYZ*?
   - **A.** 25 units^2
   - **B.** 39 units^2
   - **C.** 41 units^2
   - **D.** 82 units^2

Solve.

7. The distance between points *A* and *B* is $\sqrt{113}$. Point *A* is located at $(-3, 6)$, and point *B* is located at $(4, y)$. What is a possible value of *y*? _____

8. The distance between points *C* and *D* is $6\sqrt{2}$. Point *C* is located at the origin. Point *D* is located at the point (a, a). What is a possible value of *a*? _____

9. Triangle *FGH* is isosceles with base $\overline{GH}$. Point *M* is the midpoint of $\overline{GH}$.

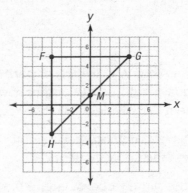

Find the length of altitude $\overline{FM}$, the perimeter of $\triangle FGH$, and the area of $\triangle FGH$.

Altitude: _____

Perimeter: _____

Area: _____

Use the information below to answer questions 10 and 11.

Rectangle *PQRS* is shown on the coordinate grid below.

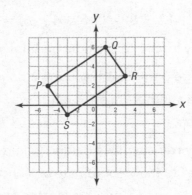

10. (PLAN) How can you find the area of rectangle *PQRS*?

_____

_____

11. (APPLY) Find the area of rectangle *PQRS*.

Area: _____

LESSON 39 Dividing Line Segments

UNDERSTAND The **midpoint** of a line segment divides, or **partitions**, the segment in half, producing two line segments of equal length, so the lengths have a ratio of 1:1. It is possible to find the point on a given line segment that divides it into two segments of any given ratio.

For a vertical or horizontal line segment, finding such a point is a straightforward process. Look at the coordinate grid.

Notice that all points on $\overline{AB}$ have the same x-coordinate, -4. So, the point $\frac{1}{3}$ of the way from A to B "rises" only $\frac{1}{3}$ of the way along the line. To find this point, add $\frac{1}{3}$ of the length of $\overline{AB}$ to the y-coordinate of A.

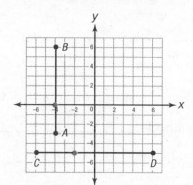

$$(-4, -3 + \tfrac{1}{3}AB) = (-4, -3 + \tfrac{1}{3} \cdot 9)$$
$$= (-4, -3 + 3) = (-4, 0)$$

The point $(-4, 0)$ is $\frac{1}{3}$ of the way from A to B, and it partitions $\overline{AB}$ in a ratio 1:2.

A similar process can be used to find the point $\frac{1}{3}$ of the way from C to D. This point "runs" only $\frac{1}{3}$ of the length along the line from C to D.

$$(-6 + \tfrac{1}{3}CD, -5) = (-6 + \tfrac{1}{3} \cdot 12, -5) = (-6 + 4, -5) = (-2, -5)$$

The point $(-2, -5)$ is $\frac{1}{3}$ of the way from C to D, and it partitions $\overline{CD}$ in a ratio 1:2.

A diagonal line segment can also be partitioned by using a point. A point that is, for example, $\frac{1}{3}$ of the way from one endpoint to another "rises" $\frac{1}{3}$ of the way along the segment and also "runs" $\frac{1}{3}$ of the way along the segment.

Look at line segment $\overline{XY}$ on the coordinate plane below. To find the point P that is $\frac{1}{3}$ of the way from X to Y, add $\frac{1}{3}$ of the "rise" to the y-coordinate of X and add $\frac{1}{3}$ of the "run" to its x-coordinate. Point X is located at $(-6, -5)$, and Y is located at $(6, 4)$.

$$rise = 4 - (-5) = 9$$

$$run = 6 - (-6) = 12$$

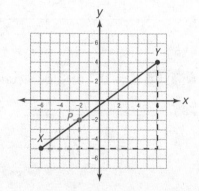

$$P = (-6 + \tfrac{1}{3} \cdot 12, -5 + \tfrac{1}{3} \cdot 9) = (-6 + 4, -5 + 3)$$
$$= (-2, -2)$$

In general, for a line segment $\overline{AB}$ with endpoints $A(x_1, y_1)$ and $B(x_2, y_2)$, to find the point that partitions the segment in a ratio of $m:n$, or lies k of the way from A to B, use the following formula:

$$(x_1 + k(x_2 - x_1), y_1 + k(y_2 - y_1)) \qquad \text{where } k = \frac{m}{m + n}$$

← Connect

The line segment $\overline{AB}$ is shown on the coordinate plane on the right.

Find the point Q that is $\frac{3}{4}$ the distance from A to B.
Then, plot and label Q on the coordinate plane.

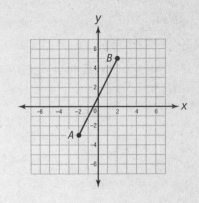

1

Identify the endpoints of $\overline{AB}$.

The coordinates of the endpoints are $A(-2, -3)$ and $B(2, 5)$.

Since the problem states that Q is $\frac{3}{4}$ the distance from A to B, let $A = (x_1, y_1)$ and $B = (x_2, y_2)$.

2

Use the formula to find point Q.

Let $k = \frac{3}{4}$, $(x_1, y_1) = (-2, -3)$, and $(x_2, y_2) = (2, 5)$.

$Q = (x_1 + k(x_2 - x_1), y_1 + k(y_2 - y_1))$

$Q = (-2 + \frac{3}{4}[2 - (-2)], -3 + \frac{3}{4}[5 - (-3)])$

$Q = (-2 + \frac{3}{4}(4), -3 + \frac{3}{4}(8))$

$Q = (-2 + 3, -3 + 6)$

$Q = (1, 3)$

▶ Point $Q(1, 3)$ is $\frac{3}{4}$ the distance from A to B.

3

Plot Q on the coordinate grid.

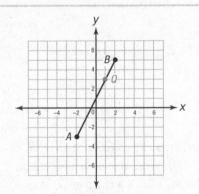

CHECK

Use the distance formula to find the lengths of $\overline{AQ}$ and $\overline{AB}$. Does $AQ = \left(\frac{3}{4}\right)AB$?

EXAMPLE A The line segment $\overline{BA}$ is shown on the coordinate plane on the right.

Find the point Q that partitions $\overline{BA}$ in a ratio of 1:3. Then, plot and label Q on the coordinate plane.

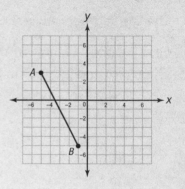

1

Identify the endpoints of $\overline{BA}$.

The coordinates of the endpoints are $A(-5, 3)$ and $B(-1, -5)$.

To partition $\overline{BA}$ in a ratio of 1:3, find the point that is $\frac{1}{1+3}$, or $\frac{1}{4}$, of the distance from B to A. Let $B = (x_1, y_1)$ and $A = (x_2, y_2)$.

2

Use the formula to find point Q.

Let $k = \frac{1}{4}$, $(x_1, y_1) = (-1, -5)$, and $(x_2, y_2) = (-5, 3)$.

$Q = (x_1 + k(x_2 - x_1), y_1 + k(y_2 - y_1))$

$Q = (-1 + \frac{1}{4}[-5 - (-1)], -5 + \frac{1}{4}[3 - (-5)])$

$Q = (-1 + \frac{1}{4}(-4), -5 + \frac{1}{4}(8))$

$Q = (-1 + (-1), -5 + 2)$

$Q = (-2, -3)$

▶ Point $Q(-2, -3)$ partitions $\overline{BA}$ in a ratio of 1:3.

3

Plot Q on the coordinate grid.

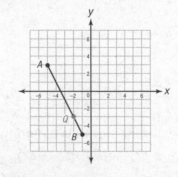

TRY

The endpoints of $\overline{CD}$ are $C(0, 3)$ and $D(12, 18)$. Find the point P that partitions $\overline{CD}$ in a ratio of 2:1.

EXAMPLE B The line segment $\overline{AB}$ is shown on the coordinate plane on the right.

Find the midpoint of $\overline{AB}$.

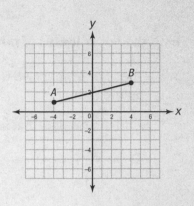

1

Identify the endpoints of $\overline{AB}$.

The coordinates of the endpoints are $A(-4, 1)$ and $B(4, 3)$.

The midpoint of $\overline{AB}$ is the point that is $\frac{1}{2}$ of the distance from A to B.

Let $A = (x_1, y_1)$ and $B = (x_2, y_2)$.

2

Use the formula to find the midpoint.

Let Q be the midpoint of $\overline{AB}$.
Let $k = \frac{1}{2}$, $(x_1, y_1) = (-4, 1)$, and $(x_2, y_2) = (4, 3)$.

$Q = (x_1 + k(x_2 - x_1), y_1 + k(y_2 - y_1))$

$Q = (-4 + \frac{1}{2}[4 - (-4)], 1 + \frac{1}{2}(3 - 1))$

$Q = (-4 + \frac{1}{2}(8), 1 + \frac{1}{2}(2))$

$Q = (-4 + 4, 1 + 1)$

$Q = (0, 2)$

▶ Point $Q(0, 2)$ is the midpoint of $\overline{AB}$.

The midpoint formula for finding the midpoint of a segment with endpoints (x_1, y_1) and (x_2, y_2) is

$$\left(\frac{x_1 + x_2}{2}, \frac{y_1 + y_2}{2}\right)$$

How does this formula relate to the formula that you have been using?

Practice

Find the coordinates of point Q.

1. The line segment $\overline{AB}$ is shown on the coordinate plane on the right.

   Find the point Q that is $\frac{1}{5}$ the distance from A to B.

   _____

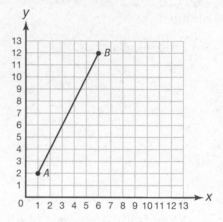

2. The line segment $\overline{CD}$ is shown on the coordinate plane on the right.

   Find the point Q that is $\frac{2}{3}$ the distance from C to D.

   _____

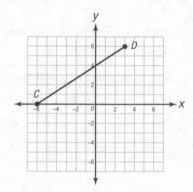

3. The line segment $\overline{GF}$ is shown on the coordinate plane on the right.

   Find the point Q that partitions $\overline{GF}$ in a ratio of 1:3.

   _____

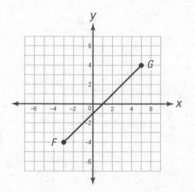

4. The line segment $\overline{JK}$ is shown on the coordinate plane on the right.

   Find the point Q that partitions $\overline{JK}$ in a ratio of 3:2.

   _____

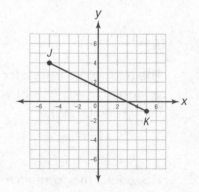

Use the information below for questions 5 and 6. Find the point described.

The endpoints of line segment $\overline{XY}$ are $X(-6, 2)$ and $Y(6, -10)$.

5. Find the point P that is $\frac{1}{3}$ the distance from X to Y. _____

6. Find the point Q that partitions $\overline{YX}$ in a ratio of 3:1. _____

Solve.

7. Point A is located at $(1, 4)$. Point P at $(3, 5)$ is $\frac{1}{3}$ the distance from A to point B. What are the coordinates of point B? _____

8. Point C is located at the origin. Point Q at $(-1, -2)$ partitions $\overline{CD}$ in a ratio of 1:6. What are the coordinates of point D? _____

9. The line segment $\overline{HJ}$ is shown on the coordinate plane below.

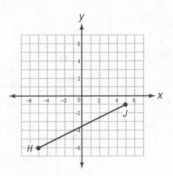

Find the point Q that is $\frac{4}{5}$ the distance from J to H. _____

Plot point Q on the coordinate plane above.

Fill in the blank.

10. **REASON** If point P is $\frac{3}{7}$ the distance from A to B, then it is _____ the distance from B to A.

Plot points L and P as described.

11. **SHOW** Point K is shown on the coordinate grid on the right.

Plot a point L so that it is 15 units from point K and so that $\overline{KL}$ is not vertical or horizontal. Then, add point P that is $\frac{1}{3}$ the distance from K to L. (Hint: Find a Pythagorean triple where the largest number is 15.)

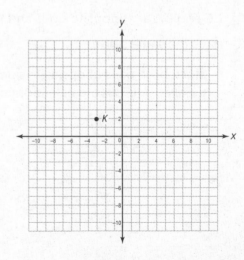

40 Proving Theorems Using Coordinate Geometry

EXAMPLE A Quadrilateral *ABCD* is shown on the coordinate grid.

Prove that *ABCD* is a parallelogram.

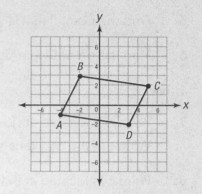

1

Make a plan.

A parallelogram is a quadrilateral in which opposite sides are parallel. To prove that *ABCD* is a parallelogram, find the slope of each side and show that the slopes of opposite sides are the same.

2

Find the slope of each side of the quadrilateral.

Use the slope formula: $m = \frac{y_2 - y_1}{x_2 - x_1}$.

$\overline{AB}$: $m = \frac{3 - (-1)}{-2 - (-4)} = \frac{4}{2} = 2$

$\overline{BC}$: $m = \frac{2 - 3}{5 - (-2)} = \frac{-1}{7} = -\frac{1}{7}$

$\overline{CD}$: $m = \frac{-2 - 2}{3 - 5} = \frac{-4}{-2} = 2$

$\overline{DA}$: $m = \frac{-1 - (-2)}{-4 - 3} = \frac{1}{-7} = -\frac{1}{7}$

3

Analyze the results.

$\overline{AB}$ and $\overline{CD}$ are opposite sides, and they have the same slope, 2.

$\overline{BC}$ and $\overline{DA}$ are opposite sides and they have the same slope, $-\frac{1}{7}$.

▶ Since both pairs of opposite sides are parallel, *ABCD* is a parallelogram.

DISCUSS

The definition of a rectangle is a parallelogram with four right angles. Is *ABCD* a rectangle? Why or why not?

EXAMPLE B Circle O in the graph on the right has center $O(1, 1)$.

The point $(-4, 1)$ lies on the circle. Prove that the point $(4, 5)$ also lies on circle O.

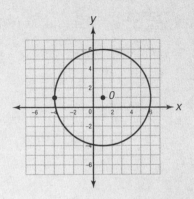

1

Make a plan.

The definition of a circle is all points that are equidistant from a given point, called the center. That distance is the radius.

So, find the length of the radius and the distance between $(4, 5)$ and the center. If those distances are equal, the point lies on the circle.

2

Find the length of the radius.

The point $(-4, 1)$ lies on the circle, so the distance between $(-4, 1)$ and the center, $(1, 1)$, is equal to the radius. Since this segment is horizontal, find the difference of their x-coordinates to find the length.

$r = |1 - (-4)| = 5$

The radius of circle O is 5 units.

3

Find the distance between point O and $(4, 5)$ and compare it to the radius.

Find the distance between $(1, 1)$ and $(4, 5)$. Use the distance formula.

$d = \sqrt{(x_2 - x_1)^2 + (y_2 - y_1)^2}$

$d = \sqrt{(5 - 1)^2 + (4 - 1)^2}$

$d = \sqrt{4^2 + 3^2}$

$d = \sqrt{25}$

$d = 5$

▶ This is equal to the radius, so the point $(4, 5)$ does lie on circle O.

TRY

Circle C has center $(-5, -6)$ and radius $2\sqrt{3}$. Is the point $(-8, -4)$ on the circle?

EXAMPLE C Triangle *JKL* is shown on the coordinate grid on the right.

Is △*JKL* a right triangle? Is it an isosceles triangle?

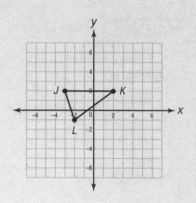

1

Make a plan.

A right triangle contains one right angle. This means that two of the sides of the triangle will be perpendicular, so they will have slopes that are opposite reciprocals. Find the slopes of all sides of △*JKL*.

An isosceles triangle has two congruent sides. Find the side lengths of △*JKL*.

2

Find the slopes of all sides and compare them.

Use the slope formula: $m = \dfrac{y_2 - y_1}{x_2 - x_1}$.

$\overline{JK}: m = \dfrac{2 - (2)}{2 - (-3)} = \dfrac{0}{5} = 0$

$\overline{KL}: m = \dfrac{2 - (-1)}{2 - (-2)} = \dfrac{3}{4}$

$\overline{JL}: m = \dfrac{2 - (-1)}{-3 - (-2)} = \dfrac{3}{-1} = -3$

▶ No two slopes are negative reciprocals of each other, so △*JKL* is not a right triangle.

3

Find the lengths of the sides and compare them.

$\overline{JK}$ is horizontal, so to find its length find the difference of the *x*-coordinates.

$JK = |2 - (-3)| = 5$

For the remaining sides, use the distance formula: $d = \sqrt{(x_2 - x_1)^2 + (y_2 - y_1)^2}$.

$KL = \sqrt{(-2 - 2)^2 + (-1 - 2)^2}$

$KL = \sqrt{25}$

$KL = 5$

$JL = \sqrt{(-2 - (-3))^2 + (-1 - 2)^2}$

$JL = \sqrt{10}$

▶ Since *JK* = *KL* = 5, △*JKL* is isosceles.

To what point could you move *L* to make *JKL* an isosceles right triangle?

EXAMPLE D Triangle *NOP* is shown on the coordinate grid on the right.

Prove that the centroid of △*NOP* divides each of the triangle's medians in a ratio of 2:1.

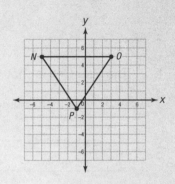

1

Find the endpoints of the medians of △*NOP*.

A median connects a vertex of a triangle to the midpoint of the opposite side. Find the midpoint of each side of the triangle. Use the formula $(x_1 + k(x_2 - x_1), y_1 + k(y_2 - y_1))$ with $k = \frac{1}{2}$.

$\overline{NO}$: $(-5 + \frac{1}{2}[3 - (-5)], 5 + \frac{1}{2}(5 - 5)) = (-1, 5)$

$\overline{OP}$: $(3 + \frac{1}{2}(-1 - 3), 5 + \frac{1}{2}(-1 - 5)) = (1, 2)$

$\overline{NP}$: $(-5 + \frac{1}{2}[-1 - (-5)], 5 + \frac{1}{2}(-1 - 5)) = (-3, 2)$

2

Graph the medians and find the centroid.

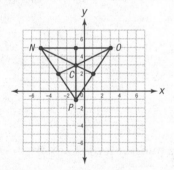

The centroid appears to be at $(-1, 3)$.

CHECK

Pick a median and find its length. Then, find the distance from the vertex of that median to *C*. Is that distance $\frac{2}{3}$ the length of the median?

3

Find the points that partition each median in a ratio of 2:1.

A ratio of 2:1 indicates the point $\frac{2}{3}$ of the way from the vertex to the opposite side. Use the partition formula and let $k = \frac{2}{3}$.

Median from *N*:

$(-5 + \frac{2}{3}[1 - (-5)], 5 + \frac{2}{3}(2 - 5)) =$

$(-5 + 4, 5 + (-2)) = (-1, 3)$

Median from *O*:

$(3 + \frac{2}{3}(-3 - 3), 5 + \frac{2}{3}(2 - 5)) =$

$(3 + (-4), 5 + (-2)) = (-1, 3)$

Median from *P*:

$(-1 + \frac{2}{3}[-1 - (-1)], -1 + \frac{2}{3}[5 - (-1)]) =$

$(-1 + 0, -1 + 4) = (-1, 3)$

▶ The centroid, $(-1, 3)$, partitions each median in a ratio of 2:1.

Practice

Solve.

1. Triangle *GHJ* is shown on the coordinate grid on the right.

   Is △*GHJ* a right triangle? Explain your answer.

   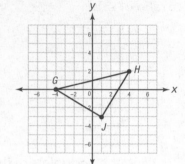

   _____

   _____

   _____

2. Quadrilateral *PQRS* is shown on the coordinate grid on the right.

   Is *PQRS* a trapezoid? Explain your answer.

   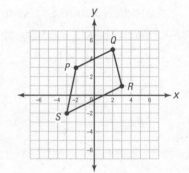

   _____

   _____

   _____

3. Triangle *ABC* is shown on the coordinate grid below.

   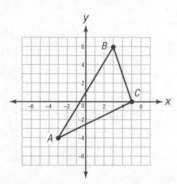

   Draw the midsegment connecting the midpoint of $\overline{AB}$ to the midpoint of $\overline{BC}$ on the coordinate grid.

   Then prove that this midsegment is parallel to $\overline{AC}$ and half of its length.

   _____

   _____

   _____

   _____

   _____

   _____

4. The diagram on the right represents a park with a grid imposed on it. Each unit length on the grid represents 1 foot. The point S represents the planned placement for a sprinkler head that sprays water in a circle. The point F represents a flowerbed.

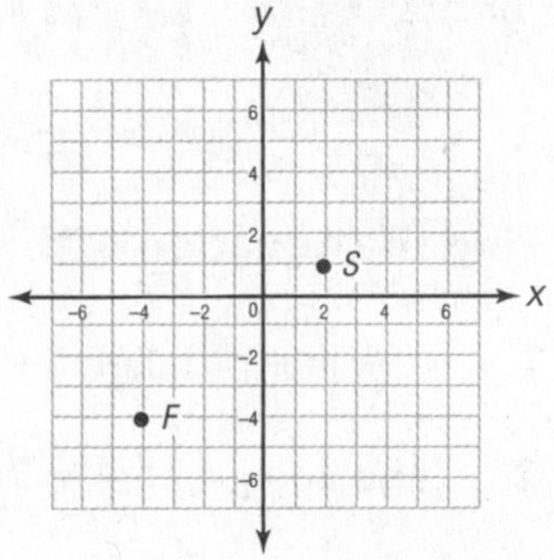

If the sprinkler has a radius of 6 feet, will the water from the sprinkler reach the flowerbed? Explain your answer.

_____

_____

5. Triangle DEF is shown on the coordinate grid on the right.

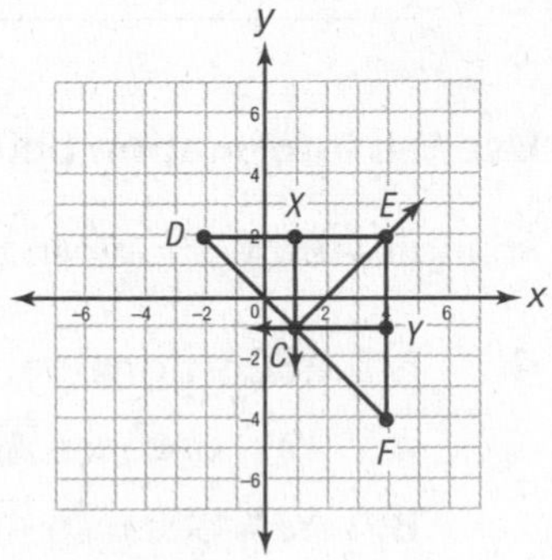

The circumcenter of a triangle is the intersection of the perpendicular bisectors of the triangle.

Prove that C is the circumcenter of $\triangle DEF$.

_____

_____

_____

_____

_____

6. **CONSTRUCT** Draw a rhombus on the coordinate grid on the right so that no side of the rhombus is vertical or horizontal.

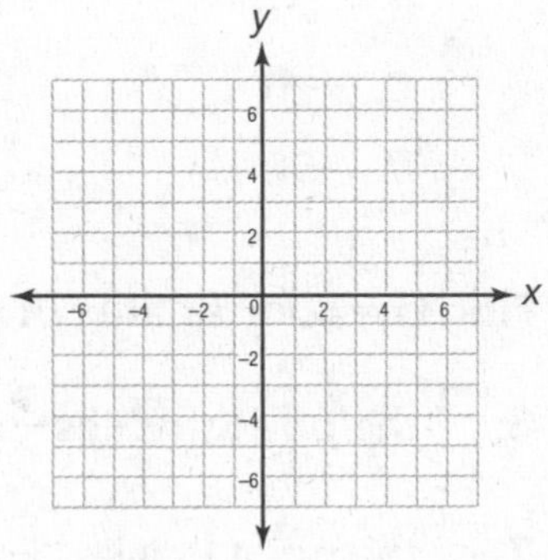

Prove that your figure is a rhombus.

_____

_____

_____

_____

_____

_____

UNIT 6 Review

Find the equation of the line that fits each description.

1. the line parallel to $y = \frac{1}{4}x + 3$ that passes through the point $(-8, -7)$ _____

2. the line parallel to $2x + 3y = 24$ that passes through the point $(12, -4)$ _____

3. the line perpendicular to $4y + x + 40 = 0$ that passes through the point $\left(\frac{1}{2}, 0\right)$

   _____

Use the information below for questions 4 and 5. Choose the best answer.

Triangle ABC is shown in the coordinate grid on the right.

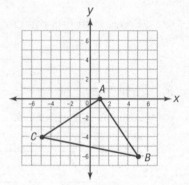

4. Is $\triangle ABC$ a right triangle?
   A. Yes, because $\overline{AB}$ is perpendicular to $\overline{BC}$.
   B. Yes, because $\overline{AB}$ is perpendicular to $\overline{AC}$.
   C. Yes, because $\overline{BC}$ is perpendicular to $\overline{AC}$.
   D. No, because none of the sides are perpendicular to one another.

5. What is the area of $\triangle ABC$ in square units?
   A. 13
   B. 21
   C. 26
   D. 52

Find the coordinates of the point that fits each description.

6. the point that lies $\frac{1}{3}$ of the distance from $(-10, 4)$ to $(14, -11)$ _____

7. the point that lies $\frac{5}{6}$ the distance from $(3, 5)$ to $(15, 23)$ _____

Use the information below for questions 8 and 9. Choose the best answer.

Quadrilateral *DFGH* is shown in the coordinate grid on the right.

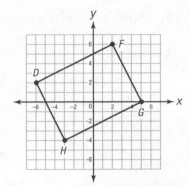

8. Is *DFGH* a square?

   A. Yes, because all of the angles are right angles and all of the sides are congruent.

   B. No, because all of the angles are not right angles.

   C. No, because opposite sides are not parallel.

   D. No, because not all of the sides are congruent.

9. What is the perimeter of *DFGH* in units?

   A. $12\sqrt{5}$

   B. $14\sqrt{5}$

   C. $16\sqrt{5}$

   D. $18\sqrt{5}$

Solve the problem and explain your answer.

10. Does the point (13, 16) lie on circle *O* with center (7, 8) and radius 10? Explain your answer.

   _____

   _____

   _____

Describe each pair of lines as parallel, perpendicular, or neither.

11.

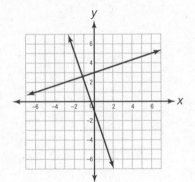

   _____

12.

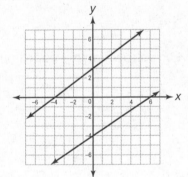

   _____

Solve.

13. Square *PQRS* is shown on the coordinate grid below.

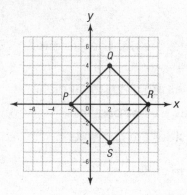

What is the area of *PQRS*? _____

14. $\overline{BA}$ is shown on the coordinate grid below.

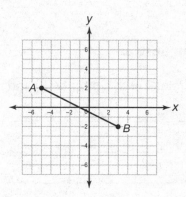

What point partitions $\overline{BA}$ in a ratio of 3:1? _____

Solve.

15. Triangle *NOP* is shown on the coordinate grid below.

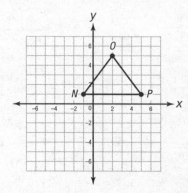

Find the perimeter of △*NOP*. _____

16. **VERIFY** $\overline{CD}$ is shown on the coordinate grid below.

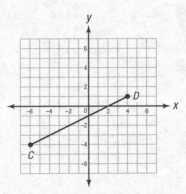

Find the point P that is $\frac{1}{5}$ the distance from C to D and plot it on the grid. Then find the lengths of $\overline{CD}$ and $\overline{CP}$. Verify that $CP = \frac{1}{5}CD$.

_____

_____

_____

17. **PROVE** Quadrilateral $JKLM$ is shown on the coordinate grid below.

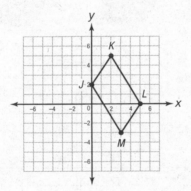

Prove that $JKLM$ is a parallelogram but not a rectangle. Give your proof in the form of a paragraph.

_____

_____

_____

_____

_____

_____

LANDSCAPE DESIGN

A landscape designer is making a plan for a client's backyard. He has made a scale drawing of the yard, shown below. Each unit on the grid represents one foot.

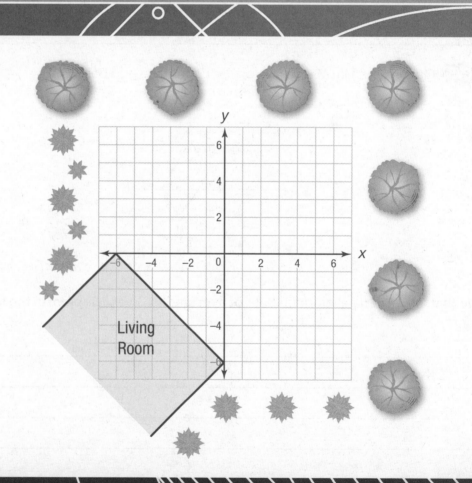

1. The yard will have several features, including a rectangular wooden deck. The corners of the deck will be $(-5, 0)$, $(-3, 2)$, $(1, -2)$, and $(-1, -4)$. Draw the deck on the scale drawing.

2. The deck will be made out of cedar or pine. Cedar costs $33 per square foot, and pine costs $28 per square foot. What would the cost be for each type of wood?

    _____

    _____

3. There will also be a circular pool with its center at $(3, 3)$ and a radius of 2 feet. There is currently a tree at $(4, 1)$. Will it need to be removed to put in the pool? Explain how you know.

    _____

    _____

4. Draw the pool on the scale drawing.

5. There is a plan for a string of lights to hang between two poles at $(-4, 5)$ and $(2, -4)$. Additional support poles will stand at $\frac{1}{3}$ the distance from each end of the lights. Where will these support poles be located?

    _____

    _____

6. On the scale drawing, draw the line segment representing the string of lights and plot the point where each support pole will stand.

7. Will the string of lights be parallel to the wall between the living room and the yard? Explain how you know.

    _____

    _____

Glossary

accuracy how close a measurement or calculation is to its actual value (Lesson 2)

additive identity the number that, when added to a number a, gives the sum a; for real numbers, the additive identity is 0: $a + 0 = a$ (Lesson 9)

additive inverse for any real number a, the number $-a$, such that their sum is the additive identity, 0: $a + (-a) = (-a) + a = 0$ (Lesson 9)

angle a figure formed by two rays or line segments that have a common endpoint (Lesson 31)

approximation a value used to represent a true measurement that is not exact when an exact answer is not possible (Lesson 2)

arithmetic sequence a sequence in which successive terms have a common difference (Lesson 22)

asymptote a line that the graph of a function continuously approaches but never touches (Lesson 14)

base the number or variable that is raised to a power in an exponential expression (Lessons 4, 8)

bimodal distribution a distribution of data that, when graphed, shows two clear peaks (Lesson 24)

bivariate data statistical data in which two variables are being studied (Lesson 29)

box plot a graph above a number line that shows the lower and upper extremes, first and third quartiles, and median of a data set; also called a box-and-whisker plot (Lesson 27)

categorical data data that cannot be measured and are generally in the form of names or labels (Lesson 28)

center of dilation a fixed point from which all points in a figure or graph are dilated, either moving away from or toward that point (Lesson 35)

center of rotation the point about which a figure is turned during a rotation (Lesson 34)

circle the set of all points that are equidistant from a point called the center (Lesson 34)

coefficient a number that is multiplied by a variable in an expression or equation (Lesson 3)

collinear line segments two or more line segments that lie on the same line (Lesson 32)

common difference the number added to find the next term in an arithmetic sequence (Lesson 22)

common ratio the number by which each term in a geometric sequence is multiplied to obtain the next term (Lesson 23)

compound inequality an inequality that has two or more boundaries (Lesson 5)

conditional frequency a relative frequency in the body of a two-way relative frequency table (Lesson 28)

constant a number with a known value that does not change in a mathematical expression (Lesson 3)

conversion factor a number used to convert from one unit to another through multiplication or division (Lesson 1)

correlation coefficient a number r, where $-1 \leq r \leq 1$, that describes the strength of the association between two variables (Lesson 30)

curve of best fit the curve that most closely represents the relationship between variables that do not have a linear association (Lesson 30)

dependent variable a variable, often y or $f(x)$, that provides the output value of an equation or function (Lesson 3)

dilation a transformation that enlarges or reduces the size of a figure or graph according to a scale factor (Lesson 35)

dimensional analysis a method of determining or checking a mathematical expression for a given context by examining units (Lesson 1)

domain the set of all the first elements (inputs) of a relation (Lesson 13)

dot plot a data display that represents data values as dots over a number line (Lesson 24)

element an individual value from a set (Lesson 13)

elimination method a method for solving systems of equations where equations are multiplied by constants and added and/or subtracted so as to eliminate all but one variable (Lesson 11)

end behavior the behavior of a graph as it is followed farther and farther in either direction (Lesson 14)

estimation a value made inexact on purpose in order to make calculations easier or to generalize about a population (Lesson 2)

experimental study a study in which the researcher controls variables in order to determine their effect (Lesson 24)

exponential decay a situation in which a population or quantity decreases at an exponential rate, or by a constant percent per unit time (Lesson 8)

exponential equation an equation in which the variable is in the exponent (Lessons 4, 8)

exponential function a function of the form $f(x) = a \cdot b^x + c$, in which the input, x, is the exponent of a constant, b (Lesson 13)

exponential growth a situation in which a population or quantity increases at an exponential rate, or by a constant percent per unit time (Lesson 8)

first quartile (Q_1) the median of the lower half of a data set (Lesson 27)

function a relation in which every input maps to exactly one output (Lesson 13)

geometric sequence a sequence in which consecutive terms have a common ratio (Lesson 23)

half-plane a portion of the coordinate plane that lies on one side of a line (Lesson 12)

histogram a data display that uses bars to show how frequently data occur within certain ranges or intervals (Lesson 24)

horizontal shrink a transformation that pushes the points of a figure or graph toward the y-axis (Lessons 20, 35)

horizontal stretch a transformation that pulls the points of a figure or graph away from the y-axis (Lessons 20, 35)

horizontal translation a slide of a graph or figure in the right or the left direction on the coordinate plane (Lessons 18, 32)

image the figure resulting from a transformation (Lesson 31)

independent variable a variable, often x, that serves as the input value of an equation or function (Lesson 3)

input the first value, often an *x*-coordinate, in an ordered pair for a function; the value that is entered into a function in order to produce the related output (Lesson 13)

interquartile range (IQR) a measure of the spread of the middle 50% of a data set; equal to the difference of the first and third quartiles of the set (Lesson 27)

joint frequency a frequency in the body of a two-way frequency table (Lesson 28)

linear equation an equation in which every variable is raised to the first power (Lesson 4)

linear function a function of the form $f(x) = mx + b$, in which the input, *x*, is raised to the first power and whose graph is a straight line (Lesson 13)

line of best fit the line that most closely represents the relationship between variables that have a linear association; also called a trend line (Lesson 30)

line of reflection the line over which a figure or graph is flipped to produce a mirror image (Lessons 19, 33)

line of symmetry a line over which a graph or figure can be reflected such that it maps back onto itself (Lesson 36)

line segment the part of a line that falls between two points on the line, which are the endpoints of the segment (Lessons 31, 32)

line symmetry characteristic of a graph or figure that can be reflected over a line to produce an identical figure or graph; also called reflectional symmetry (Lesson 36)

lower extreme the least value in a data set (Lesson 27)

marginal frequency an entry in the "Total" row or "Total" column of a two-way frequency table or a two-way relative frequency table (Lesson 28)

maximum the greatest *y*- or $f(x)$-value of a function (Lesson 14)

mean the sum of all the terms in a data set divided by the total number of elements (Lesson 25)

mean absolute deviation (MAD) a measure of the variability in a data set; the mean of the absolute values of the deviations from the mean for each data point in a data set (Lesson 26)

measure of center a value that represents the middle or average of a data set (Lesson 25)

median the middle value in a data set that is ordered from least to greatest (Lesson 25)

midpoint the center point of a line segment that divides the segment into two line segments of equal length (Lesson 39)

minimum the least *y*- or $f(x)$-value of a function (Lesson 14)

multiplicative identity the number that, when multiplied by a number *a*, gives the product *a*; for real numbers, the multiplicative identity is 1: $a \cdot 1 = a$ (Lesson 9)

multiplicative inverse for any real number *a* other than 0, the number $\frac{1}{a}$ such that their product is the multiplicative identity, 1: $a \times \frac{1}{a} = \frac{1}{a} \times a = 1$ (Lesson 9)

normal distribution a distribution of data that, when graphed, is symmetrical and resembles a bell curve (Lesson 24)

observational study a study in which variables are observed or outcomes are measured, but no attempt is made to control variables or affect outcomes (Lesson 24)

outlier an element that is very different from the other elements in the same data set (Lesson 25)

output the second value, often a *y*-coordinate, in an ordered pair for a function; the value that is produced when a function is evaluated for a given input (Lesson 13)

parallel lines lines that lie in the same plane but never intersect (Lesson 37)

parallel line segments two or more line segments that lie on parallel lines (Lesson 32)

parent function the most basic function in a family, or group, of related functions (Lesson 18)

partition to divide (Lesson 39)

perpendicular meeting at a right angle (Lesson 33)

perpendicular lines lines that intersect to form right angles (Lesson 37)

preimage an original figure that is transformed to form an image (Lesson 32)

Pythagorean Theorem theorem stating that for any right triangle with legs of lengths *a* and *b* and hypotenuse of length *c*, $a^2 + b^2 = c^2$ (Lesson 38)

quantitative data data that can be measured and are in numerical form (Lesson 28)

range (of a data set) a measure of the spread of a data set; equal to the difference of the greatest value and the least value in the set (Lesson 27)

range (of a function) the set of all the second elements (outputs) in a relation (Lesson 13)

rate of change the value by which one quantity changes when another related quantity increases by a unit amount (Lesson 15)

reciprocal the multiplicative inverse of a number (Lesson 9)

recursive process a process that requires knowing or computing previous terms in order to find the value of a desired term (Lesson 22)

reflection a transformation that flips a figure or graph over a point or line (Lessons 19, 33)

reflectional symmetry see *line symmetry* (Lesson 36)

regular polygon a polygon that has all sides equal in length and all angles equal in measure (Lesson 36)

relation a set of ordered pairs (Lesson 13)

relative frequency the ratio of a frequency for a category to the total frequencies in a row, column, or table (Lesson 28)

residual the difference of an observed *y*-value on a scatter plot and a predicted *y*-value based on a line of fit (Lesson 29)

rotation a transformation that turns a figure or graph around a point (Lesson 34)

rotational symmetry characteristic of a graph or figure that can be rotated by a measure of less than 360° to produce an identical figure or graph (Lesson 36)

scatter plot a graph that shows the relationship between two variables; a graph on which data are plotted as points (*x*, *y*) on a coordinate plane (Lesson 29)

sequence a predictable arrangement of numbers, expressions, pictures, or other objects that follows a pattern or rule (Lesson 22)

skewed distribution a distribution of data that, when graphed, shows a "tail" that extends much more to one side of the graph than the other (Lesson 24)

slope the ratio of the vertical change to the horizontal change for the graph of a linear equation (Lessons 7, 15)

slope-intercept form a form of a linear equation, $y = mx + b$, where m is the slope and b is the y-intercept of the graph (Lessons 7, 16)

spread (of a data set) a description of the distribution or grouping of data in a given set (Lesson 26)

substitution method a method for solving systems of equations where one variable is replaced by an equivalent expression in the other variable (Lesson 11)

system of linear equations a grouping of two or more linear equations written using the same variables (Lesson 11)

term (of an expression) a combination of constants and/or variables joined together through multiplication or division (Lesson 3)

term (of a sequence) a number or object in a sequence (Lesson 22)

third quartile (Q_3) the median of the upper half of a data set (Lesson 27)

transformation an operation that changes a figure or graph according to a rule (Lessons 18, 31)

translation a transformation that moves all of the points on a graph or figure the same distance in the same direction (Lessons 18, 32)

two-way frequency table a data display used to display and interpret frequencies for categorical variables (Lesson 28)

two-way relative frequency table a data display used to display and interpret relative frequencies for categorical variables (Lesson 28)

uniform distribution a distribution of data in which all values have the same frequency (Lesson 24)

upper extreme the greatest value in a data set (Lesson 27)

variable a letter or symbol that represents an unknown or changing number in an expression or equation (Lesson 3)

vertex a point at which two sides of a geometric shape intersect (Lesson 31)

vertical line test test in which if any vertical line crosses a graph at two or more points, then the graph does not represent a function (Lesson 13)

vertical shrink a transformation that pushes the points of a figure or graph toward the x-axis (Lessons 20, 35)

vertical stretch a transformation that pulls the points of a figure or graph away from the x-axis (Lessons 20, 35)

vertical translation a slide of a graph or figure up or down on the coordinate plane (Lessons 18, 32)

x-intercept a point $(a, 0)$ at which a graph crosses the x-axis (Lesson 14)

y-intercept a point $(0, b)$ at which a graph crosses the y-axis (Lessons 7, 14)

Formula Sheet

CCGPS Coordinate Algebra Formula Sheet

Below are the formulas you may find useful as you work the problems. However, some of the formulas may not be used. You may refer to this page as you take the test.

Area

Rectangle and Parallelogram $A = bh$

Triangle $A = \dfrac{1}{2}bh$

Circle $A = \pi r^2$

Trapezoid $A = \dfrac{1}{2}(h)(b_1 + b_2)$

Circumference

$C = \pi d$ $\pi \approx 3.14$

Volume

Rectangular Prism/Cylinder $V = Bh$

Pyramid/Cone $V = \dfrac{1}{3}Bh$

Sphere $V = \dfrac{4}{3}\pi r^3$

Surface Area

Rectangular Prism $SA = 2lw + 2wh + 2lh$

Cylinder $SA = 2\pi r^2 + 2\pi rh$

Pythagorean Theorem

$$a^2 + b^2 = c^2$$

Mean Absolute Deviation

$$\frac{\sum\limits_{i=1}^{n} \left| x_i - \bar{x} \right|}{n}$$

the average of the absolute deviations from the mean for a set of data

Distance Formula

$$d = \sqrt{(x_2 - x_1)^2 + (y_2 - y_1)^2}$$

Slope Formula

$$m = \frac{y_2 - y_1}{x_2 - x_1}$$

Midpoint Formula

$$M = \left(\frac{x_1 + x_2}{2}, \frac{y_1 + y_2}{2} \right)$$

Interquartile Range

the difference between the first quartile and third quartile of a set of data

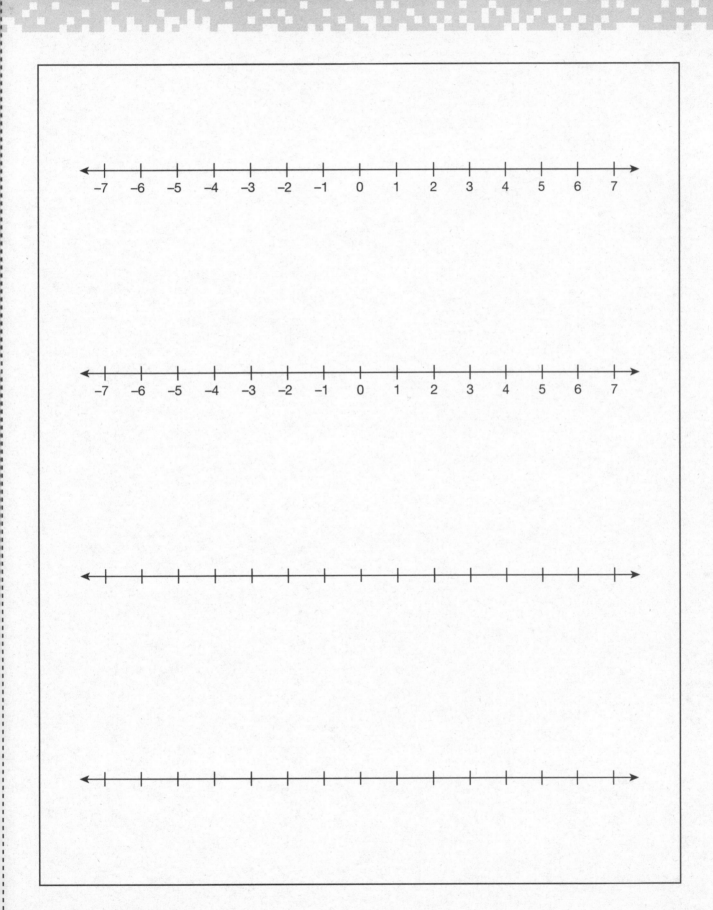

Math Tool: Coordinate Planes

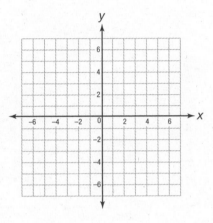

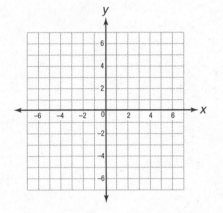

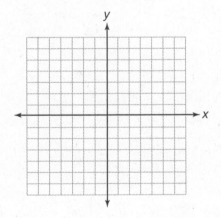

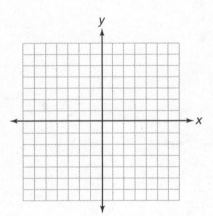

Math Tool: Coordinate Planes

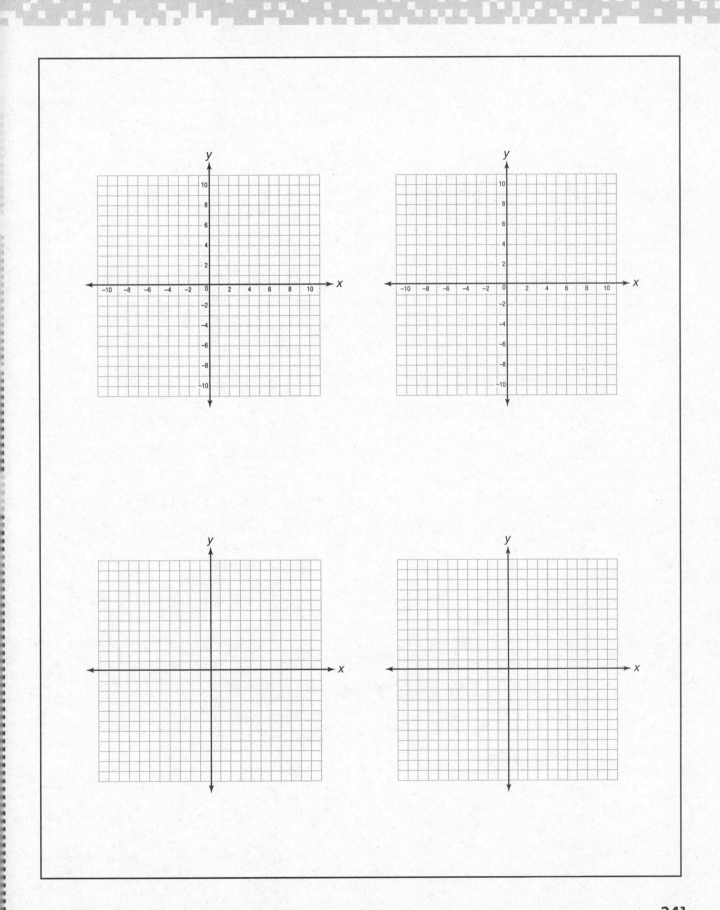

Math Tool: Coordinate Plane

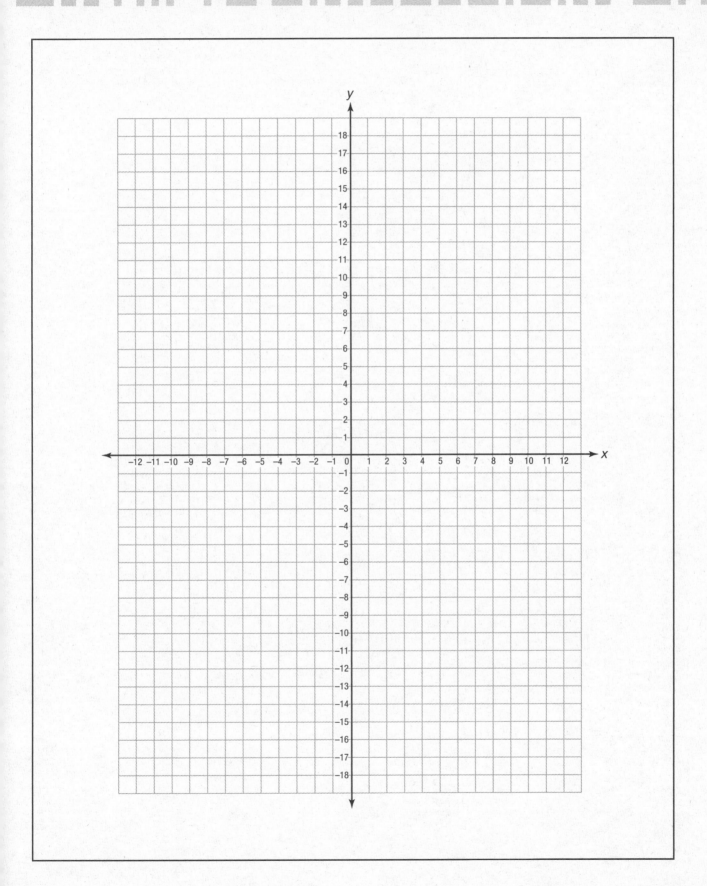

Math Tool: Coordinate Plane

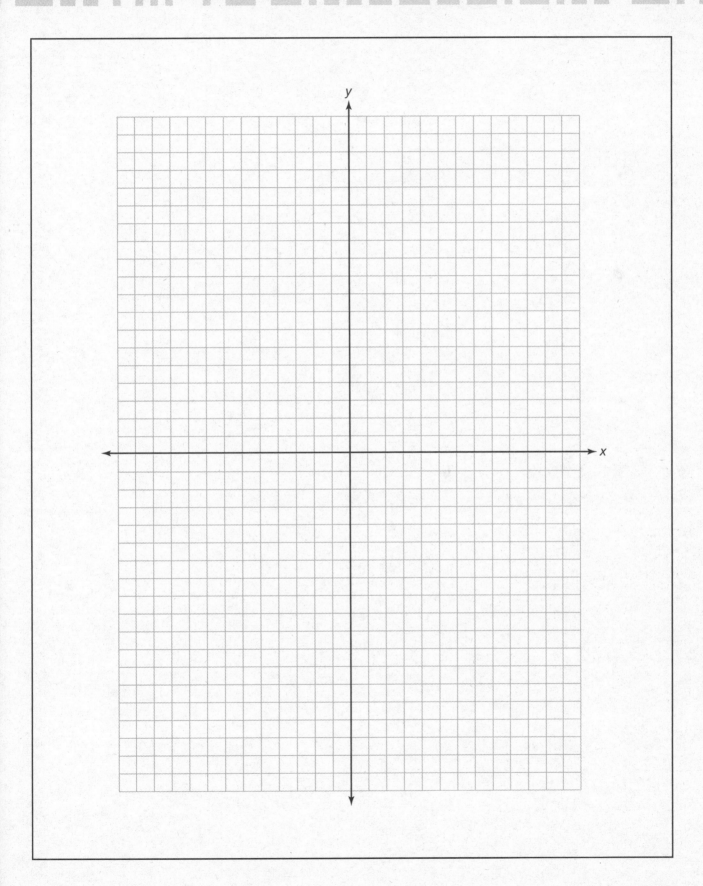

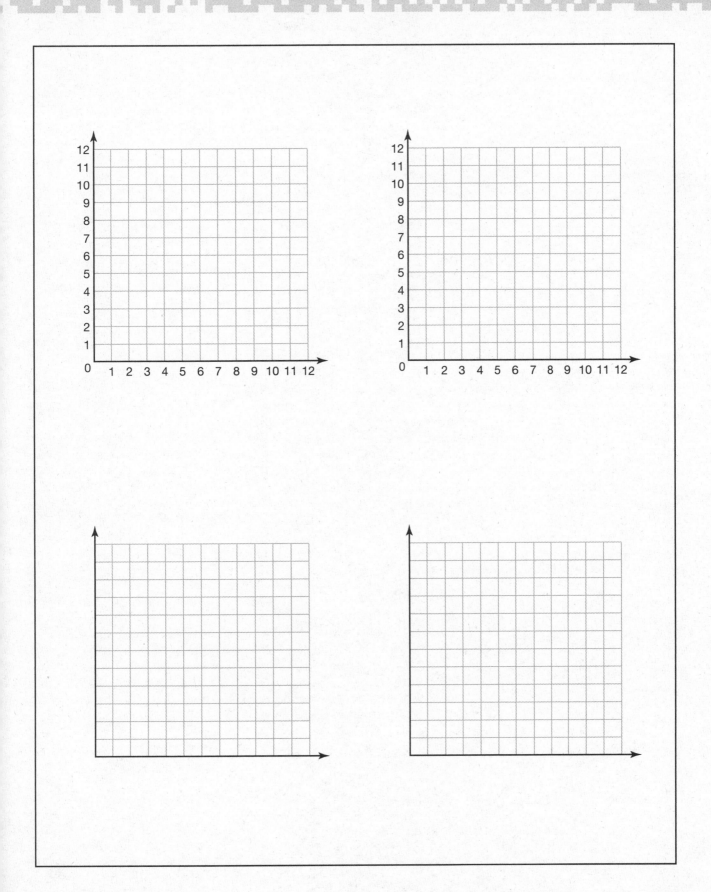

Math Tool: Grid Paper

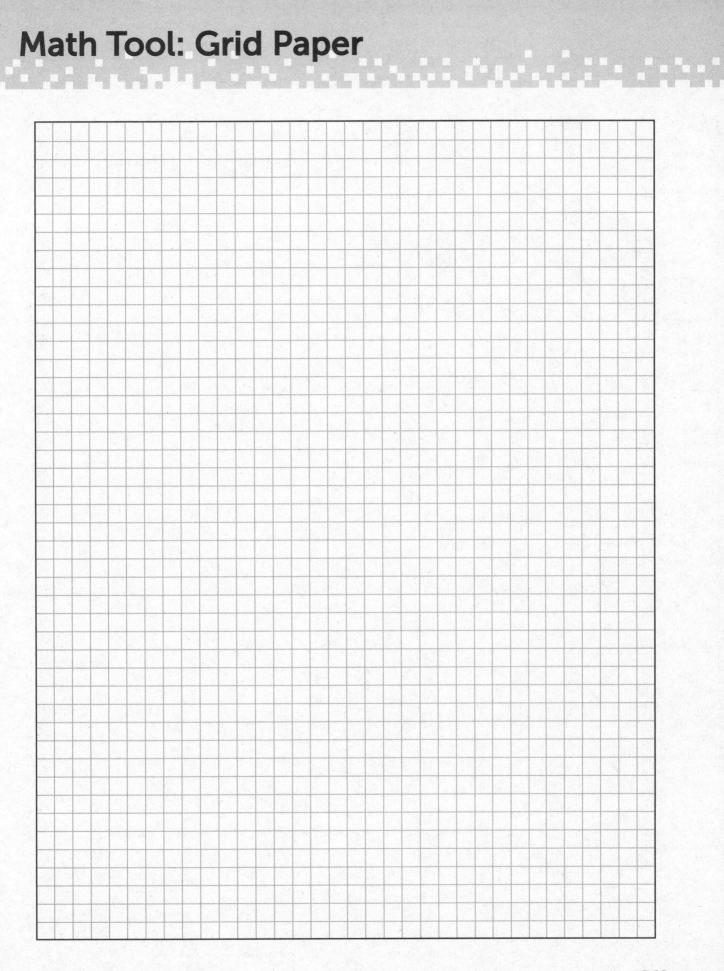

Notes

Notes